Cattle Raising on the Plains

Cattle Raising on the Plains

1900-1961

By

JOHN T. SCHLEBECKER

UNIVERSITY OF NEBRASKA PRESS

LINCOLN · 1963

Publishers on the Plains

UNP

To Toni

Cattlemen on the Plains
1900-1961

This book narrates events in the lives of cattlemen on the Great Plains in the twentieth century. The Great Plains begin at either the Missouri River, or about the ninety-sixth meridian, and tilt upward to the Rocky Mountains. Unlike the prairies to the east, the Plains are not flat, but are gently rolling to rough. They are almost entirely treeless, and receive an average annual precipitation of less than twenty inches. No state is entirely within the Great Plains, but ten states have Plains within their boundaries. Roughly, the Plains are located in: western North Dakota, western South Dakota, eastern Montana, eastern Wyoming, western Nebraska, western Kansas, eastern Colorado, western Oklahoma, western Texas, and eastern New Mexico. The region contains about 600,000 square miles. In earlier days the Plains were covered mostly with prairie grasses which provided forage for several million buffalo. The buffalo, in turn, supported a scanty but resilient Indian population.

Almost everyone knows something about the nineteenth-century cattle industry. This work carries the narrative into the twentieth century and recounts some of the adjustments which cattlemen made to their environment. The book tells something also of the ways the cattle industry evolved to meet the needs of an urban-industrial society. In this evolution, cattlemen applied science and technology to their business, and so, year by year, produced more beef on less land, with less work, and at less hazard to themselves. The narrative is primarily about cattlemen, and other plainsmen make their way into the story only insofar as they influenced the beef producers.

The narrative is composed chronologically because that seemed the most natural way to tell the story. Although grand epochs can be defined in history, the stream of events flows from year to year, and any time-divisions are bound to be arbitrary. I have arbitrarily divided the narrative in a way which seems best to fit the story of the cattlemen of the Plains.

Part of the research on this work was made possible by a grant from the American Philosophical Society in the summer of 1959. I am also particularly indebted to Wayne D. Rasmussen of the United States Department of Agriculture, Harold T. Pinkett of the Agriculture and General Services Branch of the National Archives, Angelina Carabelli of the Library of the United States Department of Agriculture, Robert G. Dunbar of Montana State College, and Gilbert C. Fite of the University of Oklahoma. Without their help, nothing would have been accomplished. Of course, I must remember my teachers who gave me the whole idea: Frederick Merk of Harvard, and Vernon Carstensen of Wisconsin.

Contents

	Cattlemen on the Plains, 1900–1961	vii
I.	The Closing of the Range, 1850–1900	1
II.	The Controlled Range, 1900–1905	17
III.	New Accommodations, 1906–1910	30
IV.	The Good Old Days, 1911–1914	44
V.	More and More Beef, 1915–1918	57
VI.	The Postwar Depression, 1919–1922	72
VII.	From Range to Pasture, 1923–1925	87
VIII.	The Good Years, 1926–1928	104
IX.	The Great Depression, 1929–1932	119
X.	The First New Deal, 1933–1935	134
XI.	The Second New Deal, 1936–1939	152
XII.	The War and the Plains, 1940–1945	169
XIII.	Reconversion with Stability, 1946–1949	186
XIV.	The Korean War and After, 1950–1955	204
XV.	The Age of Biochemistry, 1956–1961	223
XVI.	Conclusions, 1900–1961	238
	Notes	243
	Bibliography	291
	Index	311

CHAPTER I

The Closing of the Range
1850-1900

In the late nineteenth century the heroic age of the range cattle industry dribbled to an end. How and why this romantic era came to an end is fairly well known, but why this primitive phase lasted so long has not been much examined. From the beginning of settlement in America cattle grazing had been carried on by some frontiersmen. In the seventeenth-century pea-vine pastures of Georgia or the back country of North Carolina—in eighteenth-century Kentucky, Pennsylvania, or Ohio—or at countless other times and places—an equivalent of the range cattle industry has characterized the cutting edge of the frontier. Men engaged in the business were called cowherds in seventeenth-century New England, drovers in eighteenth-century Kentucky, and cowpunchers in nineteenth-century Wyoming. But despite name differences, they performed similar tasks and lived astonishingly similar lives in many ways. Only a special parochial conceit could detect any great differences in their basic business, or in the nature of the entrepreneurs.[1]

Before pioneers reached the Plains, the time during which herdsmen dominated any particular region was usually rather short. Although the days of the open range have been often described as short, the period actually endured for quite some time. Grazers held the stage from approximately 1850 to 1900, more than half a century. In no other place had frontier cattlemen remained in control for such an extended length of time. This last frontier of the cattleman was unique because of the long time during which herders dominated the physiographic province. How and why did this cattleman's frontier last so long?

Four major reasons come to mind. First, the Great Plains intimidated farmers who knew nothing of dry land farming or irrigation. Second, by the middle of the nineteenth century the American people had temporarily acquired more land than they needed for agriculture. Third, by new methods and machinery, farmers increased yields per man and per acre so much that they did not need to settle new lands to increase production. Fourth, millions of Americans and immigrants increasingly crowded into urban places, and so the cities absorbed large numbers of potential farmers. In short, to some extent people could not move onto the Plains, and in any case, they did not need to. These influences combined to retard settlement, and so delayed the movement of people onto the Plains. The hazards of life on the Plains, the lack of a need for land, and the attraction of rural population to the cities, all multiplied their effects. Farmers advanced to the edge of the Plains and halted.

In *The Great Plains*, Walter P. Webb pointed out that for nearly two hundred and fifty years American settlers had advanced on the three legs of land, water, and timber. The Great Plains were notably deficient in water and timber, and consequently the old techniques of frontier advance could not serve. To go forward, pioneers had to discover new fencing and building materials and to devise new methods of obtaining water. In addition, the exceptionally able cavalry of the Plains Indians had to be subdued. In the 1870's pioneers drew up at the Plains, and there halted because they could not, by and large, cope with the overwhelmingly strange conditions. Instead of advancing into the semiarid grassland, they crossed over to the humid lands of Oregon and California. Only the seminomadic cattle herders successfully adapted to life on the Plains because they needed little timber and water. Few in number, they placed little strain on the limited resources. The six-shooter helped them to keep the Indians at a distance, if not subdued, and the

Army helped to maintain peace for the cattlemen, and sometimes among them.[2] Barbed wire and the windmill eventually allowed farmers to migrate onto the Plains, but the inventions and the migrations became important only in the 1880's.

In some favored places farmers could irrigate, but at the time, Americans lacked the technical skill for irrigation farming. Furthermore, the riparian water code imposed legal and institutional restraints on the settlers. The earliest pioneers knew nothing of a water law which permitted a stream to be used up. The Mormons, indeed, successfully irrigated as early as 1847, but religious fervor, unusual organization, and the invention of legal ideas about the use of water accounted for their success. Some time elapsed before typical American farmers accommodated themselves and their laws to life in a semiarid region. In the meantime, the Plains remained in the cattleman's domain.

Not until the early 1890's did farmers seriously begin to move onto the Plains. From 1850 to 1880 much excellent humid land existed in various places in the United States. Although fourteen arid western states contained about 50 per cent of the land area of the United States, the humid states contained the remaining 50 per cent of the land. Between 1850 and 1890, Americans used only about half their potential humid farm land.[3] After 1890, however, farmers rather rapidly cultivated this land, and only then did other farmers begin to surge onto the Great Plains. Before 1890, however, farmers had few incentives for moving onto the inhospitable Plains.

Improvements in technology caused agricultural productivity to rise consistently, while the need for farm labor steadily declined. On the whole, the farmers quite adequately supplied the nation with food and fiber. In 1870 each farm worker supported 5.14 persons, in 1880 he supported 5.57 persons, in 1890 he supported 5.77 persons, and in 1900 he supported 6.95 persons. In 1855 it took thirty-nine man hours to harvest forty bushels of corn, but by 1894 farmers averaged only fifteen man hours for the same amount of corn. On an average, each farmer doubled the amount of corn he could handle during this period. Similar gains could be seen in most crops. In cotton, where progress was least conspicuous, labor requirements fell by one-third between 1841 and 1895.[4] With a modestly growing population, the existing farmers could handle the demands of the nation. America did not need any increases in farmers or in farm land.

Simultaneously, more and more farmers tended toward commercial specialization. Commercialization came about primarily because of improvements in transportation which brought more and more farmers within reach of the market. "The cost of shipping a bushel of wheat between Chicago and Liverpool dropped from 38.4 cents in 1860 to 13.4 cents in 1890."[5] Under these circumstances, the area of wheat specialization could obviously expand greatly. No matter what the crop, more farmers could get into commercial production as the transportation system developed. Specialization brought efficiency on a greater scale to the American farm, and with efficiency came greater yields per farm and per farmer.

The declining need for farmers affected immigrants as well as natives. From 1880 to 1890 the Great Plains always received less than its share of immigrants. In every census period the Plains received comparatively fewer immigrants than it had in the previous period. The tremendous numbers of immigrants who arrived in the late nineteenth century seldom made their way to the Great Plains. Between 1881 and 1890 over five million immigrants arrived in the United States, but no more than three hundred and ninety-six thousand of them went to the Plains. Such increase in settlers as took place came from the movement of native farmers.[6] Neither immigrant nor native farmers pressed onto the Plains, and the area went by default to the frontier cattlemen.

The cattle industry of the Great Plains began in the eighteenth century in Texas and New Mexico when Spanish herdsmen introduced cattle into the area. American settlers continued the industry, and they soon added the blood lines of American cattle to the rugged but scrawny stock of the Mexicans. The herds roamed at large on the Plains with a minimum of supervision or care. Markets for good quality beef were not readily at hand, and consequently cattlemen had no incentive for high-quality production. They sold a few cattle however. They sold some in Texas, more in New Orleans, and in 1846 herders drove a thousand head to the Ohio Valley. During the Civil War people largely neglected the herds, but they multiplied anyway, and by 1865 some five million cattle roamed about in Texas. Most of these had no owners, and for a while, they remained unclaimed. During the winter of 1865–1866 various businessmen rounded up herds and in the spring of 1866 drovers began the first long drive to northern markets. The first long drive ended at Sedalia, Missouri, but the enterprise proved commercially unsatisfactory. Then, in 1867, Joseph McCoy had cattle brought by trail to Abilene, Kansas. In that year and later, other cattlemen followed his example and repeated his success. In the 1870's and 1880's cattle left Texas and headed to northern markets at the rate of about one million head a year. As time went on, the cattlemen progressively shifted the terminals westward to Newton, to Ellsworth, to Dodge City.[7]

Meanwhile, the range cattle industry expanded. Herdsmen drove cattle from Texas to ranges in the northern and central Plains of Colorado, Wyoming, Montana, Kansas, Nebraska, and the Dakotas. Cattlemen found that cattle fattened best on the grass of the northern Plains, and so the northern Plains became a feeding ground. On the other hand, cows on the northern Plains usually lived only to have about six calves, while on the southern Plains a cow lived to have about twelve calves. So, while feeding centered on the northern Plains, breeding came to be centered on the southern Plains. As the railroad network developed on the northern and central Plains, cattlemen moved in with more and more cattle. In the 1870's cattle grazing made its first permanent appearance in the northern Plains.

Kansas cattlemen in particular had made increasing use of the Hereford. Throughout the range country, stockmen bred up their herds. They did this by bringing in both grade and purebred Hereford bulls. Raised on free grass, and transported to market on their own legs, the cattle proved to be tremendously profitable. Now and then profits reached as high as 40 per cent on the invested capital.[8] In the late 1870's and early 1880's capital flowed onto the Plains and the industry expanded continuously, particularly in the north:

STATE OR TERRITORY	CATTLE IN 1860	CATTLE IN 1880
Kansas	93,455	1,533,133
Nebraska	37,197	1,113,247
Colorado	None	791,492
Wyoming	None	521,213
Montana	None	428,279
Dakota	None	140,815

Prices were good. Between 1878 and 1899 the price for western range cattle never fell below $3.10 per hundredweight, and once it rose to $4.75. At either price cattlemen had a considerable profit margin.[9] In 1882 the cattle industry hit its peak with the price of $4.75 per hundredweight. Then in 1884 the industry of the open range began to decline. Several events brought on this slow but certain collapse: northern states passed quarantine laws against Texas cattle; farmers began to move onto the better land; and a series of severe winters hit the range.

Texas cattle carried tick fever. The disease caused only sickness in these cattle, but it killed northern cattle. To prevent the spread of the disease in the northern Plains, various states passed quarantine laws. Kansas and Missouri passed such laws as early as 1867, but these pioneer laws merely inconvenienced the cattlemen.[10] In 1884 Kansas forbade the passage of Texas steers across her borders except in December, January, and February, and soon other states followed with laws of this sort. By 1886 the states had the laws working, and so made the free transit of cattle difficult if not impossible.[11]

Beginning in the 1880's a small trickle of farmers moved onto the Plains, took up land, and fenced it. They thereby caused the herdsmen inconvenience at the least, and at the worst drove them to the less desirable land. The settlers had the law with them since they either acquired title to the land, or at least took steps to acquire title. In contrast, the cattlemen merely grazed the land without legal claim. The cattlemen were nearly, but not quite, helpless. Sometimes the cattlemen fenced their range illegally in an effort to keep possession of it, sometimes they had their cowboys take out dummy homestead claims to lands with water on it. Only a few herdsmen managed to survive with these maneuvers once the farmers began to move in.[12]

While all this went on, weather hit the stockmen with dramatic blows. The first hint of the destruction to come occurred in 1884–1885 when a severe winter struck parts of the central Plains. A Kansas census-taker wrote in 1885: "Most of the cattle died for want of food and not being acclimated & for want of shelter." [13] Then came an extensive and killing winter in 1885–1886, and the series of disasters culminated in the general blizzard of 1886–1887. In this last blizzard herdsmen lost between 30 per cent and 80 per cent of their cattle on the northern Plains.[14] The open-range cattle industry never fully recovered from this blow.

The old-style open-range cattle industry came to an end, but the number of cattle on the Plains continued to increase. This increase in cattle, however, resulted from a new organization of the cattle business. By 1890 the range cattle industry had changed considerably, although it still closely resembled the earlier frontier industry. But change did come. For example, the cowboy now and again had to get off his horse and dig a post hole, or mow a hayfield. Still, in Montana, for example, the cattlemen held the last of their old-

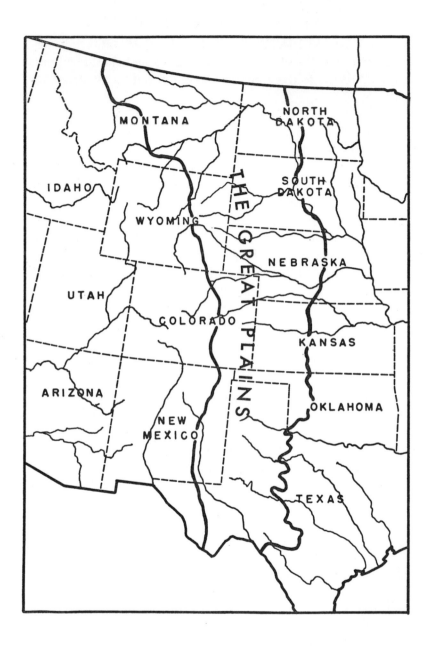

style roundups as late as 1906. The industry did not die all at once without warning.[15] The open range fell apart in a gradual crumbling.

Even so, quarantine, farmers, and blizzards failed to ruin all cattlemen. In the South some were not injured by blizzards, and even in the North a few managed to survive. Those who had grown some hay to feed animals across the winter came out fairly well. Some cattlemen even survived the influx of settlers. Stockmen who lived in places where farming was less practical avoided the first pressures. These remotely situated cattlemen often kept going by leasing public domain, and by otherwise adapting to the newer situation. Furthermore, the first advance of the farmers onto the Plains did not succeed entirely. Many farmers failed during the prolonged drouth of 1887–1897. In certain western counties of various states, farm population actually decreased. After the initial wave of homesteaders had been beaten back by the elements, some cattlemen managed to repossess the land, and of course, some of the homesteaders became cattlemen.[16]

The drouths on the Plains also hurt the open-range cattle industry. On the southern Plains especially, the drouth of 1892–1893 caused many of the cattlemen to leave the business. On the northern Plains, the drouth of 1895 hurt, as did that of 1897. Both farmers and cattlemen suffered losses and sometimes failed. Neither farmers nor herdsmen were especially fitted to survive. Toward the South, in Oklahoma and nearby regions, the severe winter of 1898–1899 killed from 20 to 50 per cent of the cattle by starvation. By 1897 only the northeastern counties of Montana could be fairly described as exclusively range in that state. Everywhere the farmers advanced at the expense of the range cattlemen.[17]

Not all the pressure on the herdsmen came from crop farmers. Part of the pressure came from a new type of cattleman who appeared on the Plains, and who cut into the available range and water resources. These pioneers rapidly became more of a threat to the old range cattlemen than the

crop farmers. The new-style cattlemen were able to survive
the assaults of nature, and at the same time they were also
equipped to force both herdsmen and farmers to the wall.
The evolution of these newer stockmen had been fairly long
in process, but after 1890 they became ever more prominent.
By the last days of the nineteenth century the future quite
obviously lay with the ranch farmers.[18]

The change in type of cattleman took place because the
need for beef continued. This need, however, could not be
met by an industry crippled by weather, homesteaders, and
cattle disease. So long as the market for meat held up, someone had to supply the commodity. Throughout the 1880's
and 1890's both the domestic and foreign markets appear to
have held up well. On the domestic scene the rising urban
population would probably have supported the market even
if per capita consumption had declined. Using the 1940
census classification (cities of 2,500 or more were considered
urban) the increases in total population and total urban
population were impressive: [19]

YEAR	TOTAL	URBAN	PER CENT OF TOTAL WHICH WAS URBAN
1880	50,155,783	14,129,735	28.1%
1890	62,947,714	22,106,265	35.1%
1900	75,994,575	30,159,921	39.6%

If these increasing millions had eaten just a little beef, the
Great Plains industry would have had plenty of customers.
Of course, whether people eat meat or not depends not only
on the number of people, but also on their income. Americans did not have large incomes. In fact, their incomes were
shamefully low. Even so, they had higher incomes than any
other people in the world, and between 1870 and 1910 economic conditions gradually improved. "Income per capita
in the United States (in terms of 1929 dollars) more than
doubled between 1870 and 1910, averaging $230 in 1870,
$315 in 1880, $385 in 1890, $458 in 1900, and $530 in 1910." [20]
Furthermore, Americans used their rising incomes to buy

better foods rather than more of the cheaper foods. A poor Boston seamstress told her butcher, "Do you suppose that because I don't come here in my carriage I don't want just as good meat as rich folks have?" [21] The demand for beef rose continually, although, unfortunately, clear statistics are not available before 1899. Americans did not necessarily want just more beef. They wanted the better kinds of beef. In a way, the increased income of the American people led them to demand a quality of beef which the open range could not, for the most part, supply. The declining number of cattle on American farms suggests more of a demand for quality than a decline in demand. Furthermore, as cattle husbandry improved, fewer head of cattle could produce the required amount and quality of meat. [22]

The open-range cattle industry had one serious flaw in that it supplied an uncertain quantity of meat of rather inferior quality. The industry could meet the demands of the expanding market only so long as cattlemen had absolutely free access to free grass, water, and trails. As these became even slightly limited, the old primitive system could not supply the consumer at a reasonable price. Most importantly, the old system was unreliable. Producers had to devise a system less subject to the assaults of nature. Cattlemen had to reach a new accommodation. They had to work out a reliable system of meat production that would meet more effectively the challenges of a hostile climate, and advancing hordes of farmers. The cattlemen of the Plains gradually adjusted to the demands of an industrial society, and they made this change within the confines of a disabling climate. Several major developments accounted for this evolution:

1. Transportation facilities continually grew and improved.
2. The tick succumbed to science and the quarantines ended.
3. Feeding of livestock supplemented open-range grazing.
4. New forage plants supplemented the native grasses.
5. Reliance on the range steadily decreased.

Continual expansion of the transportation system contributed to the evolution of the Plains cattle industry. Improvements were made also in transport. Railroads used larger rolling stock, more powerful engines, and more efficient refrigeration systems. Meat could be moved more rapidly, and thus as urban demand increased, the demand was more easily met.[23]

Quarantines against tick fever had been an important cause for the end of the old open range. Tick fever, sometimes called Texas fever, had come into this country in Colonial times, but had done its worst damage during the nineteenth century. In 1884, Theobald Smith, of the Bureau of Animal Industry, began working on the disease. In 1890 Smith began seriously to investigate the tick as a vector for the disease. He found the tick to be guilty, and in 1893 he published his results. Control of the disease now became possible. Someone merely had to find a way to eliminate the tick. At first the disease had been controlled by restricting the movement of cattle. Unquestionably quarantines had worked, but they did not control the disease where it was endemic. Quarantines also seriously hampered cattle movements. In 1897, at Fort Worth, Texas, scientists experimented with cattle-dipping to kill ticks. Dipping proved so successful that in 1898 all states removed their quarantines against southern cattle, provided these cattle had been dipped under the supervision of the Bureau of Animal Industry. Shortly thereafter, dipping stations appeared all over the South. As the twentieth century opened, the quarantine no longer completely impeded the movement of cattle.[24]

New methods of cattle husbandry formed an element in the readjustment of the industry. The older cattlemen had only owned a small amount of land, and they seldom had taken any great precautions to lay up supplies of feed for drouth or winter. In contrast, the new cattlemen raised forage crops to feed their cattle across critical seasons. They also tried to control the quality of their stock by owning and fencing part of their pasture land. They came to rotate pastures as a matter of ordinary practice, and some undertook reseeding of grasses. Where practicable the new-style cattlemen developed irrigation. None of these practices swept the industry, but, here and there, individuals began the change. Where they could not irrigate, cattlemen came (in the 1890's) to rely more and more on the new techniques of dry farming as a way of growing emergency feed supplies. All of these changes were taking place through the late 1880's and early 1890's.[25] "In northern Montana on the Sun River, T. C. Power had 5,000 acres enclosed, of which 300 were seeded with timothy and the remainder devoted to pastures and feeding grounds."[26] This happened as early as 1886. T. C. Power was not typical, but his experiment happened to point the way for the industry for the next twenty years.

The new industry chiefly depended on the growing of supplemental feeds. The introduction of various new forage and range crops reflected and contributed to this change. Alfalfa was the oldest of these crops in the United States. Alfalfa came into the country as early as the seventeenth century, but it spread most rapidly and widely after its introduction into California from Chile in 1854. Gradually it was adopted for use on the Plains. But for all its virtues, alfalfa did not prove entirely satisfactory, and apparently cattlemen seldom used it as late as 1885.[27]

In the 1870's the sorghums were introduced onto the southern Plains and soon took the area by storm.[28] At first it was the sorgo or sugar varieties that interested cattlemen, but milo, a grain variety, excited some interest in Texas as early as 1882. In the 1880's Kansas farmers raised various varieties of sorghum as forage crops. By the early 1890's most of the newer cattlemen had discovered "that sorghum was one crop that never failed—that is, almost never. Thus they had found another certainty in crop selection." By the 1890's few other crops were seriously considered as reliable for forage.[29] In the 1890's the grain sorghums also became important as forage crops for the stockmen of the southern

Plains. Sorghum was comparatively immune to drouth, a virtue cattlemen soon widely recognized. The introduction and use of this interesting plant was an important and perhaps even necessary step in the development of the new ranch farming.[30]

The grain sorghums received national recognition as drouth-resistant plants in 1892, but by then most Plains cattlemen knew about their virtues. Even in the northern Plains, where cattlemen seldom could use sorghums, scientists experimented to find varieties with a short growing season. For a while, kaffir held the stage in the Dakotas and Montana.[31]

Sorghum resisted drouth well because extensive drying did not kill the plant, and when moisture became available again the plant once again began to grow. Grasshoppers ate it only as a last resort, and in years of grasshoppers or drouth, often sorghum alone yielded a crop.[32] In places where cattlemen could not irrigate, sorghums proved to be an indispensable forage crop for the new ranch-farming complex.

In 1898, plant explorers brought crested wheatgrass to the United States from Russia. This important forage grass resisted both cold and drouth and thus was admirably suited to the needs of the northern Plains. Although introduced in 1898, no one distributed the seeds extensively until the twentieth century. Nevertheless, the new grass contributed to the changing cattle industry of the Plains.[33]

For the newer cattle industry, irrigated land provided a sure supply of forage to carry cattle through blizzards or drouth. In the 1880's and 1890's several cattlemen built small irrigation systems, and these immeasurably helped these ranch farmers in the winters of 1884–1887, and the drouth of 1887–1897. Few used irrigated pastures and hay-fields, however, because cattlemen generally found the systems too expensive to build. What some cattlemen did by irrigation suggested what others might do, but irrigation did not prevail through the Plains cattle industry. In 1894 the Congress passed the Carey Act. This law gave states land if they would construct irrigation works, but the states did virtually nothing under the act, mostly because the Panic of 1893 left them too weak financially to undertake public works. The Newlands Act of 1902 called for federal building of some irrigation projects on the Plains, but this came in the twentieth century.[34]

New patterns of land tenure also indicated the changes in the cattle business. More cattlemen owned a larger share of their land. From 1870 to 1900 the average size of a Great Plains farm or ranch consistently increased. In 1870 Plains farms averaged 169.1 acres; in 1880 they averaged 207.5 acres; in 1890, 267.7 acres; and in 1900 the average came to 491.8 acres. Simultaneously, the number of cattle on these farms and ranches constantly increased.[35] Of course, almost all cattlemen still relied heavily on the federal range. Nevertheless, the cattle industry was becoming less an adventure and more a business.

The changes, although impressive, only pointed out a trend. The nineteenth-century cattle industry remained a range enterprise, even if the range was no longer fully open, and the grass no longer completely free. In 1880, for example, over 96 per cent of all livestock feed came from the range. In 1890, this figure had lowered slightly to 95 per cent, and in 1900, 92 per cent of the feed came from this source. This slightly decreased reliance on the range did not amount to a revolution in the cattle industry, but the change did outline a path of evolution.[36]

As cattlemen came to rely less on the range, some of them tried to get the federal government to control the public lands more effectively. As early as 1899, cattlemen sought laws to bring about closer federal control of the public range. No altruism was involved. Primarily these cattlemen wanted to have the grazing lands more nearly restricted to themselves. Nevertheless, their request for some control indicated a new approach to the range and to the cattle business. The bill of 1899 did not pass.[37]

The simple and primitive cattle-herding business began

in Texas; by the 1870's it had spread to all the Plains. Quarantine, homesteaders, blizzards, and drouths all conspired to force the old open-range herdsmen out of business. The ever-growing urban population of the Republic still needed beef, however, and so the industry of the Plains was transformed rather than killed. The newer stockmen made greater use of supplemental feeds, they cared for their stock more carefully, they owned a larger amount of their land, and by all these and other methods, they increased both the quantity and quality of beef. At the close of the nineteenth century per capita consumption of beef and veal came to 72.4 pounds. In response to this demand plainsmen undertook a major revision of the cattle industry on the Great Plains.[38]

CHAPTER II

The Controlled Range
1900-1905

In the first years of the twentieth century, Americans ate more beef than ever before, with the cattlemen of the Plains developing methods for supplying the people. From 1900 to 1905, each person ate an average of 74.7 pounds of beef. In 1900, per capita consumption stood at 72.3 pounds, but by 1905, it stood at 77.9 pounds for each American. Since the number of people constantly was increasing, the people ate much more meat than the per capita figures suggest.[1]

Furthermore, the human population grew much faster than the cattle population. Cattle numbers reached a peak in 1900, and then actually declined on American farms. The higher beef-consumption levels indicated that fewer cattle were producing more meat. Americans ate more beef, but they also insisted on higher quality and so cattlemen had to produce higher-quality cattle. Many Plains stockmen responded to the changed conditions. Those who successfully continued in the business discovered that only more careful husbandry could meet the new challenge; the old herdsmen either changed their methods or got out.[2]

Although population grew in all parts of America, it grew most spectacularly on the West Coast. Throughout the twentieth century, cattlemen of the Plains found ever-greater markets there. The growth of this new urban market, apparent even as early as 1900, caused some Plains stockmen to accommodate to two different selling conditions. All over the country, however, consumers were demanding quality;

the increase in Western consumers merely gave cattlemen greater opportunities.[3]

Simultaneously, the foreign market held up well. Between 1900 and 1905, fresh-beef exports increased greatly. Even so, however, each year the American cattleman's share of the foreign market decreased because even though foreign demand was growing, other beef-producing countries were exporting more. Argentina, for example, rose rapidly as a meat exporter. Nevertheless, in 1905, the United States still led the world in beef exports. The English bought more beef than any other people, and Englishmen, like Americans, insisted on quality as well as quantity. Foreign consumers thus also helped force Plains stockmen to improve both their methods of breeding and of feeding.[4]

The export market brought other changes in American beef production. Europeans sometimes complained about the impurity of American meat. In order that Americans might continue to sell to Europeans, the Bureau of Animal Industry as early as 1891 had been authorized to inspect the processing of meat at slaughterhouses when the meat went into interstate or foreign commerce. In 1903, and in 1905, Congress also authorized the Bureau to prevent the interstate and foreign shipment of diseased animals. These regulations changed some packing practices. They also forced stockmen to take better care of their cattle.[5]

Changes in the meat-packing industry also affected the Plains cattlemen. Although a centralized packing industry had begun in the nineteenth century, the industry had migrated westward rather slowly. In the early twentieth century, however, meat slaughtering fell precipitously in eastern cities, while it boomed in western cities. For example, the value of meat products slaughtered at Boston fell from $7,096,777 in 1880, to $1,392,010 in 1900. At the same time, the value of meat products slaughtered at Chicago rose from $85,324,371 in 1880, to $256,752,949 in 1900. As the packers moved west, the cattlemen of the Great Plains had more opportunities to supply the ever-increasing urban population. The increase in consumers also gave Plains cattlemen incentives for more efficient production.[6]

Cattlemen enjoyed these incentives for a little while, and then around 1903 the packers set up the Beef Trust. This combine tended to deprive cattlemen of the price incentives which they might have had in a freer market. Cattlemen protested the monopolistic tendencies in the packing industry, but the complaints reached a crescendo only after 1905.[7] Meanwhile, as the packing industry moved westward, so did the center of beef cattle production. In 1900 the center stood at Waverly, Kansas. The center of beef production had shifted south and westward since the nineteenth century. Southwestern cattlemen had apparently recovered from the drouth, and they were also achieving control of the tick.[8] Consequently, their beef production actually grew.

Americans were eating more and more beef, but at no time did the price of western cattle reflect this demand accurately. Between 1900 and 1902 prices for western range cattle increased steadily, but between 1903 and 1905 they fell sharply. In 1900 western cattle averaged $4.35 a hundredweight, but by 1905 western cattle sold for only $3.80 a hundred. This price trend proved temporary, however, and in 1906 Plains cattle brought an average of $4.40 per hundred.[9] Even at these prices cattlemen could have profited if their costs had not risen because they were being deprived of the free grass of the open range. Furthermore, as cattlemen and farmers competed for land, cattlemen had to buy or lease expensive land. This also raised costs. Then too, the incoming farmers demanded more governmental services. These services in turn required heavier taxes which produced another rise in costs. The cutting-up of the open range generally restricted stockmen to the least productive, that is, the most expensive land. Nevertheless, cattlemen could make out, particularly if they shifted to ranch farming.[10]

Some cattlemen, of course, complained about the poor cattle prices, and when they did they most often blamed the

Beef Trust for the situation. The prices for ordinary range cattle might have been low, however, even if a beef trust had never existed. Range cattle, after all, very often did not meet the quality standards demanded by many domestic consumers. Whatever the reason, low prices hurt even more because of the difficulty many cattlemen had of getting credit. When they did find credit they paid very high interest rates. And it was certainly true that cattlemen found it hard to pay off their debts even when they found someone to lend them money. When cattlemen shifted to ranch farming they had to invest more heavily in land and cattle. Often the shift in method cost more than the producer could afford at the existing beef prices. Their dilemma arose from their realization that, for the most part, they could survive only if they took up the new way of life. One Montana editor commented on the new-style cattlemen: "The indications now are that eighty per cent. of these adventurers will succeed and now when they get out of debt they will be fixed for life." [11] The editor may have been too optimistic in his prediction. Still, as he noted: "We know a few men who refused to make the investment in range lands who amassed between fifteen and twenty thousand dollars but they are now virtually out of the business." [12] Economic events helped push stockmen into a newer form of cattle husbandry. Unquestionably, higher meat prices would have made the transition easier for them.

In short, the evolution of the cattle industry was accelerated by (1) the demand for higher-quality beef (2) the lower cattle prices, and (3) the continually rising costs of production. In addition, cattlemen continually had to adapt to the never-ending pressures of weather. On the northern Plains stockmen suffered from drouths in 1900, 1902, and 1903. On the southern Plains their worst years were 1900 and 1902. Bad as these drouths were, they merely speeded changes in cattle husbandry. They did not destroy very many cattle. The weather was good, however, in 1904 and 1905.[13]

The railroads also continued to plague cattlemen. For a generation or more, western farmers had viewed the railroads ambivalently. The railroads were indispensable to successful farming, and were abominable because they were so necessary. The open-range herdsmen had early come to dislike the railroads, and with reason, because the railroads hastened the end of the open range. As the twentieth century opened, the railroads continued to produce changes in the cattle industry. For one thing, railroad mileage on the Plains increased steadily. The railroads also systematically destroyed what remained of the open range. In doing this they speeded the evolution of the cattle industry from herding to ranch farming. The railroaders themselves apparently thought that they were introducing crop farming. In reality, they were setting the stage for the misery and failure of crop farmers. Without knowing what they were doing, the railroaders inadvertently helped convert cattlemen to ranch farming.

The railroad builders particularly urged the development of dry farming on the Plains. Settlers came from the East, enticed by the propaganda of the railroaders. James J. Hill, a phenomenal promoter, especially urged more and more dry farming on the Plains. Even some of the older settlers on the Plains welcomed both the farmers and the railroad.[14] Thus, as the railroad advanced, so also did the dry farmer. Railroads in the Plains states increased from 42,601 miles in 1900 to 57,902 miles in 1910. Not all of this was on the Plains proper, but much of it was.[15] For example, the Chicago, Milwaukee, St. Paul and Pacific Railroad began to build onto the Plains in 1906, and in 1907 reached Butte. By 1909 the line ran to Seattle. Other railroads showed similar expansion. The Rock Island consolidated roads, and built into Texas and other areas between 1901 and 1906.[16] Similar tales could be told for other parts of the Plains.

The railroads kept coming and so did the farmers. These farmers usually engaged in dry farming. Their method of agriculture involved some fairly precise principles:

1. They fallowed or summer fallowed in order to allow a reserve of moisture to accumulate so that they could grow a crop.

2. They spaced their crops widely, and carefully eradicated weeds in order to reduce the drain on vital water.

3. They grew drouth-resistant plants whenever possible and profitable.[17]

Dry farming worked rather well in some years. Between 1900 and 1905 the system got its first real hold on the Plains, and editors and others saw it as the route to economic improvement. Even cattlemen were not always hostile to the new crop-farming method. They saw it as a way of producing fodder for drouth or winter feeding. The fallow period, however, was especially dangerous, for then the land lay open to dust blowing, and the loss of precious topsoil could ruin the farmers. Jim Hill, Hardy W. Campbell, and the other apostles of dry farming did not immediately recognize this hazard. Old-time cattlemen, among others, saw the danger, but they were pretty largely silenced as the dry farming boom hit the Plains in the early twentieth century.[18]

Dry farmers flooded onto the Plains. The population of the Plains states rose steadily. Between 1900 and 1910 the number of people increased from 8,167,482 to 11,246,147, or 37.6 per cent. The four southern Plains states got more immigrants than the rest of the Plains together. Southern population rose 46 per cent between 1900 and 1910. The six northern Plains states increased only 27 per cent in the same period. The new settlers unavoidably moved onto the former grazing land of some cattleman. While the farmers pressed onto the grazing land, herdsmen of the open range transferred their cattle to the east. The earlier farming boom of the 1880's and 1890's had failed, but failure had taught people virtually nothing. As one old cattleman saw it, the earlier boom only ". . . opened the eyes of hundreds of thousands of Eastern and Middle States farmers to the possibilities of the West. It showed what might be done if agriculture could conquer the lands that had been included in the semi-arid region. This agriculture has proceeded to do." [19]

Agriculture conquered the arid Plains, but in a peculiar fashion. The early dry farmers soon found that livestock was their most profitable enterprise. They plowed the fields, but the haystack was the common visible evidence of their occupation. In legions the nesters went quickly into the cattle business. The crops they most often mentioned as profitable were sorghum and alfalfa. Neither was a cereal crop, but both were fed to cattle.[20]

Northern plainsmen needed feed for the winter, and southern plainsmen needed feed for the dry summer. These needs accounted for most of the farmer and stockman interest in the ranch-farming complex. By 1900 only 5 per cent of the cattle on the Plains were kept exclusively on the open range. The remaining cattle all received some supplemental feed, or grazed on owned or leased land. By 1903, for example, practically all Montana cattlemen joined the ranks of winter feeders, although they sometimes fed only a portion of their stock for a few weeks. On the whole, they shifted only a little, since in 1900 some 92 per cent of all their livestock feed still came from the range. Trivial as the remaining 8 per cent seems, it indicated a complete revolution in the cattle industry of the Plains.[21]

On the northern Plains some cattlemen adopted winter feeding as enthusiastically as they had previously embraced herding. A few even devoted their full attention to hay ranches and ceased breeding in favor of winter feeding. Whether the cattlemen followed full winter feeding, or only supplementary feeding, they usually did not follow very advanced methods. They cut the hay by mower, gathered by horse rake, and stacked by hand.

While this aspect of the enterprise remained comparatively primitive, scientists introduced new hays which brought greater profit to those who used them. Alfalfa became increasingly more prominent on the ranch farms, and successful stockmen continually expounded on its virtues.

A few pioneers introduced and grew bromegrass (*Bromus enctus* and *Bromus inermis*). On the southern Plains, experiments with the sorghums continued, and around 1904 experimenters tried to introduce the grain sorghums onto the Plains. "It was soon found that the drouth-resisting qualities of the grain sorghums would let them serve as the corn of the plains." [22] Which they did. In time, newer cattle feeds gradually appeared all over the semiarid Plains.

The ranch farmers, large and small, favored the Hereford as their beef animal. For half a century Herefords dominated the Great Plains. Nevertheless, at the turn of the century a few cattlemen challenged the position of the Herefords. One of the important events in the history of breeds and breeding took place in 1904 at the St. Louis Exposition. Here, Carl Hagenbeck, of Germany, exhibited some "Sacred Humpbacked Zebus from India." One Al McFaddin of Texas was so taken by the strange animals that he bought a pair. The cow died shortly, but using the bull, McFaddin began breeding grade Brahman cattle on his ranch. In 1905 the Secretary of Agriculture, James Wilson, visited Texas and quickly became interested in the cattle. Wilson cleared away some red tape and authorized O. P. Borden to import more of the cattle. In 1905, Borden left the United States for India, and in 1906 brought back the first purebred Brahma herd to enter the country. At first only a few enthusiasts favored the strange-looking zebus, but in time other cattlemen developed an interest in the breed.[23]

Cattlemen not only employed new plants and new animals, but new methods. Aside from dry farming, these new methods centered chiefly on range management, or techniques for making the best possible use of the natural pastures of the Plains. Overstocking and overgrazing had slowly injured both cattlemen and their range. On the southern Plains some cattlemen noted the damages of overgrazing at least as early as 1902, but no one did anything to halt the destruction. Texas changed her range-leasing law in 1901 in a way which tended to reduce the problem of overgrazing, but this was nearly the only significant development in range management in the South. On the northern Plains, as early as 1901, Elias Nelson, of the Wyoming Experiment Station, suggested rotation of grazing to stop grass and soil depletion. His ideas impressed a later generation more than they did his own. On the whole, few ranch farmers did anything to halt the destruction of the range.[24] Of course, ranch farmers automatically followed some conservation methods. So long as they did not increase their herds, their shift to a dependence on forage crops resulted in less damage to pastures.

Many cattlemen reduced the use of their range by growing supplemental feeds on irrigated fields. Irrigation apparently became commoner as the century wore on. In the Southwest the stockmen in certain favored areas tried irrigation, and indeed, experiments in irrigation extended northward through Kansas to Montana. The chief forage crop grown on irrigated land was alfalfa. In some cases, farmers got large alfalfa yields, and the irrigation proved extremely successful. In other cases, stockmen who tried irrigation barely produced drinking water for cattle.[25] In 1902, when Congress passed the Newlands Act under which the federal government built irrigation systems, the act did not produce any great benefits for cattlemen on the Plains.

Out on the Plains, nothing spectacular happened in the early twentieth century, but certain obvious changes took place in the cattle industry: cattlemen in the North fully adopted winter feeding; more cattlemen used alfalfa and sorghum for fodder; stockmen adopted dry farming techniques oftener; and more stockmen practiced irrigation for feed production. Several results flowed from these changes. For one thing, the number of farms in the Plains states increased regularly between 1890 and 1900. Percentage increases in numbers of farms ranged from 608.1 per cent in Oklahoma to 3.9 per cent in Kansas. The median average increase in farms was 59.3 per cent for the Great Plains, compared to an increase for the United States of only 25.7 per cent. Taking one place with another, the number of farms started on the Plains dwarfed the national growth.[26]

At the same time, the number of cattle per farm or ranch decreased as ranch farming developed. Between 1900 and 1910 the number of cattle on the Plains states fell 36.7 per cent, dropping from 23,298,140 head down to 17,040,795 head. In part, declining cattle numbers probably resulted from a more rapid turnover of livestock. For example, in 1900, on the average, cattlemen sold their fat steers six months younger than they had back in 1890. Since Americans did not import much beef and at the same time ate more, the beef obviously came from American farms and ranches.[27] More cattle came from the Midwest than from the Plains, but even so, total American production also declined. A more rapid marketing could very easily account for the phenomenon of declining cattle and increased beef.

In the first instance, then, the developing ranch farming led in part to quality beef, and in part to a reduction in the number of cattle kept on each ranch farm. This change also resulted from more careful husbandry, more careful culling of herds, and better breeding with higher calf-crops.

As their whole complex of ranch farming developed, cattlemen came to adopt new views of the public domain. In 1900 the National Cattlemen's Association lobbied in Congress for a federal land-leasing bill. The sponsors intended to keep the range under the control of those who were then using it, but leasing ran counter to that herdsman instinct which still predominated in some places. In 1900, for example, the Montana stockgrowers opposed a federal leasing bill. They wanted the range free, and to secure this they even proposed that the federal domain be turned over to the states. This idea of surrender to the states came up again and again right on up to 1906. By 1906, however, Montana cattlemen, and presumably cattlemen in other places, reluctantly advocated the leasing of the federal domain.[28] However, no law passed;

most of the domain remained uncontrolled; and each year less of it was left.

Some Forest Reserves had been created from federal land as early as 1891, and from time to time some grazing land had been declared forest and reserved from entry. In 1900 the Foresters first required cattlemen to obtain permits before grazing cattle on the National Forests. Forest supervisors gave residents within the reserve first chance for permits. Others could also receive permits. The order of claim went from nonresident ranchers on down to rank outsiders.[29]

At this time the Department of Interior controlled the Forests. Cattlemen near the Forests who wanted even less control than they were getting, thought they would be less regulated by the Department of Agriculture. So various sources pressured the Congress (for a variety of reasons), and in 1905 Congress transferred the Forests to Agriculture. Before long, some cattlemen, particularly holdovers from the heroic age, complained because they could not do exactly as they pleased with the National Forests.[30] An unending controversy between private greed and public good opened in 1905. For the most part, the protagonists rarely saw any way to compromise their viewpoints. But at any rate, overgrazing on the Forests declined to negligible proportions.

Federal activity extended well beyond tentative efforts to control the range. In 1901 the Division of Animal Husbandry was formed with the appointment of an expert in the breeding and management of livestock. The federal government tried also to improve the quality of beef by quarantining livestock in order to prevent interstate shipment of diseased animals; the acts of 1903 and 1905 prevented international trade in diseased livestock. Congress also established enforcement agencies in the Department of Agriculture. Thus the earlier state efforts at disease control came to be supplemented by federal laws.[31]

Meanwhile, scientists of the Bureau of Animal Industry continued to work on eliminating the tick. They tried various cattle dips, but they found crude mineral oil to be most effective. Workers and scientists used it "almost exclusively from 1903 to 1911. . . ." Having hit on a satisfactory dip in 1903, the bureau began a systematic plan for eradication in 1905. The workers in the bureau relied on state and local help. In a few years their program achieved remarkable results. Even as early as 1905 they had gotten better control of the ticks than before.[32]

New circumstances in the industry seemed to require new institutions. Sectional disagreements among cattlemen (possibly about quarantines and the open range) led to the first chipping away of the old National Cattlemen's Association. In 1901 some stockmen formed the American Cattle Growers' Association. In 1905, however, the National Cattlemen's Association really split when a large number of dissidents walked out and formed the American Stock Growers' Association, later to become the American National Livestock Association. Will Barnes, one of the founders and first secretary, recalled that the row which led to the break came about, in part, because the packers tried to influence the affairs of the older organization. Barnes observed, "we cowmen had a foolish idea that the packers, the live-stock commission men, the stock-yard owners, and the railroad officials were responsible for most of our sorrows. (There was no Forest Service then to blame it all on.)" In retrospect, it appears possible that the new-style cattlemen needed an organization which would represent the ranch farmer rather than the open-range herder. In any case, the new Stock Growers' Association, with Murdo Mackenzie at the head, reflected a newer approach to the problems of the Great Plains cattleman.[33]

In the first six years of the twentieth century, this then, briefly, is what happened. Cattlemen were forced, some of them reluctantly, to produce higher-quality beef on fewer acres. Changes in meat packing and consumer demand partly introduced the new approach. As settlers flooded onto the Plains they compelled cattlemen to readjust. The pioneer farmers undertook a gigantic experiment in dry farming, and although the techniques turned out to be less than over-whelmingly successful for crop farmers, they proved valuable for stockmen. Cattlemen almost all turned to raising some supplementary feed, and on the northern Plains winter feeding became customary. In spite of these developments, most cattlemen continued to depend on the range for most of their feed.

The raising of supplemental feed speeded the adoption of new forage plants. In conjunction with feeding, some few cattlemen placed a slight emphasis on range management. This evolutionary alteration did not extend to cattle breeding, except that some stockmen improved their herds of Herefords. Irrigation remained unimportant to most cattlemen. Ranchers did come to own more land and fewer cattle, but at the same time they increased their meat production. More meat for each animal characterized the period of change.

The federal government increasingly entered the business scene in the twentieth century. This development could be noted even on the Plains where government actively intervened in land policy and disease control. Policy on the National Forests was already irritating some cattlemen. Meanwhile, the stockmen formed new institutions to lobby for them. The evolution of the Plains cattle industry continued.

CHAPTER III

New Accommodations
1906-1910

By births and by immigration the population of the United States rose between 1906 and 1910. In 1906 the people of the United States numbered an estimated 85,837,000, but by 1910 they had increased to 92,267,000—a growth of 7.4 per cent. Most of the increase was urban. In 1900 the urban count came to 30,380,000, or 40 per cent of the total. By 1910 urbanites numbered 42,166,000, or 45.8 per cent of the total.[1]

The chief challenge to the Plains cattle producers was to supply these ever-multiplying consumers, and they, along with stockmen from all parts of the country, apparently responded to the challenge since per capita meat consumption continued to rise. The per capita consumption of beef and veal that had averaged only 77.9 pounds between 1900 and 1905 rose one pound between 1906 and 1910. Between 1906 and 1910 Americans consumed 78.9 pounds of beef and veal per capita each year. In 1910 per capita consumption fell to a low of 77.6 pounds, but even this was not much below the average of the preceding five years.[2] Whatever their problems, cattlemen did not suffer from a shrinking market.

The total commercial slaughter of cattle and calves increased between 1907 and 1910. Only in 1908 did slaughter drop rather significantly. On the whole, the increasing population and growing meat consumption provided potential rewards for more intensive meat production.[3]

People ate more meat, and cattlemen could have responded in several ways. First of all, stockmen could have embraced more fully the ranch farming techniques then in vogue. They could have used more supplemental fodder, they could have managed the range better, and they could have employed both dry farming and irrigation more intensively. In short, the cattlemen could have committed themselves more wholeheartedly to intensive cattle raising, and they probably could have done this within the existing financial structure. They could have, but many of them considered ranch farming an unpleasant and temporary makeshift. They changed their methods, but reluctantly and incompletely.

Second, the cattlemen might have more completely recognized the pre-eminent rights of the American people. For example, cattlemen might have more readily accommodated themselves to federal intervention in their affairs. In particular, the objectives of the Forest Service might have been more quickly and gracefully accepted. Furthermore, cattlemen might have offered less resistance to tick eradication programs. Cattlemen hurt themselves as they strove against the public good.

Other possible adjustments could not be directly controlled by the cattlemen. For example, the packers might have taken a smaller profit on their operations, and they might have attempted less control over the market place. If packers had been less acquisitive, the period of transition might have been less difficult for the cattlemen. In addition, beef consumption in the United States might have increased more than it did. Packer collusion penalized consumers as well as producers.

In the general adjustment, railroad officials might have spent less effort booming the wheat industry, and more effort improving the cattle industry. Admittedly, dry farming on the Plains was inevitable, and in many areas the change was economically sound. Railroad officials, however, emphasized wheat in a way which neither helped the plainsmen, nor benefited the cattle industry. In short, although cattlemen and others made the necessary accommodations, the changes could have been quicker and smoother. Still, cattlemen did make some remarkable adjustments between 1906 and 1910.

Farmers flooding onto the Plains presented the cattlemen with their first challenge. In 1906 Congress established a Bureau of Dry Land Agriculture in the Department of Agriculture, and this event stimulated a new advance of farmers. On the northern Plains homesteading went forward rapidly. The total area put to the plow was not great, probably not more than 10 per cent of the total, but it was the best land. The rush of settlers really began in 1908, or thereabouts, and continued in volume past 1910. Early settlers had good luck, and in favored areas commonly received yields of forty to fifty bushels of wheat to an acre. The word spread to the East. Then, in 1909, Congress passed the Enlarged Homestead Act which gave settlers three hundred and twenty acres of dry land, provided that they cultivated one-fourth of it. This act encouraged more settlers to move onto the Plains. The farmers continually deprived cattlemen of more and more pasture lands.[4] After 1909 most of the settlers in the northern Plains had to take up dry lands with scanty water resources.[5] This hurt cattlemen some, but created a potentially more dangerous situation for farmers.

Although the dry farmers almost all specialized in wheat, they almost all kept some livestock also. Farmers who raised nothing but wheat were particularly vulnerable to weather and markets. Even some of the apostles of dry farming worried about this instability. Scientists and others increasingly talked about "diversified farming." They used the term rather imprecisely, but when all is said and done, most of them meant a form of ranch farming with major reliance on beef steers. Not all of them meant this. Thomas Shaw of the Montana Experiment Station urged farmers to think in terms of livestock, and Shaw meant a varied livestock composed of more than just steers. Nevertheless, most farmers apparently understood him to mean mostly steers. As time went on, fewer and fewer farmers relied on wheat alone, and in time of drouth, livestock sometimes enabled the dry farmers to survive. Between 1906 and 1910, the amount of wheat produced on the Plains apparently actually decreased. Drouth in 1910 hurt that crop, but production had been going down anyhow. In 1906 farmers harvested some 209,348,000 bushels of wheat on the Plains; by 1910 wheat farmers harvested only 177,903,000 bushels on the Plains.[6] Nevertheless, farmers on the Plains preponderantly depended on wheat, and the flood of settlers became ever more important for cattlemen as time went on.[7]

Wheat farmers, however, had not yet been conspicuously successful, and so stockmen managed to continue in their business. When dry farmers gave up, as they sometimes did, they saddled the land with an inflated value and an inflated tax assessment which in turn left cattlemen with high and unrealistic costs. More to the point, the cattlemen remained. Those cattlemen who stayed relied more heavily on crops and less on range pasturage. Improved ranch farming overcame some of the costs, met the challenge of the market, and permitted some agricultural use of the land.[8]

To some extent the government restricted the surge of settlers, but the old-timers saw this as a mixed blessing. The creation of National Forests prevented homesteading of some land, but at the same time, the Foresters supervised grazing on the Forests. Formerly free range shrank not only because of settlers moving in, but also because the federal government created Forests. To assist in grazing supervision, and to make the Forests carry their own expenses, in 1906 the Department of Agriculture assessed grazing fees on all Forest users. The fees not only produced a modest revenue, but made control of grazing easier.[9]

The permit system of the Forest Service accomplished more than a leasing system could have. Under the permit system the Foresters could restrict the number of animals grazed. Under a leasing system, especially for short-term leases, grazing would have remained uncontrolled, and cattlemen would have had an incentive for overstocking. Apparently some cattlemen wanted to overstock. At any rate, various herdsmen were continually suggesting the creation of a leasing system. Usually cattlemen wanted almost all of the public lands reserved from entry and put on a leasing arrangement. Had this program been adopted, cattlemen would have been free from both settlers and regulation. Such a system would have delayed the full adoption of ranch-farming techniques, and would have led to further destruction of the range. Congress rejected it.[10]

As homesteading continued, cattlemen had to use the Forests for summer grazing more frequently. The shortage of well-managed range became more acute when Congress passed a Forest Homestead Act in 1906. This act made homesteading possible in some Forests under certain conditions, and thus tended to reduce the amount of Forest grazing land.[11]

From the first the Forest Service encountered opposition from cattlemen who objected to paying for grazing privileges, and at first fees were more easily assessed than collected. Further, cattlemen were not accustomed to thinking in terms of restricted allotments, and as Supervisor E. C. Russell observed, they "took personal offence at Forest officers when they moved them back to the range allotted to them." [12] But these problems were only temporary. Stockmen adjusted to the regulations even though they did not always like them. On this point cattlemen did not all agree because some of them considered the regulations to be a good method for preserving the range. In any case, the Forests did inhibit the influx of settlers. Cattlemen in Wyoming even passed resolutions praising the Forest Service, its program, and its protector, President Theodore Roosevelt.[13]

Between 1906 and 1909 Forest Service officers worked out the details of Forest administration. Forest acreage amounted to little on the Plains, but it was here that government officials first developed techniques of range regulation. Generally, the service aimed to have the land grazed, but sought to restrict use to a level which the range could support. At the same time the service definitely discouraged the use of the grass by herdsmen, or, as they were coming to be called, "tramp cattlemen." In this period the amount of land under supervision nearly doubled. By 1909 nearly 100 million acres of land were controlled by the Forest Service. In 1909, Albert F. Potter, Chief of Grazing, met with Forest users in Washington, and as a result of the conference, he had the administration of the Forests transferred from Washington to six western Forest Districts. Thereafter, stockmen seem to have approved of the Forest Service and its activities, although they occasionally protested the grazing fees.[14]

In 1907 Congress set the minimum grazing fees at twenty to thirty-five cents per animal unit, or thirty-five to fifty cents per unit per annum.[15] The Congress also provided that as the Forest range came into greater demand the fees could be raised. In 1910 the service raised fees slightly on some Forests. The new charges ranged from thirty-five to sixty cents per animal unit. Around 1910 the Forest Service also began systematic codification of regulations, and although these were too rigid and later had to be changed, they at least established a formal base for the operation of the service. On the whole, the grazing regulations were clear and direct, and greatly facilitated the operation of the Forests.[16]

Whether they admitted it or not, the Foresters aimed, in part, to encourage cattlemen to rely less on the range and more on ranch farming. Or, as one commentator put it, they aimed at "the elimination of tramp and alien stockmen, and the encouragement of citizens and home builders. . . ."[17] The Forest Service ultimately achieved this. Of course, the Forest supervisors were not fully responsible, and probably not even chiefly responsible for the changing pattern of the cattle industry. Still, they did their bit, and ranch farming progressed rapidly after 1906. In 1910 Plains cattlemen obtained only 84 per cent of their feed from the range. Range pasture had not yet become unimportant, but cattlemen no longer relied on it so much.[18] In this developing ranch-farming technique, four major changes took place: cattlemen managed their range better; experimenters introduced and cattlemen used more and different forage crops; breeders introduced new breeds, and cattlemen made better use of the older breeds; federal and state officials, with some producer cooperation, made serious efforts to eradicate tick fever.

In range management, Plains stockmen tended not so much toward an overpublicized diversification, but instead they used land, labor, and capital more intensively. An expanding world metropolis required the end of the wasteful misuse of resources in areas close to the great urban concentrations.[19] Consequently, intensive agriculture developed everywhere. It developed most impressively on the Plains where intensity took shape as the ranch-farming complex.

Both state and federal lands played increasingly greater roles in range management practices. Cattlemen sometimes leased state lands, or obtained Forest permits. In either case, cattlemen tended to use these governmental lands as seasonal ranges. This enabled stockmen to reduce their grazing of other lands, and this in turn undoubtedly benefited the Plains as a whole. Occasionally, cattlemen used drift fences to divide their various pastures, but they could not legally do this on federal lands. Illegal or not, they sometimes fenced the public domain. In 1908, for example, approximately 150,000 acres of land were illegally fenced in Montana, and this figure covered only the fencing done by persons actually brought to trial in one state. Because of federal efforts to end fencing on the range, many cattlemen did not like to risk the investment in fences. They preferred to use state or federal lands as their alternate range. In this way other people bore the cost of segregating the cattleman's stock.[20]

Almost no one actually improved the range, and most cattlemen did not even take much interest in the ever-encroaching mesquite brush. The primitive range management of most cattlemen consisted simply in putting livestock on state and federal land at certain seasons. Real management was left to government employees.[21]

Similarly, few people did anything about bringing new plants to the Plains. Although crested wheatgrass had been introduced as early as 1898, the experiment stations did not undertake extensive work with the grass until the twentieth century. In 1906 plant explorers sent back more seeds from Russia, and experimental plantings were undertaken on the northern Plains. This winter-hardy perennial showed much promise. Since few reseeding projects were undertaken before 1910, the grass remained valuable only in prospect. Nevertheless, some scientists realized its potential.[22]

At least one, and probably more, experiments in seeding sweet clover on the range were undertaken by cattlemen. The crop did not become as important as alfalfa as a legume (nitrogen-restoring plant) but some stockmen did seem to recognize that clover might be a useful forage crop.[23]

Meanwhile, ranchers on the southern Plains grew larger amounts of sorghum. In 1899, they harvested 5,169,000 bushels of grain sorghums; by 1909 the harvest had increased to 17,597,000 bushels. Not all of this was grown on the Plains, but most of it was. The new interest was more unusual in that Sudangrass, the most outstanding of the grain sorghums, was unknown. Sudangrass came in comparatively late for it was introduced only in 1909. Thereafter, it rapidly became the chief sorghum fodder of the southern Plains.[24] On the northern Plains scientists pushed forward their experiments with sorghum, but the crop made virtually no impression on farmers or cattlemen.[25]

Progress in cattle breeding, in contrast, did take place. Several significant advances were made between 1906 and 1910. For one thing, a new breed was firmly established with the importation of zebus, or Brahman cattle. In 1905, O. P. Borden had gone to India to get some zebus, and by 1906 he had selected a herd for importation into the United States. Before he shipped the cattle he had their blood tested twice, and had all the cattle inoculated against rinderpest. Borden discarded several animals on suspicion of being diseased, and in the end he shipped only forty-six bulls, two cows, one heifer, and two calves. Seven weeks later (June 16, 1906) the animals reached New York without loss. They were unloaded at Simonson Island, and the entire shipment was put through another series of tests. Three animals reacted to tests for surra, a deadly cattle disease, and these were immediately slaughtered and the carcasses burned. Seven more animals later reacted to surra tests and were also destroyed.

Although the remaining animals appeared to be perfectly healthy, officials held the shipment, and bit by bit caused the herd to be decimated. Altogether they ordered the slaughter of eighteen animals for one reason or another. Borden came to think that the Treasury officials consulted something other than the interests of the American people. The quarantine continued. Borden suspected Machiavellian maneuvers by partisans of rival breeds, but his suspicions have never been substantiated. Anyhow, Borden went to Washington, saw President Theodore Roosevelt, and explained the situation. Roosevelt had Lyman Gage, Secretary of the Treasury, release the animals. On November 14, 1906, the remnant, some thirty-three head, went off to Texas where they fully established the Brahman cattle industry in the United States. The importation of 1906 was the last from India, and nearly the last from outside the United States.[26]

Of the cattle shipped from India, sixteen went to Tom O'Connor of Victoria, Texas. O'Connor in turn gave a half-breed Brahman-Shorthorn bull to Robert J. Kleberg, Sr., of the King Ranch. From this bull Kleberg bred several grades, and of these he kept one male bull calf called Chemera. The other grade Brahman cattle did so well that Kleberg concluded that the breed had a future in Texas. The crosses excelled in hardihood, size, and ability to fatten. As a result of his early impressions, Kleberg continued his experiments with the breed using Chemera for breeding.[27]

Most breed improvements, however, centered on the older breeds. Primarily, stockmen tried to improve the quality of the existing range livestock. Various state laws had been passed to force cattlemen to keep high-quality bulls on the range, and to keep them in a definite ratio to the cows. Apparently, the laws were haphazardly enforced. Consequently, in 1908 some cattlemen appealed to the Forest Service to have rules passed to keep the quality of cattle high on the Forests. Foresters reviewed the suggestion reluctantly, but they eventually presented regulations to the Secretary of Agriculture, James Wilson. Wilson established these general rules under authority which had already been delegated to him by the Congress. "The Secretary of Agriculture approved a regulation to the effect that whenever an association . . . asked for the enforcement of some "special rule" . . . it would be enforced upon all users of the particular range . . . whether they were members or not." [28] Under the regulation Forest users soon controlled the age, number, and breed of bulls on the Forests. They even had the right to remove bulls which did not meet the specifications of the cattlemen's associations. Some old-time cattlemen protested, but they were such a small minority that they could be, and were ignored. In this fashion, the federal government assisted the cattle industry of the Plains. [29]

In the meantime, the science of veterinary medicine had advanced. Systematic eradication of the tick, for example, began in 1906. Also in that year Dr. Joseph W. Parker began experiments with an arsenical dip for cattle. The dip was soon shown to be superior to previous dips. Cattle were dipped every fourteen days for a year, and thus ended the life cycle of the tick. As usual, cattlemen did not cooperate very well at first. They ridiculed and hampered many inspectors in their work. Foresters also worked to eradicate ticks, and as usual many cattlemen opposed the program and the Forest Service. Objectors dynamited dipping vats and killed some workers, but the dipping program continued. In spite of the sometimes violent opposition, the scientists of the Bureau of Animal Industry persisted and eventually succeeded. By 1910 the tick was well on its way to oblivion. [30]

Although tick fever was the only disease vigorously attacked in the field, some other significant scientific discoveries were made between 1906 and 1910. In 1908 Johne's

Disease, or paratuberculosis, was diagnosed for the first time in the United States. The disease subsequently appeared all over the country, but no one found a cure for it, and no one began any systematic campaign for its eradication. Then, in 1910, Arnold Theiler showed that a separate disease, which he called anaplasmosis, could be, and often was, confused with tick fever, or prioplasmosis.[31] Theiler's discovery made no impact at that time, at least not on cattlemen. They had trouble enough with the tick, and whether they liked it or not, the fight against the tick continued.

In short, between 1906 and 1910, cattlemen of the Plains accommodated themselves to the changing conditions of the industry. The challenges of increased meat consumption, the steady advance of settlers, and the ever-present hazards of climate and disease, were all met by new developments in science, and in ranch farming. These advances accompanied, and resulted from greater federal activity in science and regulation. The responses of the stockmen adequately met the problems set by nature, but mostly because nature behaved well. Exceptionally good weather, for example, prevailed between 1906 and 1908. All the Plains got sufficient rainfall, and some areas got more than enough.[32]

Furthermore, between 1908 and 1909, Forest Supervisors reported generally good cattle and range conditions. In part, good weather accounted for good cattle and range, but in part the excellent conditions resulted from a greater use of ranch farming, and from the regulations of the Forest Service.[33] Then trouble came. Bad weather struck in 1909 as a late spring and a shortage of summer rain hit the Plains. This caused cattlemen some difficulties, but most managed to survive. A decade earlier many of them would probably have succumbed. Cattlemen sent their weakened cattle long distances to recover in the Forests. The Supervisor of the Forest in Nebraska reported: "Seven thousand head of cattle were shipped in from New and Old Mexico, these were very thin on arriving here." [34]

The dry year of 1909 was followed by the severe winter

of 1909–1910. Once again cattlemen turned to the Forests as a place for the recuperation of their cattle. Once again stock came from afar, but even so, not all survived. In Wyoming, Forest Supervisor E. N. Kavanagh reported:

Many applications were refused, however, and the parties who had made the applications were in nearly every case compelled to ship their stock out of the country. Some of the stock were shipped into Nebraska where range had been leased, while those owners who were not fortunate enough to secure range were compelled to place their stock upon the market. Stock that were shipped to market were usually in very poor condition, having been held until the owners were certain that it would be impossible to secure feed. Consequently this stock sold at a big loss, and many small owners doing business on borrowed capital were compelled to go out of business.[35]

And the drouth had just begun.

Throughout the Great Plains the grazing season of 1910 was one of the driest ever known. Streams which had provided drinking water for cattle dwindled, and some even went dry. In their extremity, cattlemen moved livestock onto the Forests, but even there the range often gave out quickly. The hay crop, relied on for emergencies of this sort, fell to a third, or fourth, of what it had been. Many more cattlemen were forced to liquidate. The disaster overwhelmed southern plainsmen. Desert climate dominated Kansas, Colorado, Oklahoma, and Texas.[36] The drouth following the destructive winter of 1909–1910, forced cattlemen to adjust rapidly to the weather. To survive cattlemen had to rely even more on supplemental feeds. Ranch farming increasingly came to be usual, rather than exceptional.

Except in 1910, the responses chosen by Plains cattlemen worked fairly well. Limited ranch farming met most of the challenges of nature. Cattlemen found even more satisfactory responses to the economic challenges of the era. Between 1906 and 1910 the average price of range cattle rose continually. Range cattle in 1906 sold for an average of

$4.40 a hundredweight; in 1910 they sold for an average of $5.40 a hundred.[37] Through most of the period consumption increased and prices rose, but most stockmen also had increased costs which reduced their margin of profit. The Panic of 1907 seemed to stimulate sales of range cattle, mostly because of a newer demand for cheap meat. Apparently the demand for cheap meat continued on into 1908. As a result, the number of breeding cattle on the Plains fell markedly. Probably this helped the producers because they sold their worst cattle first.[38]

By 1909, at least on the northern Plains, cattlemen had vigorously culled and reduced their herds. Meanwhile, range cattle continued to command high prices. In October, 1909, some Montana cattle sold for $8.90 a hundred. The drouth of 1910 helped keep the market price high, although, of course, many cattlemen could not then take advantage of the high prices.[39] In short, cattlemen prospered if they did not depend entirely on the range, and if they kept their other costs low. Many cattlemen managed to do all of this between 1906 and 1910.

The rising cattle markets were largely a domestic phenomenon. In 1906 the German government virtually outlawed American cattle and meat, and in 1907 France restricted American meat imports. Throughout the period American meat exports declined relatively, and the foreign market became increasingly less important to Plains cattlemen.[40] This turn of events meant very little to American cattlemen at the beginning of the twentieth century.

As drouth hit the Southwest, cattle liquidation reached astounding heights. Texas and Oklahoma cattlemen alone sold some four million head. As a result a very small displacement in the center of cattle production occurred. The center shifted slightly northwestward to a point about forty miles southwest of Topeka. The center still moved westward.[41] Coincidentally, the number and acres of farms steadily increased on the Plains. This reflected, to some extent, the changing pattern in the cattle industry.

The number of farms increased 37 per cent between 1900 and 1910 on the ten Great Plains states. In 1900 there were 863,738 farms; in 1910 there were 1,186,532 farms. The acreage increased less. Only a 14 per cent increase occurred between 1900 and 1910. Acreage increased from 282,288,000 acres in 1900 to 324,635,000 acres in 1910. The comparatively slight increase probably reflected the movement of dry farmers onto the Plains, and suggests that the full development of ranch farming was still some distance away.[42]

Out on the Plains a great deal happened between 1906 and 1910. Ranch farming got started, Brahman cattle appeared, dry farmers sprouted everywhere, and livestock husbandry became more intensive. Of all the events, however, nothing proved so fateful as the appearance of the Forest Service with the myriad of consequences which came from it. The Foresters did not dominate the Plains either then, or later, but they were the vanguard of that legion of federal servants who so markedly transformed the cattle industry of the Great Plains. As the advance party they did much to shape the later course of events.

CHAPTER IV

The Good Old Days
1911-1914

Just before the First World War Americans went on a reforming binge. Government was their chosen vehicle for change. In those days the Bull Moose and Teddy Roosevelt, the New Freedom and Woodrow Wilson, the Progressives and Bob La Follette, all paraded across the political platform. Zeal for change characterized the era, and the fervor even spread a bit to the Great Plains. Here the forces of nature and of business gave additional impetus to the spirit of the times. Laissez-faire cattle raising no longer worked on the range. In common with other Americans, cattlemen came to expect more help from their government.

Probably few cattlemen thought government could do much about the weather. Still, the plainsmen may have thought it could do something to make the weather more bearable. The drouth which began in 1909 continued into 1911. The drouth of 1911 did not strike all of the Plains states alike. South Dakota, Montana, and Wyoming were particularly dry, but Texas, Oklahoma, Colorado, and North Dakota suffered less. On the southern and central Plains, 1911 began as a dry year, but rainfall increased after July. No place, however, received very much moisture.[1]

The drouth disappeared across the Plains in 1912. In some southern areas the precipitation of 1912 fell a bit lower than in 1911, but generally the Plains got more than adequate rainfall. On the drier northern Plains a heavy snow in the winter of 1911–1912, coupled with adequate rain, produced lush grass. In Colorado, Forest Supervisor A. W. Cook estimated the grass of 1912 to be 100 per cent more abundant than it had been at any time after 1909. Nebraska suffered a bit in places, and so did some few spots in Montana, but on the whole, the picture was bright.[2]

Precipitation declined most places in 1913, but not enough to do extensive damage. Where rainfall amounted to less than in 1912, the rains fell during the growing season and so were well used. In New Mexico, and probably Texas, more rain fell in 1913 than in 1912, but this was exceptional and local. On the whole, in 1913 cattlemen had few weather problems.[3]

Drouth came again to most of the Plains in 1914. In some places the dry spell struck more severely than at any previous time in the twentieth century. The drouth began slowly and spottily. Many localities in Texas suffered in 1914; in Wyoming some areas had practically no precipitation, and when the rains came, they came at the wrong time.[4] In both Wyoming and Montana the lack of rainfall damaged the range and destroyed the grass. Nevertheless, cattle and humans generally had enough water for drinking.[5] From Nebraska to Oklahoma the drouth of 1914 hit rather generally and severely. Some areas escaped, however: the drouth was slight and limited in New Mexico, Colorado, and South Dakota; many in New Mexico even counted 1914 a wet year. In short, the dryness was damaging, but not widespread; the abundant rains of the previous two years had, at worst, produced fair grass which carried cattle through one dry year. But although cattlemen did not know it, an extended and destructive drouth had begun.[6]

In this environment of intermittent drouth, cattlemen struggled along, sometimes successfully. Their stock did not always do well. Because of the rather prolonged winter of 1910–1911, and the drouth of 1910, stock went into the spring of 1911 in an underfed condition. Crop failures in 1910 and 1911 made it virtually impossible for cattlemen of the northern Plains to feed their cattle well during the winter. The range grass was seriously depleted. As 1911 closed, the future looked black to many cattlemen and farmers of the northern Plains. Even with fairly good prices, cattlemen did not yet get very high returns because their stock went to market weighing less than usual.[7]

On the central Plains, in 1911, cattlemen suffered less than those in the North. Cattle in Colorado came into the spring in good condition and put on fat quickly. Little overgrazing took place, and the rains kept the grass green and the streams full. On the southern Plains cattle hardly even suffered, and as far north as Nebraska, cattlemen reported stock and range conditions to be about average in 1911.[8]

The severe winter of 1911–1912 hurt cattlemen all over the Plains. Cattle came on the summer range in poor condition in 1912. Rich grasses, however, caused cattle on the Plains to gain rapidly. The range was in good condition in 1912, chiefly because the previous drouths had forced cattlemen to liquidate their herds, and consequently the range had been saved. The Supervisor of the Sundance Forest in Wyoming summed up for all, from Texas to North Dakota, when he observed:

The drouth conditions that prevailed during the Summer of 1910 and 1911, caused heavy selling of all kinds of livestock in this region. This selling was supplemented by a severe loss during the winter of 1911–12 and the stock throughout the region was reduced fully 70% in numbers since the beginning of the grazing season of 1910. Forest users as well as all other stockmen in the region are endeavoring to restock their farms and ranches, but as the scarcity of cattle seems to be general throughout the country, the restocking of this region will probably be comparatively slow. . . .[9]

The cattlemen had received such a blow from nature that they recovered slowly, if at all. Some, indeed, did not recover.

In one sense the damage was a blessing. The forced liquidation reduced overgrazing, and at the same time made more fodder available to carry the remaining stock. In October, 1913, the *Miles City American* summed up in a head-line: "Lots of Fodder on Hand But Scarcity of Stock." Oddly, cattlemen did not rejoice. Instead of being thankful for the relative security of plentiful feed, cattlemen hankered after the good, old, uncertain days of boom and bust.[10]

From all reports, rain fell abundantly on the Plains in 1913. Cattle grew sleek and fat. Most cattlemen, however, still had rather small herds. As 1913 closed, the future looked bright, and the low number of cattle meant that even if drouth should come, the cattlemen of the Plains could prob-ably survive.[11] Consequently, most plainsmen hardly noticed the drouth which appeared here and there in 1914. They did, however, notice the shortage of cattle; by 1914 the shrinking herds had produced near-famine in the major cattle markets. On the range this shortage produced high-quality livestock and adequate feed supplies. Through most of the Plains, the drouth of 1914 did little damage, and both cattle and range remained in good condition.[12]

Although drouth hit only intermittently, the dry seasons of 1911–1914 hurt the cattlemen of the Plains economically. The decline in cattle numbers reflected the injury done by the weather. The comparatively good condition of range and cattle could not obscure the loss of stock and income for many producers. More importantly, the vagaries of the weather added additional irritation to cattlemen as other assaults were made on them by nature and by middlemen.

Prairie dogs, rustlers, packers, and railroads had been around before, but cattlemen had not come to like them any more for all that. Between 1911 and 1914 cattlemen concentrated on getting the government to do something about the pests. One of their earliest requests was directed to the United States Biological Survey. Cattlemen in some areas wanted the prairie dogs exterminated since the ani-mals damaged the range. At first cattlemen applied to the Forest Service for help, but the Foresters passed the buck, perhaps to avoid interservice disputes. Apparently the Bio-logical Survey could not do the work, and so the Foresters reluctantly added prairie-dog eradication to their list of activities. The fiddling around undoubtedly annoyed some cattlemen. In the confusion no one solved the problem of the dog towns. The destructiveness of the little rodents was most pronounced in time of drouth, and the existence of the dogs was one more irritant for cattlemen.[13]

Meanwhile, rustling continued much as it ever had, except that methods had become more refined. Simultaneously, railroad rates excited some comment by cattlemen. Then too, the Beef Trust continued its activities, and even expanded them, but not until Wilson became President was any real investigation begun. The investigation, undertaken at the insistence of the cattlemen, showed the virtual strangle hold of the packers on the industry. The near monopoly surprised no one, and neither was anyone surprised at the comparative lack of action to correct abuses. What was surprising was the vigor with which cattlemen complained about rustlers and packers.[14]

In addition to these problems, disease continued to hurt the Plains cattlemen. Tick fever still plagued the industry. Control became increasingly nearer, however. In 1911 the federal government adopted the arsenical solution as the official cattle dip for all cattle originating in a quarantined area and moving in interstate commerce. At least producers now had the technique for eradication at hand. Then, in 1912, Congress set up the Field Inspection Division to direct eradication of the disease. So far as anyone could see at the time, the institution promised to be permanent, in part because of the obstructionist attitude of some cattlemen. But from 1911 to 1914 the infested area gradually shrank.[15]

The Bureau of Animal Industry also took active steps to control other diseases. Beginning in 1897, and increasing by 1914, the bureau distributed free blackleg vaccine to cattlemen on the Plains. Congress authorized this partly to help end the disease, and partly to protect cattlemen from worthless products. An act of 1913 had closely regulated the manufacture, importation, sale, and distribution of serums, toxins, and other biologicals, but possibly the laws did not do the job.[16]

Bang's Disease (brucellosis) did not affect range cattle as seriously as it did dairy cattle, but nevertheless the disease caused some losses. Experiments with vaccines began in earnest in 1911, and ultimately, scientists developed a calf vaccine, although the first experiments of Mohler and Traum failed to produce very encouraging results. Still, in this area as in others, veterinary scientists diligently sought cures and preventives. The work was largely prosecuted by the federal government, and apparently few cattlemen thought this at all strange.[17]

Foot-and-mouth disease presented Plains cattlemen with their most serious threat. In 1914 the disease broke out in virulent and epidemic form. The disease had struck as early as 1902, and had appeared again in 1908 but each time it had been quickly stamped out by a vigorous slaughter campaign. The disease was extremely contagious, and no cure or vaccine was known for it. The disease invariably killed cattle. Because of this, all infected cattle plus all cattle on the infected premises, had to be destroyed immediately and the carcasses burned or buried. In 1914, however, the disease was well established before it was diagnosed. Consequently, the problem of eradication reached monumental proportions. The attack was complicated for stockmen because they had to bear most of the loss of the slaughtered cattle. Understandably they sometimes opposed the apparently indiscriminate slaughter which necessarily characterized eradication.[18]

Veterinarians in southern Michigan first identified the outbreak in 1914. Apparently hogs shipped from Michigan to Chicago carried the disease to the stockyards. From there the disease quickly and easily spread to stock in transit. All sorts of livestock, especially breeding animals, passed through Chicago or else were shipped on contaminated cars. In no time the contagion spread and the disease appeared almost instantaneously from Iowa to Massachusetts. In the ensuing months it spread even farther.[19]

The disease had to be stopped, but eradication proved to be appallingly expensive. The federal government compensated owners for half the value of the destroyed cattle. Only in this way could federal officers get even a minimum of cooperation from cattlemen. Anyhow, social justice demanded some federal compensation. Losses to private individuals and to the government ran high. In one year in Montana alone, the disease cost cattlemen over twenty thousand dollars. And this represented only part of the total cost, because in order for producers to receive federal payments, a region had to be placed under quarantine. Cattlemen could not thereafter move cattle, and this cost them untold additional amounts. By the end of 1914, the disease had struck twenty-two states. This was the worst epidemic of its kind in history. But under the direction of the federal agents, the disease was eradicated in the United States.[20]

Meanwhile, the old problems of settlers, dry farming, prices, and meat-consumption trends, continued. For the most part, plainsmen sought government help in their efforts to solve these problems. Nesters came first in point of seriousness. In 1904 Congress passed the Kinkaid Act which applied only to western Nebraska, and which allowed homesteading of one section.[21] By 1912 most of the Kinkaid Act farmers had been broken by drouth, and one observer estimated that perhaps 75 per cent of the homesteads had been abandoned or sold as soon as the settlers had made final proof. Some cattlemen believed the homesteaders were less interested in dry farming than in land speculation. H. E. French claimed:

In a great many cases it has apparently been the intention of the entryman to sell his homestead to some large cattle outfit on whose range he has located as soon as patent has been obtained. In this manner nearly all of the outside range at the present time has been entered under the homestead

laws. During the residence period required by the homestead act the lands are sometimes leased to cattle men. Often
times, however, the rental asked by the entrymen is exhorbi-
tant [sic], and cannot be met with the profits accruing from
cattle raising. For the reasons stated many cattle outfits have
been forced to cut down on their herds materially, and in
numerous other cases these outfits have retired from business
altogether.[22]

Cattlemen not only found the nesters annoying, they also
found them plentiful. In 1912 the land office at Havre, Montana, for example, recorded about three thousand entries for
land. In 1913, entries for 1,182,433 acres of land were made
in Colorado alone; in 1914, New Mexico showed 848,544
acres entered. For the Plains as a whole, between 1911
and 1914, settlers entered over 38,000,000 acres. The Plains
entries for 1911 totaled more than all entries for the United
States in 1904, or in 1909.[23] As the settlers came, they pressed
cattlemen who did not own their land.

All the laws tended to lure settlers to the Plains. Cattlemen found the law of June 11, 1906, particularly obnoxious
because it permitted homesteading on the National Forests.
This homesteading cut into the grazing lands of the cattlemen, and in time forced more changes in the conduct of
the stock business. Cattlemen had to get by with less grazing land, which meant they depended more on fodder and
less on range. Naturally they resisted any further efforts to
reduce the National Forests, and they continued to object
to the law of June 11th.[24]

Meanwhile, settlers continued to come, enticed not only
by good rainfall and easy land laws, but also by fairly high
wheat prices, and new or improved machinery. Wheat prices
rose between 1911 and 1914. Wheat at Kansas City averaged
$0.97 a bushel in 1911, and $1.05 in 1914; at Minneapolis,
prices averaged $1.07 in 1911, and rose to $1.20 in 1914. Dry
farming appeared profitable, and the farmers continued to
advance in hordes.[25]

Furthermore, between 1911 and 1914 both the gasoline

tractor and the gasoline combine came to be increasingly employed in Great Plains agriculture. Neither was used widely, but even limited use speeded the conquest of the Plains. Meanwhile, local enthusiasts and special interests kept urging the agricultural conquest of the Plains. Information and propaganda for dry farming came from a variety of sources, such as bankers' associations, chambers of commerce, railroads, experiment stations, and farmers' organizations of all sorts. As before, the zealots emphasized the need for livestock in the dry-farming complex. Between 1911 and 1914, however, they urged farmers to undertake dairying rather than beef production. Alfalfa, red clover, corn, and always livestock, were presented to the farmers as essential ingredients in successful dry farming. The agitation reached new heights after 1913, and the settlers continued to come in a steady stream. Cattlemen could not help but be, and were, alarmed.[26]

On the Plains, as in the United States, the number of cattle steadily fell. The decline in cattle caused, in part, a general rise in beef prices. Viewed by themselves, cattle prices indicated prosperity for Plains cattlemen: in 1911 Plains cattle brought an average of $5.65 a hundred; in 1912 they averaged $7.60; in 1913, $7.40; and in 1914, $7.65 a hundredweight. Cattlemen were not disturbed by falling prices. Still, with their reduced herds and higher costs, not many cattlemen became rich.[27]

Most cattle, of course, were sold by the head. Figures given in these terms are a bit more appropriate. Large shipments made in 1912 brought $30 to $40 a head. By 1913, the prices ran from $65 to $75 a head in the North, and $30 to $35 in the South. The editor of the *Miles City American* commented: "The Custer county rancher who sold his cattle for $65 a head says that if this is what Democratic hard times means he is sorry he did not experience them during former administrations." [28] Because of a shortage of breeding stock, most cattlemen held many of their cattle, and prices continued to rise through 1914. One stockman in Montana received $157.20 a head, or $10 a hundred. He got this price at Chicago for plain, ordinary, grass-fed steers.[29]

Several consequences followed from the high prices. For one thing, old-style herdsmen, or near-herdsmen, who had liquidated during the drouth were now doubly hurt. They could not restock because of high prices for cattle. Their re-entry into the business was impeded, if not prevented. Since many of them operated on borrowed capital, they could not remain in the business. The old-timers were slowly being eliminated. The more up-to-date cattlemen could, and often did, hold their cattle for breeding, and for future high profits. Furthermore, as Forest Supervisor A. W. Cook noted: "General interest in large natural increase has the tendency of arousing more interest in intensive range management."[30]

The decline in cattle numbers, and the resulting high prices, had other consequences. Cattle exports decreased. In 1913 American exports of fresh and other beef practically ceased, and in 1914 the United States imported approximately 170 million pounds of meat over exports. America thus changed, for one year at least, from a nation with a beef surplus to one with a beef deficiency.[31]

The extent of drouth damage on the Plains appeared not only in the status of meat exports, but also in the consumption of meat. Although cattle declined in numbers and rose in price, meat consumption fell per capita across the period 1911 to 1914. Each American consumed an average of 75.6 pounds of beef and veal in 1911, but only 67.8 pounds in 1914. And every year consumption declined. So did commercial slaughter. Viewed from every aspect except prices, the cattlemen of the Plains were in trouble just before the First World War began. Those who survived did so by following the best ranching techniques, and by using the help given by the federal government.[32]

Survival in the business demanded good range management. Cattlemen were continually impressed with the need for deferred grazing. In 1913 Arthur W. Sampson showed conclusively that even moderate grazing in the growing season, if persisted in, deteriorated the range. To keep the range useful, cattlemen had to hold their livestock off the range at certain times. This in turn required range management, and the raising of some supplemental feed.[33]

Range management by cattlemen continually improved. The drouths of the early twentieth century caused a fair turnover of ranch property. As the old-timers left the business, cattlemen with newer vision took over. Each year, the appeals for range management fell on more receptive ears. One Forester observed, unkindly, but accurately: "The new owners are almost always an improvement over the old, showing an interest and intelligence in modern methods of stock handling that argues well for . . . the welfare of the country. They appreciate the need for a Governmental supervision of the range, which many old timers will not admit." [34] The Foresters were still not the prime movers in range management, but at least they were making progress.

Unquestionably, fencing the range greatly facilitated range management, and although it was illegal, some cattlemen still fenced. Their illegal fencing held less promise than their attempts at cooperative range ownership. These experiments at cooperation apparently did not come to much on the Plains, but a few cattlemen tried it, and this alone was rather unusual.[35] Not until the twenties did cattlemen show conclusively that cooperative ownership of range could work.

Actually, ranch farming methods more seriously applied, yielded better results. Among these methods, the recurring attempts to heighten the quality of their range stock by breeding ranked high among the newer cattlemen. Some old longhorns appeared from time to time, but these apparently came in from Mexico. The Plains cattlemen were, on the whole, devoted to improving the breeds.[36] But aside from this, no startling advances or changes took place in the area of breeds and breeding.

Most advances and improvements continued to be made under the auspices of civil servants. Although the Forests comprised only a very small part of the grazing land in the

Plains, the Foresters did more for cattlemen than practically any of the other federal agents. What the Foresters did, or attempted to do, transcended the boundaries of the Forests and affected the whole of the cattle kingdom. Cattlemen increasingly depended on the Foresters as teachers and guardians between 1911 and 1914. After all, the Foresters seemed to be the only people capable of restraining the tide of settlers, and the Foresters also seemed to be about the only ones seriously interested in range management. In earlier periods, stockmen had organized to limit the activities of the Forest Service. After 1911, cattlemen's associations increased, but the newer groups assisted the Foresters in many ways, particularly in range management.

Of course the old herdsmen still resisted the Forest Service, but in 1911 they were also brought into line. In 1908 the United States had gotten an injunction against one Fred Light which restrained him from running cattle on the Holy Cross National Forest unless he obtained the proper permission from the Secretary of Agriculture. Light protested that the Forest Service and the Secretary had no constitutional right to do this. He appealed to the United States Supreme Court, hoping to break the regulatory power of the Forest Service. In a decision of May 1, 1911, the Court upheld the Service, the Secretary, and the Circuit Court of Colorado. Fred Light, and those of like mind, could be excluded from the Forests. Thereafter, the legality of the rulings of the Forest Service was not open to much dispute.[37]

The Forests continued to be expanded. In 1911 the Congress moved to increase the area under Forest supervision. Congress passed the Weeks Law which authorized the Secretary of Agriculture to purchase land for formation into National Forests. Congress also appropriated two million dollars for every year up to 1916 for the purchase of these tracts. At first most of the purchases were in the East, but under the act, as extended and amended, the Forest Service could purchase land which had come into possession of private individuals. Thereafter, the Foresters were no longer restricted to just the public domain.[38]

Grazing fees were raised slightly on the Forests in 1912, but the event excited almost no opposition. On the whole, cattlemen saw no great advantages in opposing the Service on this issue or on any other. About the only complaints from cattlemen centered on the use of the Forests by sheepmen. This ancient feud was so well institutionalized, however, that it excited no comment or hard feelings. Little could be, or was, done to favor either side. By 1911 cattlemen rather generally supported the Forest Service, their only protector, and the only conservator of their grazing lands.[39]

In July, 1914, World War I began. The results of this first general conflict were not immediately felt on the Plains, but, in the long run, cattle and grain production were stimulated. Both stockmen and farmers competed for the same land. The liquidation in the livestock industry came to a halt. Many cattlemen sought to consolidate their holdings, and in doing so borrowed money with which to buy their range. The foreign market, shrunken to insignificance in 1914, suddenly became important again. The war revitalized the cattle industry on the Plains, although at the same time cattlemen had to struggle to maintain their position vis-à-vis dry farming wheat growers. But a period which had opened dismally with drouth, closed brightly on the prospects of newer markets and rising prices.[40]

Clearly, the predominant theme in the history of the Plains between 1911 and 1914 was the greater activity by the federal government. Sometimes, as in their struggles with prairie dogs or packers, the cattlemen asked for the intervention, and sometimes, as in their struggles with disease or settlers, the cattlemen only welcomed the intervention. No matter how viewed, Plains stockmen did not protest the modest invasions of the federal government into what had formerly been private affairs, or sometimes, no one's affairs. In this regard, the attitudes of the cattlemen definitely changed. In a way, the outbreak of the war merely caused the acceleration of federal activity which had been under way since the opening of the century.

CHAPTER V

More and More Beef

1915-1918

For the people of the United States, World War I did not become a total war; nevertheless, it dominated the economic lives of the people, and did so long before Americans joined in the hostilities. The war strongly affected the people of the Plains also. Between 1915 and 1918 the Great Plains cattle industry rapidly evolved in response to this major disturbance in the world metropolis.

At first the war produced only a certain amount of financial uncertainty in America, and on the Plains. Apparently, few cattlemen thought the war would create any great demand for American beef either here or abroad. In any case, high cattle prices prevailed before the war began, and, for the most part, cattlemen did not expect any remarkable increases. They had grown accustomed to thinking primarily in terms of the domestic market.

As European hostilities continued past 1915 and on into 1916, however, Europeans increasingly came to buy all manner of goods in America. To meet the demand, the industrial production of the United States expanded tremendously. Consequently, American urban workers enjoyed both a level of employment and a measure of prosperity they had not known for nearly a century. Quite naturally, these urban workers wanted and ate more meat.

For cattlemen, the domestic market expanded first. Later on, the metropolitan market of Europe expanded. Thus the war, with its attendant economic changes, created an increasing demand for beef. People could afford larger amounts of meat, even though it came to be high-priced. Livestock slaughter rose in response to the wartime demand.[1]

Although Plains cattlemen found the market of 1915 good, they found the market of 1916 better. When the United States entered the war on the Allied side in 1917, the demand for meat once again rose tremendously. By this time, the United States not only served as the Allied food center, but in addition, with direct American participation in the war, the whole national economy boomed. As the war continued, urbanites ate more and more meat. Plains cattlemen profited directly and indirectly as consumption levels rose.[2]

Cattle production expanded on the Plains under the stimulus of the war. Of course, the weather did not always favor the Allied cause. Neither did it necessarily favor the cattlemen. Drouth hit after 1916, and as it did, the federal government strove to keep meat production rising. The Department of Agriculture opened the National Forests on an emergency basis. Temporarily the Foresters allowed more cattle on the range than could be comfortably carried. In addition, the government tried to assure stockmen of reasonably priced supplemental feeds, particularly cottonseed.

At the same time, cattlemen had to depend on a railroad system that showed definite symptoms of a complete breakdown. A shortage of rolling rail stock hampered adjustments in the Plains cattle industry. The federal government tried to remedy this too. To some extent, however, the difficulties persisted even after the government assumed operation of the railroads in December of 1917. Nevertheless, cattlemen adjusted rapidly and well in 1917, and beef production continued to rise in spite of all obstacles.[3]

By 1918 the demand for beef swelled to unprecedented proportions. Cattlemen sold all they could, raised all they could, and got the highest prices they could. Prices shot up to the highest levels in history. Plainsmen did all this in spite of a congested and nearly demoralized railroad system. In 1918 drouth disrupted production on the southern Plains. Beef production rose anyhow. The demand for beef exceeded what the cattlemen could supply, however, and so the government urged beefless days for American consumers. On June 12, 1918, the Food Administration suggested that Americans substitute pork for beef whenever possible. The administration also suggested that people should eat no more than one and one-quarter pounds of beef per person, each week.

The best laid plans go oft astray. Back on the ranches, drouth forced cattlemen to sell lightweight stock at ruinously low prices. In order to rescue these stockmen, the Food Administration reversed itself and urged patriotic citizens to eat lightweight beef. The American people apparently responded as best they could, but in spite of these varied patriotic eating and fasting efforts, beef continued in short supply.[4] Part of the shortage stemmed from American shipments abroad. In 1918, for example, the United States exported to its allies three and one-half times more beef than had been exported on an average during 1911, 1912, and 1913. In 1914 American fresh beef exports had amounted to only 6 million pounds, but by 1918 exports came to over 514 million pounds.[5]

This, in short, was what the war meant to the cattlemen of the Plains. The entire industry geared itself to a war economy. Perhaps the producers adjusted inefficiently, but undeniably they did adjust. The chief question is, how did they do it?

Beef prices rose ever higher, and should have gone above the levels many consumers could afford. At the same time, the Food Administration under Herbert Hoover strove to reduce meat consumption. In spite of all this, per capita beef consumption steadily increased between 1915 and 1918. Beef eating almost reached pre–1910 levels. In 1915 each American ate an average of 62.3 pounds of beef and veal; by 1918 each American ate an average of 75.8 pounds. In every year Americans ate more beef, and this, combined with increasing urban populations and increasing exports, imposed greater and greater demands on the Plains cattlemen.[6]

Plainsmen could not supply this growing demand. Consequently, beef prices rose persistently, not only at the retail
level, but at the Plains level as well. Back in 1914 range cattle
had averaged $7.65 a hundredweight. At the time, the price
had seemed fantastically high. In 1915 range cattle brought
$7.75 a hundred. By 1918 prices for range cattle finally
reached $14.50 a hundred. Prices this high would have been
unusual in 1945. For many cattlemen, the prices of 1918 approached the fantastic.[7]

In this market any kind of stock went. In 1916, for example,
Dan Adamson, Nebraska rancher, sold forty-eight spayed,
three-year-old heifers for an average of $6.65 a hundred. The
cattle market of 1916 took any sort of cattle at high prices.
In fact, feeders begged cattlemen to hold some cattle until
the corn crop matured. Consumers did not insist on well-
finished beef, and feeders had to protect themselves in some
way. In spite of the prices, not all ranchers profited from the
beef boom. The King Ranch of Texas, for example, showed
net losses in both 1917 and 1918. High labor costs hurt the
cattle kings. So did the comparative inefficiency of larger
operations particularly in time of drouth. In contrast, small
cattlemen who followed ranch farming methods broke even,
or better.[8]

As prices mounted, Plains cattlemen often succumbed to
a speculative fever. The disease spread in even more virulent
form to the bankers of the region. In order to get in on the
rising prices, many cattlemen needed loans for expansion.
On the whole, they found lenders eager to advance money in
1916. Actually, bankers often forced expansion on the cattlemen. "There were many authentic instances of banks bringing strong pressure to bear upon their clients, forcing them to
accept more loans for expansion or feeding." [9] The bankers
hated to see cattlemen have all those profits for themselves.
The bankers had usually been among the overlords of the
cattlemen, and these "lords of creation" took steps to maintain their position over the stockmen.

As part of the credit machinery, Congress created Federal

Land Banks in 1916. Ostensibly these banks provided long-term agricultural credit for farmers. In reality, however, the banks were not organized to assist cattlemen very well. The $10,000 limit on loans was particularly unsuited for range cattlemen. Very few livestock producers received loans from the land banks. In 1918, when disaster hit the Plains, and drouth threatened to ruin many cattlemen, then, the bankers and the land banks either could not or would not lend money for the emergency. Bankers were in business chiefly for profit, and only incidentally for public service. In their extremity, stockmen once again turned to the federal government for help. They got it. In 1918 the War Finance Corporation (which had been designed to do other things) agreed to lend money to the hard-pressed cattlemen. The corporation loaned for just one year, for the drouth emergency only, but it loaned at the comparatively low rate of 8 per cent per annum. Cattlemen could borrow as much as 75 per cent of the value of their livestock. In Texas alone, by late 1918, cattlemen had applied for some $10 million in loans. The War Finance Corporation managed to save many cattlemen who would otherwise have perished if left to the tender assistance of private bankers.[10]

Assaults of nature also somewhat marred these happy years. Not that things looked bad at the start. Throughout the Plains, 1915 was the wettest year known. Only parts of Texas, northern Montana, and South Dakota experienced the normally dry weather of the Plains. In Nebraska, meadows flooded. In South Dakota summer came late enough to retard plant growth. But water was generally abundant. Here and there Plains cattlemen discovered, somewhat to their surprise, that too much water could be as injurious as too little.[11]

Good weather continued into 1916 for the most part. The Dakotas, Wyoming, and southern Texas suffered from drouth, but for most of the Plains, 1916 was a wet year.[12] The next year was not as good. Drouth struck parts of Texas in 1916, and spread throughout the southern Plains in 1917. In southwestern Texas as much as 90 per cent of the cattle had to be fed both summer and winter. One Congressman from the area reported:

Ranches are without grass and water. In some places creeks have not run for over two years. Even immediate shipment of cattle will not prevent great loss. Cattle are weak and a large percentage are actually unable to withstand shipment and would die in transit, hence only salvation is concentrating and feeding on ranches throughout winter wherever there is available water.[13]

Mostly as a result of this drouth, the King Ranch owners lost $77,266 on their operations in 1917.

Drouth also killed and destroyed in New Mexico, Oklahoma, and southeastern Colorado. In contrast, most of the northern Plains received plenty of moisture. Reports from Montana and Wyoming, however, indicated scattered drouth in those states. Drouth forced cattlemen to cut herds considerably, but for most of them the high prices made the liquidation less painful than it might have been. As usual, conditions were not uniform throughout the Plains. In Texas, for example, stock glutted the markets, and prices for these lightweight cattle fell drastically. Texas appeared to be an exceptional case.[14]

The drouth began to break around the middle of 1918. The rains came in scattered places, and although precipitation was not always heavy, the range improved. Relief also came to stockmen in Texas and New Mexico where the drouth had been long and damaging. Throughout most of the Plains sufficient moisture appeared. Drouth afflicted only the northern Plains. But the worst had passed by 1918, and the weather relaxed its pressure on the plainsmen. In 1917 and 1918, wartime prosperity obscured the drouth on the northern Plains. On the southern Plains, however, cattlemen had been to the gates of hell and back. They had found the trip unnerving.[15]

During the war, cattle and range conditions did not always

correspond to weather conditions. Weather, range, and cattle generally excelled in 1915. Late or cold springs on most of the Plains retarded plant growth, but by the end of the season both animals and grasses had prospered.[16] In 1916, however, in spite of a shortage of moisture in some places, the range grasses remained good. In a few places the dry weather actually caused grass to cure better. Even in large parts of drouth-stricken Texas, grass continued to be relatively abundant in 1916.

The winter of 1916–1917 began early throughout the Plains, and in Montana and Wyoming cattlemen began feeding six weeks earlier than usual. This circumstance had no immediate consequence, and on the northern and central Plains, cattle appeared to be in better condition at the end of 1916 than they had been at the close of 1915, and 1915 had been a wet year.[17] The hard winter of 1916–1917 was followed by drouth in 1917. Range grasses deteriorated generally throughout the Plains. Still, forage crops continued to be adequate in most places, although nearly everywhere cattle suffered some. On the other hand, cattlemen in a few isolated places indicated that their cattle were in better than usual condition in 1917. On the southern Plains, however, cattle and range ended the season in very poor condition.[18]

In response to the weather, in 1917 and 1918, southern cattlemen moved comparatively large numbers of cattle to northern ranges. The drouth ended on the southern Plains in 1918, but the rains came too late to halt the general emergency movement of cattle. Throughout the Plains, cattle and range improved in 1918, not quickly, but surely. Summing up for 1918 a Montana Forester declared: "Condition of the range at close of the season was better than usual and much better than the season of 1917." [19] On the whole, cattlemen avoided severe damage to the range by keeping their herds small during the worst years of drouth.

Now and then plainsmen got unwanted help in culling their herds. Predatory animals continually destroyed livestock. During the war stockmen received important federal help in reducing these losses. Assistance had come earlier, for the Forest Service had begun predator control in 1911. Apparently the Foresters could not do the work effectively, and do everything else too. In 1915, Smith Riley, District Forester at Denver, commented:

The figures indicate that either predatory animals are decidedly on the decrease or that Forest officers are losing enthusiasm in this line of work. It is not thought that predatory animals are decreasing, at any rate not in the proportion that the figures would indicate.[20]

In 1915 the work was transferred to the Biological Survey. From then on, the survey conducted the war on predators and prairie dogs. The Foresters assumed the less demanding role of auxiliaries.[21]

The change made sense from several standpoints. Most obviously, predatory animals roamed everywhere, even on the range outside the Forests. For stockmen, predator control ranked highly as an economic activity. Between 1915 and 1918, predators each year destroyed from $20 million to $30 million worth of livestock. The figure included sheep and other domestic stock in addition to cattle, but the losses were impressive anyway. After 1915 the Biological Survey worked vigorously at control. They attacked the large timber wolves first, and then gradually expanded their war to include the eradication of other destructive animals. Between 1915 and 1918 federal agents killed 70,713 predatory animals. Their kill included 60,473 coyotes, 8,094 bobcats, and 1,829 wolves. At a conservative estimate this saved cattlemen $6 million a year. Few could despise savings of that magnitude.[22] As before, nearly everyone attacked prairie dogs, but although the rodents had few friends, they apparently ranked far down in priority for extinction.[23]

Cattle diseases also inflicted losses on plainsmen. The nation could ill afford these losses in wartime, and so the federal government continued to carry on its veterinary programs. Foot-and-mouth disease broke out again in 1915, but far less seriously than in 1914. The new epidemic was largely confined to stockyards, and was quickly ended.

Meanwhile, the Department of Agriculture took new measures against tick fever. In 1917 Congress set up a Division of Tick Eradication in the Department. The new division worked with state authorities and individuals in the apparently unending battle against ticks. Except for parts of Texas, however, ticks had been brought under control on the Plains by 1917. Even in Texas, the tide of battle pointed to human victory.

The Bureau of Animal Industry received auxiliary help in disease control from the newly created Extension Service. In 1916 the Extension Agents began assisting in education programs, and, nearly as importantly, they distributed the free, federal blackleg vaccine. Agents were instructed in vaccination procedures, and were provided with hypodermic needles. This once-serious disease was nearly under control. Simultaneously in 1916, vesicular stomatitis was discovered in the United States, although its appearance was not widespread. Nothing much could be, or was done about the disease which superficially resembled foot-and-mouth disease.[24] In short, disease still ranked as a major problem on the Plains, but during the war years concerted federal efforts were increased in an effort to cut losses from disease.

Well before the United States entered the First World War, Europeans were buying large amounts of food in America. The most remarkable consequence of these purchases was an increased area devoted to wheat in the United States. Farmers grew wheat in heavily settled regions where it had dropped to a minor position years before. On the Plains, farmers put new acres to the plow in an attempt to profit from the high prices.[25] Drouth and black stem rust damaged the crops of 1916 and 1917, however, and dry land wheat farmers barely managed to survive. Indeed, many failed. In North Dakota, for example, the average yield fell from 18.2 bushels per acre in 1915 to less than 5 bushels per acre in 1917. Over the Plains the story was much the same.

Even with wheat at $2.20 a bushel in 1918, farmers lost money. Simultaneously, beef growers did well enough, and so, in the Dakotas, for example, many farmers shifted to cattle. In spite of the difficulty of change caused by a shortage of breeding stock, the evolution from farmer to stockman took place as early as 1915. Concurrently, dry farming enthusiasts continued to urge Plains farmers to emphasize animal husbandry.[26]

In 1917 the dry farming story was about the same all over the Great Plains. On the whole, farmers harvested a bit more than they had in 1916, but their increased harvests were not impressive. In Texas, for example, in 1915, total wheat production had been 25,575,000 bushels, but by 1917 this had actually fallen to 16,200,000 bushels. By 1917 dry farmers in Montana and Wyoming were so few in number, and so uncertain in tenure, that they had little influence on the Plains cattle industry. Of South Dakota, Mary Hargreaves noted: "Farmers who succeeded in this period were generally those who relied upon cropping innovations in combination with livestock. . . ." [27]

In 1918, dry wheat farmers fared better on the Plains than they had in any year except 1915. Wheat production rose on the northern and central Plains, although it declined in Texas and Oklahoma. On the northern Plains, however, yields per acre fell, sometimes sharply. In Montana, land which had once produced as much as twenty-five bushels to the acre grew only three bushels or less by 1918. Farmers produced the over-all larger yield by plowing more land. Aside from the greater use of machinery, the only important technological change in the period occurred in Canada in 1918 when a few farmers experimented with strip cropping. The new method reduced wind erosion, but it was still just an experiment. On the whole, even though this total production rose, dry farmers got low crop yields between 1916 and 1918.[28]

Since wheat farming was often unprofitable in spite of high prices, some farmers turned to fodder crops, and some tried their hand at feeding livestock. Ironically, in the heyday of wheat, dry farmers tended to shift to some form of ranch farming. Ranchers sometimes turned to feeding too. During the war years, the most successful of these experiments were carried out on the northern Plains.[29]

In the meantime, year by year, more cattlemen employed ranch farming techniques on the Plains. Nature forced cattlemen to recognize the need for supplemental feeding. Ranch farmers also came to use better-quality cattle. In New Mexico some cattlemen still produced scrubby, off-color cattle, but even there this approach to animal husbandry became unprofitable during the war. The ranch-farming complex yearly won more converts. Most cattlemen commonly built dams for gathering rain water, and many of them fenced their cattle on ranch-owned land.[30]

During the war, techniques of ranch farming evolved slowly and a bit unevenly. Ranch farming had always included the growing of drouth-resistant forage crops. In 1915 change along this line came about when crested wheatgrass made its first significant entry onto the American scene. Of course, experimental introductions had been made as early as 1898, but in 1915 the grass was first grown on a commercial scale in the northern Plains. From that date forward, stockmen grew increasing acreages of the grass.[31] Some years elapsed before any varieties of wheatgrass could be successfully grown on the southern Plains.

Southerners did not miss the wheatgrass because they had other supplemental feeds readily at hand, particularly cottonseed, and cottonseed cake. Cottonseed products had to be bought, but southern cattlemen could buy it cheaply, and cottonseed was rich in proteins. Of course, cattlemen could not readily control the quality of the feed they bought. In 1917 some Texas cattlemen sought strict regulation of the cottonseed crushers. In the end, the stockmen managed to have some quality standards established and enforced. Late in 1918 the Federal Food Administration took over the task of quality control, and, in addition, set prices for various qualities and types of cottonseed products. Cake and meal with 43 per cent protein, for example, were to sell for not more than $57 a ton. Cattlemen showed great interest in this matter, which suggested that for ranch farmers of the southern Plains, cottonseed products were a staple supplemental feed, and as such were an integral part of the ranch-farming complex.[32]

Texas cattlemen also took some interest in silos during the First World War. Their interest was neither deep nor broad. Still, their increased use of silage was unusual. At the time, ranch farmers of the northern Plains took less interest in silos than did their southern brethren. The King Ranch prominently led in the use of silos, especially trench silos. The Texans reputedly got the idea from Denmark. However that may be, such silos had been used in the United States since at least 1875.[33]

In general, although the number of ranch farmers increased, their techniques remained virtually unchanged between 1915 and 1918. As late as 1918, strip cropping (first begun in dry land farming), and the use of the forage plant, crested wheatgrass, were still only potentially important.

Work with Brahman cattle continued in Texas. In 1918 the Klebergs of the King Ranch obtained more Brahman breeding stock in a desperate effort to do something to counteract the effects of the drouth. As the new breeding program began, the Klebergs crossed Brahmans with Shorthorns, and awaited the results with anticipation. Scarcely anyone on the southern Plains knew that an important experiment was under way.[34]

The war required the federal government, acting as agent of the people, to take a greater part in every phase of the cattle business. Consequently, no one was much surprised to find the Forest Service assuming more importance in the lives of the cattlemen. Probably the comparatively good condition of Forest range caused cattlemen to turn to the Forests when nature threatened. Consequently, the number of cattle on the Forests rose consistently between 1915 and 1918. The

Forests were not always crowded, but the number of cattle did increase.[35]

Cattlemen and Foresters also joined to effect changes in the industry, because a people at war could not permit wasteful use of grazing land. Both Foresters and cattlemen strove to improve the quality of cattle, and to clear the range of scrubs and wild horses. Local livestock associations multiplied, and regulations for range bulls proliferated. Most of the regulations had two features in common: (1) every cattleman using the Forest had to keep one bull for every twenty-five head of breeding cattle, and (2) the bulls had to be purebreds of some recognized breed. Foresters cooperated in the enforcement of the regulations which were also frequently extended outside the Forest by state law, and enforced by state officials. Together, state and federal governments gradually forced an upgrading of the quality of stock. These programs had been in operation before, but they were given new impetus by the requirements of a people at war.[36] The changes thus created in the industry seldom overwhelmed anyone, but both range management and cattle husbandry slowly improved.

During the war the Forest officials apparently decided that the time had come to make the Forests genuinely self-sustaining. High beef prices seemed to make such action appropriate. In 1915 the Foresters raised grazing fees sharply (from 50 per cent to 75 per cent above the 1906 fees), and in 1916 they raised them again. In 1917 the fees were raised very substantially in an effort to have them conform to the actual value of the Forest grazing land. The sentiments of cattlemen were by no means unanimous. In some places Forest users stoutly opposed fee increases. Most of the protests arose over the largest raises of 1915 and 1917. The protests were not effective, although they began to smoulder below the surface.[37] Many cattlemen had once seen the Foresters as a bulwark against change. Increasingly, however, cattlemen discovered that the Forest Service offered no protection from change, and that the Foresters could not stop the disappearance of free range either. The Foresters, consequently, began to lose some of their erstwhile friends.

Use of the public domain, outside the Forests, attracted more attention during the war years. By 1916 the deterioration of the unregulated range had become clearly apparent. In an effort to retard the destruction, Congress passed the Stock Raising Homestead Act of December 29, 1916. Congress thought that homesteading by cattlemen would reduce the domain, and also put it under some sort of supervision. The act must also have been some sort of concession to the ranch farmers. The law tended to compel more intensive use of the range by those who acquired their six hundred and forty acres under the act.[38]

Under the act of 1916, the Secretary of Interior could prohibit anyone from claiming land which had generally needed water holes, and rights-of-way. The Secretary was also supposed to reserve land from entry if it was irrigable, or if it could not support a family raising stock on six hundred and forty acres. In response to the act, settlers flooded onto the Plains. Within four months of its passage, the Department of Interior received applications for 24 million acres. The supply of open range really became limited then, and almost all cattlemen either intensified their operations by ranch farming, or else sought state-owned lands for lease or purchase. Many of the entrymen could not succeed on six hundred and forty acres, and so they leased their land to other cattlemen. Cattlemen often felt that most of the homesteaders were actually speculators attempting to profit from the discomfiture of legitimate cattlemen.[39] Anyhow, the act effectively required further changes in animal husbandry on the Plains.

Throughout its long history, the cattle industry of the Plains changed to meet the demands of an ever more urbanized and industrialized civilization. For the most part, cattlemen adjusted by using land, labor, and capital more intensively. Specifically, cattlemen intensified their operations by adopting the particular techniques of ranch farming. Two chief elements characterized the development of the cattle industry: (1) wider use of ranch farming methods, and (2) greater reliance on federal aid and regulation. While this general course of events persisted throughout the twentieth century, the urban-industrial growth of the First World War accelerated the evolution.

Techniques of ranch farming made no important advances. If prices had not been so good during the war, greater technical changes might have come to the industry. As it was, with high prices, cattlemen often managed to keep going without really adjusting to urban-industrial America.

The natural hazards of life on the Plains always conditioned the responses of westerners, but in terms of survival, plainsmen had long since learned to adapt to nature. During the First World War, cattlemen had to do more than just survive the assaults of nature. They had to adapt in a way which would maximize production for an industrial society. This is what they did—imperfectly, but certainly.

CHAPTER VI

The Postwar Depression

1919-1922

A depression began about the middle of 1919 and lasted until around 1923. As unemployment spread, American urban workers cut down their meat consumption, and this inevitably hurt the Plains cattlemen. Between 1919 and 1922, each American consumed an average of only 66.4 pounds of beef and veal each year. This averaged 2.5 pounds below the average of 1915–1918. Cattle prices also fell.[1]

For Plains stockmen, trouble arose chiefly from the general economic conditions of postwar America. Stockmen from Texas to Montana had surplus cattle in 1919. They dumped their livestock on the market at the same time that a general depression spurred a consumer campaign against the high cost of living. As consumer resistance grew, northern cattlemen hesitated to buy cattle for summer grazing, and their decision in turn hurt the southern plainsmen. At the same time, a railroad snarl on the Plains hindered cattle movements from range to range, and from range to market. The depression deepened.[2]

Hoping for prosperity, Corn-Belt cattle feeders bought many cattle through 1919 and 1920. Plains cattlemen took advantage of feeder optimism and liquidated as much as they could. Because Americans ate less beef, however, prices progressively deteriorated through 1921. At length, Corn-Belt feeders cut back their buying. Plainsmen lost heavily from start to finish, but the ruined market had not yet caused them to despair.[3]

Beef consumption declined steadily as the depression grew

72

worse and people shifted to other foods. By 1921 Plains cattlemen suffered too from the forced selling of much of their stock; they also suffered from a general shortage of stock, caused in part by the forced selling. The number of range cattle declined and soon reached the lowest point in decades. All over the Plains, cattlemen ended 1921 in the worst shape they had been in since the century began. Jay Higgins reported a typical Plains tale:

The market and financial conditions have been such that stockmen generally have suffered heavy losses and many have been practically put out of the business. Many were required by bankers to sell off their stock very closely and have been unable to refinance the purchase of other stock. This condition will probably result in an understocked condition . . . for some years to come.[4]

All these troubles spurred cattlemen, economists, and editors to devise remedies. Solutions ranged from a plan for direct buying by Corn-Belt feeders (to cut out the central market), to the development of higher-quality beef animals. The central markets proved durable, but no doubt improved quality would have helped the Plains cattlemen some. Observers had already noted that the few remaining beef consumers preferred baby beef of high finish and light weight. Cattlemen might have done more to capture this market. Still, the producers could not force people to eat beef just by improving quality.[5] The urban depression lay at the heart of the problem, and, as it continued, the market for cheap western steers fell apart.

Well-to-do Americans (a tiny minority even in the Roaring Twenties) demanded finished beef. These discriminating people absorbed only a small number of Plains cattle, however, and in the end, producers had to find other solutions to the depression. Cattlemen had no shortage of advisers. In 1922 would-be saviors suggested such diverse solutions as: (1) production of high-quality beef (2) sale at the newly opened Los Angeles stockyards (3) cooperative marketing (a Texas experiment), and (4) more opportune marketing, based on data issued by the newly formed Livestock Reporting Service. All these measures probably helped some, but none really approached the fundamental problems of the urban depression. Many people simply refused to believe in the depression. This attitude did not help anyone meet the problem.

Unfortunately, Europeans cut back on their meat eating too. Plainsmen dumped more cattle on the market than Americans could use, and then sent the rest of their surplus to Europe. It did not sell there, either. As early as 1919, American meat stocks abroad exceeded European needs. By 1920, beef exports had shrunk to insignificance. Other nations captured what there was of a European market. In short, the European customer suddenly disappeared, the American customer stopped buying, and the Plains cattle industry very nearly collapsed.[6]

Domestic prices for range cattle dropped steadily. In 1918 the peak wartime price had been $14.50 a hundredweight. In 1919 the price dropped to $11.25 a hundred, and fell sharply to $8.80 in 1920. In 1921 Plains cattle prices fell more than two dollars to $6.15 a hundred, and by 1922 ranged around $6.00 a hundred (the low was $5.00 in New Mexico, the high $7.75 in Montana). Almost all costs remained at near 1918 levels, and so Plains cattlemen lost steadily.[7]

The depression of 1922 intensified when Texans dumped their cattle on an already demoralized market. By then cattlemen were against the wall. In New Mexico and Colorado, cattlemen spent an average of $27.98 to produce a calf which sold for $21.50.[8]

Under these circumstances cattlemen cast about for cheap loans with which to continue their business. Cattle financiers panicked almost immediately. Financing was undeniably hazardous. The state of Montana, for example, loaned school funds for ranch land, but in the end recovered only about 25 per cent of the loans. On the southern Plains, cattlemen who had borrowed from the War Finance Corporation were pressed for repayment as the corporation sought to wind up its affairs. In Texas, Oklahoma, and New Mexico, cattlemen were stretched over the barrel.

As credit became harder to secure, the Federal Reserve System intervened to make borrowing more difficult. In 1920 the Federal Reserve Banks imposed progressive rediscount rates on livestock loans. When the local bank borrowed from a Federal Reserve Bank, the rate of interest rose progressively on cattle loans. The larger the loans, the heavier the interest. The amount local bankers could borrow was thus effectively, and sharply, cut off. When interest got too high for local bankers, cattlemen could no longer borrow.[9]

The Federal Reserve progressive rediscount rate seriously hampered cattle movements in 1921. To counteract banker policy, cattlemen of the southern Plains actually tinkered with cooperative financing of cattle shipments. A few eastern bankers organized the Stock Growers' Finance Corporation to lend some $50 million on livestock. The bankers did this mostly to head off cattlemen's demand that the War Finance Corporation extend money for livestock loans. The bankers delayed doing anything, however, and at length the Federal Reserve Board recommended that the War Finance Corporation lend the money. Bankers fought the proposal, but to no avail. In August, 1921, Congress authorized the War Finance Corporation to lend on livestock. By late October, 1921, the Corporation, through newly created agencies, was lending money to cattlemen. The Corporation advanced one billion dollars through thirty-three new lending agencies. Altogether stockmen borrowed some $100 million, and the more painful pressure subsided.[10]

Meanwhile, on August 1, 1921, the Federal Reserve Board had ended the progressive rediscount rate. The editor of *The Producer* expressed the sentiments of most cattlemen when he wrote of the defunct rule:

Few will mourn its passing. Its sponsors claimed that it was correct in principle; its opponents charged that it was abominable in practice. During its short existence it was responsible for much liquidation of breeding stock. It prevented those banks that were disposed to aid stockmen in an emergency from doing so except at a ruinous penalty. It was the inspiration for much profiteering in interest charges.

Peace to its ashes! [11]

The Federal Reserve Board had acted, but belatedly. Once again the War Finance Corporation had rescued the beleaguered cattlemen.

The rescue operation had several consequences. First, interest rates declined as bankers competed with the federal corporation. Second, with money advanced by the government, cattlemen could move cattle either to market or to other ranges. Even so, small operators often found themselves in trouble, and, as Will C. Barnes put it, many were "wiped off the map. . . ." [12]

The whole mess produced another interesting subsidiary consequence. Cattlemen and farmers tried to have Congress provide permanent agencies for intermediate agricultural credit. Sooner or later, many cattlemen thought, the War Finance Corporation would end, and something should be devised to take its place. Cattlemen, for the most part, no longer wanted to be left to the mercy of private bankers and wild free enterprise. A great many changes had taken place since the turn of the century. [13]

Meanwhile, various cattlemen's organizations continually requested a serious investigation of the Big Five meat-packing monopoly. Finally, in 1919, the Federal Trade Commission discovered that the Big Five controlled the industry. The commissioners suggested that Congress divest packers of their control over stockyards, refrigerator cars, and cold-storage facilities. The commissioners held that the monopoly of meat processing stemmed from packer control of these subsidiary industries. Congress almost, but not quite, acted. On February 24, 1919, the Senate Committee on Agriculture and Forestry took up a bill which would have licensed live-stock dealers, prohibited packers from owning terminal stockyards, and required railroads and packers to make refrigerator cars available to any person requesting them. Then, in the fall of 1919, the Senate stopped hearings, killed the bills, and waited for the Justice Department to begin antitrust prosecution of the packers.[14]

The threatened antitrust suit stirred the packers into negotiating with Attorney General A. Mitchell Palmer. On August 31, 1920, the packers secured the famous Packer Consent Decree. Under the decree the packers did not admit to any guilt, but they did agree to get out of all food businesses, except meat packing, within two years. The decree did not require them to give up their refrigerator cars or cold-storage warehouses. The Consent Decree was not exactly what cattlemen wanted, and from the first they criticized it, mostly because it left the packers in control of their distribution network. Many cattlemen felt that Congress should still legislate.[15]

In January, 1921, in order to calm the stockmen, packers lobbied at the meeting of the American National Livestock Association. The packers irritated the cattlemen, but accomplished nothing more. Cattlemen persisted in lobbying for a packer control act. On August 15, 1921, they got what they wanted when President Warren G. Harding signed the Packer and Stockyards Act. The law provided that:

1. Packers were not to discriminate in commerce in favor of, or against any person or locality, nor were they to apportion among themselves in buying or selling.

2. Packers were forbidden to control prices or create a monopoly.

3. The Secretary of Agriculture was empowered to enforce the law, and could declare existing or prospective rates or regulations unreasonable, and might prescribe rates and practices to be adopted.[16]

The Packer and Stockyards Act went into force on November 1, 1921, when sixty-six yards passed under the supervision of the Secretary of Agriculture. Immediately, the packers contested the constitutionality of the law, but on May 1, 1922, the United States Supreme Court upheld all provisions of the act. The law at last gave cattlemen some protection from the oppressions of the packers.[17]

Congressional action, however, could not stop the drouth. The northern Great Plains are dry at best, and in 1919 they were far from their best; drouth had struck Montana, North Dakota, South Dakota, and Wyoming. Even Nebraska suffered some. In contrast, plenty of rain fell in Texas, New Mexico, Oklahoma, Colorado, and Kansas. By the middle of 1919, northern cattlemen were shipping stock either south or east. Stockmen decreased their shipments to southern ranges toward the end of 1919, but by that time large numbers of northern cattle had been liquidated.[18]

Again drouth struck in 1920. Northern Plains cattlemen suffered most, and they suffered more than in 1919. Cattle by the thousands were shipped to the relatively moist southern Plains. Blizzards which swept the northern Plains intensified the damage, and after two successive years, northern plainsmen were left in a quandary, or worse.[19]

Drouth continued through 1921, but now the South had its turn for a change as rains fell on the northern Plains, but bypassed southern areas. Not all the northern Plains were wet, but generally the drouth let up there; where rainfall was light, it was at least opportune.[20]

Cattlemen just about stopped complaining about the weather in 1922. The winter had been hard, and on the northern Plains cattlemen had trouble restocking, but 1922 was a good wet year all over. Stock were fat and healthy, and the range was generally good from north to south.[21] Taking one thing with another, no single section of the Great Plains suffered from prolonged drouth between 1919 and 1922.

Dry weather did less damage than it might have, partly because railroads lowered rates for the emergency. Railroads in the northern Plains set up special rates for hay in 1919 and 1920. Railroads began this benevolent policy while they were still government-operated. After the railroads returned to private management, they found the precedent difficult to reverse. In 1921 the Interstate Commerce Commission recommended that railroads lower rates on feed and stock to assist drouth-plagued cattlemen. Railroad managers acted on the recommendation to some extent. In 1922 the Santa Fe, and the Rock Island reduced rates one-half on feed for the southern and central Plains. The rate reductions unquestionably assisted cattlemen in this trying period. Railroad managers had also come a long way since 1900.[22]

Meanwhile, cattlemen suffered from grasshopper scourges as well as from drouth. Grasshoppers had regularly ravaged the Plains since time immemorial and new outbreaks occurred in 1921 and 1922. In the more primitive open-range era, cattlemen had not been bothered much by these pests. Grasshopper plagues assumed new importance, however, as the range shrank, and as cattlemen turned to supplemental feeds. In 1921, hordes of grasshoppers appeared in Montana and Wyoming. The insects destroyed so much feed and grass that cattle had to be moved to other ranges. On much of the northern Plains grasshoppers damaged the hay crop, and in some places they literally devoured grass and fodder. In 1922 the grasshoppers appeared in greater numbers and their attacks spread eastward to the Dakotas. Cattlemen sought government help in spreading poison bait, but help usually came too late, if at all. Fortunately, moist weather rescued the northern cattlemen; grasshoppers generally reproduced slowly in wet years and their numbers were thus reduced.[23]

Prairie dogs also took their toll from the cattlemen, causing considerable losses. Scientists estimated that on the southern Plains ten prairie dogs to an acre used almost all of one year's grass. In 1919 some 60 million dogs in New Mexico alone destroyed the equivalent of the hay and forage production of at least 12 million acres. The Biological Survey continually tried to exterminate the animals who in turn resisted extermination fairly well. In 1922 the war in Wyoming was considered moderately successful, but the dogs were far from eradicated.

Meanwhile, predators continued their destructive ways. The buzzard—previously considered only a scavenger—was discovered to be a bird of prey. Buzzards particularly attacked and killed newborn calves. In the early twenties, Texans strove to exterminate the birds. They killed some three thousand in 1920 alone. At the same time, the wars against mountain lions, coyotes, and wolves continued. The United States Biological Survey directed the several wars, but neither side scored any decisive victories.[24]

The battle against animal disease was not as dramatic, but was probably more significant. Here cattlemen achieved some success. Between 1906 and 1920, the tick-infested area decreased by 70 per cent. Of the remaining 30 per cent, only a small part was in the Great Plains. Congress strengthened the laws on quarantining in 1920, and thus permitted agents of the United States to exercise even more control over cattle shipments. By 1922 the Plains were remarkably free from ticks, largely because of federal eradication programs.[25]

In 1922 extension agents developed blackleg vaccination into a fine art. They discovered that with community vaccination "bees" they accomplished more than they did with the instruction of individual cattlemen. In 1922, however, Congress stopped the distribution of free vaccine. The program had been marvelously effective up to that time. Between 1897, when free distribution began, and 1922, when it ended, per capita cattle losses from blackleg fell from 10 per cent to less than one-half of 1 per cent per annum.[26]

In short, between 1919 and 1922, the cattlemen of the Plains struggled against drouth, blizzard, insects, and depression. The plainsmen did not always win. Some shifted to sheep, and some left as sheepmen entered. Feed rose outrageously in spite of reduced rail rates, and many stockmen sent cattle to other ranges during drouth. Many cattlemen simply failed altogether. B. F. Gordon, of Lewistown, Montana, recalled: "many well to do farmers and stockmen were forced to surrender, and flock to the towns and become . . . the unemployed, dependent on the government or charity for their existence."[27] Montana and the Dakotas suffered from all calamities in 1921, and thousands of cattle were thrown on the market. The same tale was told of Texas in 1922. From north to south, cattlemen painfully readjusted their operations.[28]

Of course, the First World War had stimulated the cattle industry, but in spite of this the number of cattle on the Great Plains scarcely increased between 1910 and 1920. In 1910 the Plains states had 17,040,795 head of beef cattle. By 1920 these had increased 2.5 per cent to 17,491,712 head.[29] No doubt, in part, the slow growth resulted from the developing ranch-farming complex which permitted more meat to be produced with fewer cattle. While the Plains cattle population remained almost stable, the cattle population in the eastern states declined. As a result, in 1920 the Great Plains accounted for 49.5 per cent of all the beef cattle in the United States. The center of beef production shifted westward again in 1920.[30]

And then there were the dry farmers. Although all agricultural prices slumped after 1919, wheat dropped less than cattle. On the other hand, drouth and grasshoppers injured dry farmers more than cattlemen. Nevertheless, farmers steadily increased their wheat acreage. The amount of Plains land in wheat increased 43.6 per cent between 1910 and 1920, although the amount of Plains land in farms increased only 18.8 per cent. Viewed from another way, however, the gross increase was modest. In 1909, wheat was grown on only 6.8 per cent of the total Plains farm acreage. Ten years, and many dry farmers later, only 9.7 per cent of the Plains was in wheat. Cattlemen seemed more contemptuous of, than disturbed by, the dry farmers. Yields from wheat continued to decline in many places on the Plains. Even though settlers continued to come west, wheat farming offered few good prospects. Dry farmers increased in numbers, but they also added more cattle to their operations. This did annoy cattlemen.[31]

All over the northern Plains, dry farmers failed as the

drouth persisted through 1919 and 1920. The government loaned money for seed in 1921 and 1922, but even so, many farmers were forced out as depression continued. In Kansas, farmers went bankrupt, and some committed suicide. "Rarely does a day pass now that the telegraph does not tick out a half dozen or more bits of news telling of the ill fortune of Kansas farmers." [32] South Dakota farmers lost their farms by the hundreds, while over in Wyoming farmers broke the sod with an optimism soon turned to despair.[33]

Cattlemen had hard going, but they were not that badly off. In 1919, cattle were in fairly good shape everywhere. In 1920, in spite of drouth, the range was fairly good even in the North, and cattle came out of the season in good condition. In general, the range was not overgrazed in 1921, and such cattle as remained were in fair condition. In 1922, throughout the Plains, although the weather was good, the range showed the drouth of previous years. Reports from all over indicated a little deterioration in grasses and cattle. The range had been overstocked in 1919, but thereafter expensive liquidations kept the grass in shape and cattle numbers low.[34]

Cattlemen prospered more than wheat farmers, in part, because ranch farming continually improved and increased. The number of cattle on the Plains, for example, increased only 2.5 per cent between 1909 and 1919, but at the same time, the acreages for hay and sorghum increased 14.2 per cent. On the Plains, in 1910, 84 per cent of all livestock feed had been derived from the range. By 1920 only 80 per cent came from the range. The additional 20 per cent came from hay and forage crops.[35]

On the southern Plains, almost all cattlemen converted to ranch farming. Some ranch farmers built silos, and many also built dams for water storage. Southerners had learned not to depend on fodder grown off the ranch, and whenever possible, they raised supplemental feed. Northern plainsmen at the same time developed a "vastly expanded stock industry supported by a well-developed feed-crop program. . . ." [36] Up and down the Great Plains, by 1922 almost every farmer kept cattle and grew fodder crops. Dry farmers came to realize that they could not depend on wheat alone, and so ranch farming methods appeared everywhere in the farm community.

In the North, and to a somewhat lesser extent in the South, large outfits were broken up. The commercial, family-sized ranch farm had more staying power than the giant spread. Ranch farmers quickly shifted from winter feeding to maintenance feeding. The need for fodder increased labor costs, but ranch farming also cut down the general hazards of the cattle business. Wheat farmers in the North, and cotton farmers in the South, both tended to become cattlemen. The evolution accelerated as drouth and depression struck first north and then south.[37]

Meanwhile, ranch farmers often used the basic dry farming methods of the time. The combination was often essential, for as J. L. Humphrey wrote of a dying ranch: "In other words, dry farming methods will have to be successfully followed to make this four thousand acre ranch of any great value unless it is run in connection with a large amount of other grazing land which at present is not available." [38] So, as the settlers moved in, the pattern of cattle raising changed. Silos, for example, were sometimes adopted by farmers in the northern Plains. Maintenance feeding became nearly an economic necessity by 1922. Urban America prospered most when the Great Plains were fully productive, and so full production became necessary.[39]

Stockmen incorporated various forage crops into the ranch-farming system. Sorghums continued to be important, but were widely grown only on the southern Plains. Alfalfa, inoculated with nitrate-producing bacteria, increased in use both north and south. By 1919 over 92 per cent of the alfalfa was grown west of the Mississippi. Alfalfa resisted drouth and also produced large amounts of forage. It thus especially appealed to Plains cattlemen. In the United States, timothy was the most important forage crop, but it was not very successful on the Great Plains. On the northern Plains, crested wheatgrass proved to be the most useful forage plant. This Russian immigrant attracted attention because it was superior to the native grasses.

Cattlemen on the southern and central Plains also discovered particularly useful feeds. Southern cattlemen continued to depend heavily on cottonseed products. Cattlemen of the central Plains discovered the superior feeding qualities of sugar-beet by-products. On the central and northern Plains sugar beets attracted more and more attention, and ranch farmers were urged to grow beets for supplemental feed, and for cash.[40] Thus, in a variety of ways, cattlemen produced more beef on less land with less risk.

Full production required advanced methods of range management as well as ranch farming. By 1919 cattlemen everywhere tried to use grazing lands efficiently. In 1919 James Jardine and Mark Anderson published *Range Management on the National Forests,* and in the same year Arthur W. Sampson brought out the first thorough study of range grasses entitled *Plant Succession in Relation to Range Management.* These books assisted both Foresters and cattlemen in their efforts to save the sadly depleted resources of the Great Plains.[41]

Changes in the industry also involved the use of more purebred cattle. Throughout the Plains, Herefords and Shorthorns still predominated. Cattlemen's associations generally insisted that only registered bulls of these two breeds be allowed on the range. Herefords were more numerous, and in some cattle markets they made up nearly 75 per cent of the cattle sold.[42] But with each passing year the old breeds faced more competition. In 1920, Texas ranchers Fred W. Turner and Karl Thomas, managed to import a herd of Charolais cattle from France by way of Mexico. After the great foot-and-mouth outbreaks of 1915, laws made it nearly impossible for breeders to import foreign cattle. Under the circumstances, any importation was a major achievement even if it was not economically important.[43]

Brahman cattle were already in the country, and apparently found favor with some Texans. Meanwhile, the Klebergs of the King Ranch continued their experiments with the breed. In 1920 they chanced to produce a bull they named Monkey (he was partly Shorthorn and partly Brahman), whose offspring astonishingly bred true. From Monkey the Klebergs produced a new breed of cattle which they called Santa Gertrudis. The Santa Gertrudis resisted great heat, had the tough, insect-proof skin of the zebu, gained well on grass alone, and also showed the heavier, deeper meat conformation of the Shorthorn. In short, Monkey combined the best characteristics of both breeds. In 1920, however, the Santa Gertrudis had yet to be developed.[44] By 1923 the breed was tentatively in existence, but Herefords and Shorthorns still reigned on the Plains.

The years of hardship were mitigated a bit for National Forest users because they were permitted to delay payment of their grazing fees. Five-year permits on the Forests were also inaugurated in 1919. In 1920 some Congressmen attempted to have the fees raised to equal private rates. The effort stimulated the Foresters into making a survey of the grasslands in 1921 to see if fees could be established for different qualities of range.

In spite of a fee increase in 1919, hardly any cattlemen complained about the operation of the Forests. The Forest Service returned 35 per cent of the grazing fees to the states for schools and roads. In this way Congress greatly reduced complaints by stockmen about federal interference in the cattle business.[45] Indeed, cattlemen found the National Forests so successful that they sought some extension of the program. In 1919 bills were presented in Congress which would have extended federal supervision of grazing to the remaining public domain, but no act passed. As cattlemen observed the consequences of the Stock Raising Homestead Act of 1916, they came to favor stricter federal regulation of the range. Under this act, about 42 million acres had come into the possession of entrymen in four years. However Congress might view these entries, cattlemen disapproved.[46]

To sum up: between 1919 and 1922 a host of troubles beset stockmen. Meat consumption declined; beef prices fell;
drouth hit the Plains; grasshoppers, prairie dogs, and diseases
destroyed crops and cattle; and meanwhile, bankers and
packers hovered like Harpies to finish off any surviving
cattlemen. In their extremity cattlemen called for and got
government assistance in combating their adversaries. Farmers and cattlemen had changed their minds about government assistance. The change had been coming since the century began, but it reached a new stage after the war. Demanding federal aid, the editor of *The Producer* declared:

Paternalism in government may be a hinderance rather
than a help to the sound economic development of a nation.
Too much coddling may dull initiative. Insurance against
risk and losses of all kinds may soften the fiber of the industrial fabric. Our formularies have taught us this. But the
state that takes into its own hands the vigilant supervision
of fundamental activities, exercising its perogative to protect
them against disaster in critical periods, while it may be as-
sailed by political theorists with all manner of dogmatic am-
munition, will at any rate not lay itself open to the charge of
indifference that, once invited, both aims straighter and
scores more effectively.[47]

Between 1919 and 1922 cattlemen engaged in ranch farming
on an ever greater scale, and they also asked for and got more
federal help in surviving the attacks of nature and the market.
Ranch farming and federal help—these two—still characterized the evolving cattle industry.

CHAPTER VII

From Range to Pasture
1923-1925

The population of the United States grew rather slowly after the First World War. The restrictive immigration laws of 1923 and 1924, and the sharply falling birth rate, both slowed down the arrival of new Americans. Nevertheless, the number of potential beef eaters steadily increased. In 1920 the American population came to 105,710,000. In 1923 population was estimated at 111,537,000, and in 1925 at 114,867,000.[1] Per capita and gross consumption of beef increased. In 1923, 21,810,000 pounds of beef and veal were slaughtered under federal inspection; by 1925, this had risen to 23,106,000 pounds.[2] The Great Plains cattlemen somehow managed to supply most of this beef.

Cattlemen raised the beef while land available to them continually decreased. They did it chiefly by using new techniques and new approaches to the range. Ranch farming increased. At the same time, ranchers devised a new set of methods which can best be called pasture farming. Both ranch farmers and pasture farmers needed greater control of grazing land. They wanted laws which would stabilize the use of the public domain and protect their tenure.

While cattlemen changed their methods and ideas, nature remained benign. Rains fell abundantly on the northern Plains as far south as Kansas and Colorado in 1923. New Mexico was dry, but in Oklahoma and Texas rainfall was only slightly worse than usual.[3] In 1924 all the Plains states were fairly moist, except for the southern states.[4] Then, in 1925, drouth again struck briefly on the southern Plains. All of

Texas, New Mexico, and a bit of Oklahoma suffered early in the year. By April of 1925, however, the rains came in Texas and Oklahoma, and by August the drouth broke in New Mexico. Cattlemen of the southern Plains had had a close shave, but they came through without too much trouble. On the northern Plains, as far south as Kansas and Colorado, the weather continued moist. Cattle and feed were in good condition. Cattlemen found the weather pretty good between 1923 and 1925.[5]

Animal and plant diseases, however, continued to plague them. Even there the situation improved. By 1923 tick fever hardly bothered cattlemen. Of nine hundred and seventy-five counties under tick quarantine in 1906, some six hundred and ninety-five had been released by 1923, and in 1924 the Department of Agriculture released an additional seventy-three counties. Federal and state officials had nearly eliminated the disease.[6]

No such good luck attended the war on foot-and-mouth disease. In 1924 a new plague broke out in California. A vigorous slaughter campaign stamped out the disease. Then suddenly it reappeared in Texas. By the middle of September, however, eradication was well under way. Some three thousand cattle were condemned on three Texas ranches. By October all of the diseased animals had been slaughtered at a cost to the federal government of more than $380,000. The new outbreak stimulated Congress to appoint a commission to study foot-and-mouth disease in Europe where it was endemic. In 1924 the commissioners reported that eradication by slaughter was the cheapest method for the United States because the disease had not become permanently established in the country.

In 1924, Heinrich Forsch and Robert Dahmen of the Berlin Veterinary Research Institute discovered the bacteria which caused foot-and-mouth disease. Ultimately, scientists developed a vaccine. Even so, Americans still found slaughter the cheaper method of control.[7] In 1925 another epidemic of foot-and-mouth disease occurred in Texas. In spite of some bad-tempered protests, diseased animals were again slaughtered. Altogether 21,263 cattle had to be destroyed before the disease was eliminated.[8]

Meanwhile, the battle against bovine tuberculosis continued. The disease harmed dairymen more than beef producers, but beef cattle did get it. In 1917 the federal government had undertaken an eradication program, and, as a result, tubercular reactors in America decreased, between 1918 and 1924, from 4.9 per cent of all cattle to 3.4 per cent.

Cattlemen also contended with plant diseases. Smut, a disease of certain grasses, particularly wheat, had not previously hurt cattlemen much. As stockmen increasingly depended on forage crops, however, smut became economically significant for them. Because smut attacked sorghums, the disease became especially important for southern plainsmen. Smut could be controlled by treating the seeds so as to destroy the spores before planting, and cattlemen increasingly used this technique. Ergot, a fungus of flowers and grasses, both injured crops and poisoned cattle; however, it presented few problems because cattlemen could easily control it. They merely avoided feeding infected grains, except by accident. Diseases of animals and plants cost cattlemen plenty, but the losses did not ruin the industry.[9]

Economic losses did not ruin the industry either. Montana cattlemen did poorly in 1924. Presumably other cattlemen in other areas also found 1924 a poor year. Prices sank so low that Corn-Belt feeders sometimes suspected a trick and hesitated to buy. Cattle prices averaged $6.87 a hundred between 1923 and 1925. In 1923 cattlemen seemed to consider the market good.[10] A dissenting opinion came from Oklahoma where one observer insisted: "Market conditions are still bad. Few if any of the cattlemen have made money this season. Quite a few have realy lost money."[11]

As usual, economic disturbances most seriously hurt those least able to resist. Stockmen with less-than-carload lots took lower prices for their cattle. The larger outfits shipped in larger quantities, and the difference sometimes came to as much as $5 or $10 a head.[12] Furthermore, cattle prices were not only low, but were low in relation to all other commodities. Prices were especially low in relation to taxes and other costs. Still, the industry survived. In 1925 the general economy began to improve and cattlemen came into fairly good times.[13]

Hard times for cattlemen seemed to cause increased meat consumption. Between 1923 and 1925, each American ate an average of 68.0 pounds of beef and veal. Americans thus consumed slightly more in the middle twenties than they had consumed just after the war. Undoubtedly they increased their beef eating because of the lower cattle prices.[14]

Consumers ate more beef and veal, but they still wanted it to be tender. To meet the demand, cattlemen marketed cattle at two years or younger. The age of cattle at marketing thus decreased, but so did the price per head. At the same time, however, earlier marketing caused greater turnover, which meant more meat produced on less land.[15] On the other hand, costs continued to rise, and stockmen found credit hard to come by. On the Great Plains, many of the troubles of cattlemen stemmed from this shortage of credit. The old problem thus remained. Since 1919 cattlemen had wanted the government to set up some sources of intermediate credit because stockmen regularly needed assistance across difficult periods. Prior to 1923 the War Finance Corporation had helped them out. Then, in 1923, Congress set up twelve Intermediate Credit Banks which, among other things, supposedly rediscounted livestock loans. Each bank received $5 million from the federal treasury. Congress intended that the new banks should lend for one to three years. The Intermediate Credit Banks supplied some credit to cattlemen, but not much. Plainsmen continued to suffer from a shortage of capital, and in 1923 many local banks and their clients failed for want of ready cash. In South Dakota a rash of mortgage foreclosures broke out in the twenty-three Great Plains counties.[16]

Congress next removed the War Finance Corporation from

the farm-loan business. In February, 1924, the Agricultural Credit Corporation replaced the War Finance Corporation. The Agricultural Credit Corporation apparently quickly fell under the spell of the Federal Reserve System. The Federal Reserve System policies helped neither cattlemen nor bankers. Congressman Usher L. Burdick of North Dakota charged: "It was not intended that any cash should be sent to small banks to keep them from closing." [17] He may have been right. Anyhow, the results of the policy were terrible.

On the northern Plains bankers failed in legions. One-third of Montana's banks closed between 1920 and 1924. Bankers in North and South Dakota went to the wall, and many of them ceased to operate. At the same time, cattlemen were heavily in debt throughout the Plains. In 1924, for example, over 79 per cent of the ranchers in Montana were in debt. Furthermore, they could seldom find new credit, and their old debts had grown oppressive. All over the Plains, cattlemen decreased herds, or went out of business. The trouble continued well into 1925 as cattlemen, farmers, and bankers were ruined. Land prices fell. Throughout, no federal institution could lend directly to cattlemen, and no other solution appeared workable.[18] No wonder that under the circumstances, cattlemen tended to support the McNary-Haugen agricultural relief bill of 1924. The House of Representatives turned it down on June 3, 1924, but plainsmen hoped for better luck at the next session of Congress.[19]

Cattlemen looked for help in other areas of federal administration, and sometimes found it. In 1923 the Secretary of Agriculture amended the rules of the Packers and Stockyards Act so that commission firms had to post bond assuring prompt sale of cattle consigned to them. Cattlemen liked this change, but apparently they did not much approve the nonenforcement of the Packer's Consent Decree of 1920. Packers protested that the Packers and Stockyards Act of 1921 abrogated the decree, but the members of the American Livestock Association felt otherwise. Cattlemen protested that three years after acceptance of the decree, the packers still ignored it. Then, in April of 1923, the Court of the District of Columbia suspended the decree indefinitely. A business-oriented administration and court seemed determined to abandon cattlemen to the collusive power of the packers. From the cattlemen's viewpoint, however, they had not quite lost everything because the court had not invalidated the whole decree. As 1925 drew to a close, cattlemen still strove to have the decree enforced, and packers still resisted enforcement.[20]

Cattlemen felt a certain urgency in their efforts to control the packers. Producers worried about the Consent Decree as Armour and Morris merged. The merger first made the news in January, 1923, and was completed on March 29, 1923. The Big Five became the Big Four. They did not thereby become less formidable. Some cattlemen thought that collusion might soon be replaced by outright monopoly in the packing business. Others thought the merger opened the possibility of a competitive struggle between the giants which might benefit the stockmen.[21] Neither view proved correct.

Out on the Plains, range depletion continued between 1923 and 1925. Still, the range appeared comparatively good in 1923. On the southern Plains grasses were a bit sparse and short, but forage was plentiful on the rest of the Plains. In 1924 the range was not quite as good as it had been, but it was good enough. The range tended to deteriorate, however, and some cattlemen felt slight but certain pressures. In 1925 the range was generally good over all the Plains. Changes in range management took place without much prodding from nature.[22]

Cattlemen did introduce changes. Some cattlemen with only a few head would lease range land, and then for a fee would graze the cattle of other nearby ranchers. The other cattlemen thus protected their own range, and the herder made a living without investing much money in cattle. In addition to this development, between 1923 and 1925, cattlemen increasingly deferred grazing, or controlled their range. Stockmen reserved land for grazing at certain seasons, and kept cattle off at other times. This sort of range management permitted cattlemen to carry more cattle at less risk. Unfortunately, the system sometimes encouraged overgrazing. This happened because more cattle could be carried in the winter than the range could reasonably accommodate at other seasons. Range management did not solve all problems. Combined with supplemental feeding, however, management greatly increased the amount of meat produced on an acre.[23]

Greater production of beef per acre also took place as the horse population declined both on the Plains and in the United States because of automobiles and tractors. Feed and range once needed for horses became available for cattle. Cattlemen could raise more cattle without increasing land or crops. Horse population declined drastically. Between 1923 and 1925, the number of horses fell at a rate of about seven hundred and fifty thousand head each year. At this rate of decline, the feed released equaled at least an amount needed to grow an additional 337 million pounds of meat each year.

As the number of horses declined, the feed released was nearly as important as the rising crop yields produced by other means. Between 1921 and 1924, for example, the released grain equaled about two-thirds of the increased corn crop, and the released hay equaled one-third of the increased hay production. After 1925, the released hay actually equaled half the increase in hay production. The simple decline in the number of horses completely altered the Great Plains cattle industry. Without changing a single land or crop statistic, cattlemen raised more beef. Not that horses disappeared by 1925. In 1924, for example, horses still came to 16 per cent of the livestock on Montana ranches and farms, but this was less than before, and from then on horse population fell continually.[24]

Meanwhile, dry farming on the Plains changed. On the southern Plains, many of the larger ranchers broke up their holdings and sold them for farms. Relatively low prices discouraged stockmen. At the same time, relatively high cotton prices enticed farmers onto the land. The development of drouth-resistant cotton and wheat accelerated the spread of southern dry farming.[25] The greatest plow-up of the southern Plains took place just after the First World War. By 1924 farmers of the Plains grew 17 million more acres of wheat than they had grown in 1909. Farmers expanded production mostly in the South, particularly in Texas, Oklahoma, Kansas, and New Mexico. In order to provide land for dry farming the old ranches had to be broken up. In December, 1923, R. R. Hammond, cattle baron of Texas sold out, saying: "There goes the last of the herd, and I am out of the cow business forever." [26] He was, of course, and so were many others.

Through 1923 and 1924 the lists of sold and parceled ranches ran like a catalogue of fallen empires. Yellow House and South Matador; the Cowden 6 and the Flagg; the realms of Parramore, Howard, Higginbotham, and Waring; of Dalmont, Jeter, Kirkland, and Herring; the James Brothers' Ranch and the Slaughter Estate, all were broken up and sold. And this was just the beginning.[27]

As the larger outfits disappeared and the smaller outfits arose, some observers noted that even on the southern Plains dry farmers could best adapt by shifting to ranch farming. Slowly but surely, southern plainsmen found that ranch farmers prospered more than the old-style farmers or ranchers. The cattlemen with smaller holdings gave more careful attention to breeding, they produced a greater calf-crop, and they used manure more. The ranch farmers also had clear advantages over their predecessors because they used concentrated feeds more effectively to produce higher gains in less time. The ranch farmers also achieved a more rapid turnover of cattle, with higher profits as a result. The shift to ranch farming did not occur immediately on the southern Plains. Cattle prices rose very slightly in comparison with the prices of other commodities, and so farmers at first had little incentive for changing over to cattle.[28] They did change, nevertheless.

In contrast, on the northern Plains, hordes of dry farmers either quit, or shifted to cattle. The trend toward ranch farming continued. "As scores of dry-land settlers abandoned their homesteads, the zone of agricultural development retreated in large part to the area east of the river. Farmers who remained turned increasingly to stock raising, with tillage operations merely subsidiary."[29] Thousands of farmers left the northern Plains. Between 1920 and 1925, one-half of Montana's farmers lost their farms by foreclosure. Other Plains farmers turned to livestock. Between 1923 and 1925 in Nebraska, for example, livestock and livestock products accounted for 75 per cent of all gross farm income.[30]

From all sides came evidence of the advantages of ranch farming. (Some called it diversified farming.) Studies of one sort or another indicated that cattlemen prospered more when they relied less on the range. On the other hand, simple diversification went too far. A study in Utah indicated that often the least prosperous farmers were those who took the advice to "diversify" literally. These farmers spread their efforts too thinly for profit. Major reliance on livestock and minor reliance on range; only this sort of diversity worked.

In terms of animal husbandry the advance of the farmer turned out rather well. The new plainsmen intensified livestock production, used the range better (partly because they had less available), developed water facilities better, and lost less from weather and diseases because, as ranch farmers, they supervised their cattle. Not that everything they did turned out well. They plowed some grass, and some cattlemen had to buy out farmers at high prices, but on the whole, the benefits of the invasion far outweighed the injuries. Needless to say, the old-style ranchers, and even some of the ranch farmers, refused to call the change progress.[31]

The newer system being developed by the cattlemen was pasture farming. Pasture farming differed from ranch farming mostly in that pasture farmers used very little range.

They used so little that their range often became a sort of meadow. Furthermore, pasture farmers usually controlled more land than the typical dry farmer, or for that matter, the typical rancher. Nevertheless, the ordinary pasture farm was not as large as the fully evolved ranch farm. These specific characteristics of the pasture farm were less important than the attitudes of these new cattlemen. Generally, they were not ranchers who reluctantly adopted a disliked makeshift. Neither were they just broken and disappointed dry farmers who hesitantly accommodated to survive. Most pasture farmers embraced grassland farming, supplemental feeding, water development, advanced breeding, and pasture management as profitable goals in themselves.[32]

Pasture farming developed along with the older ranch farming, but neither completely conquered the Plains. In 1924 a study in southeastern Montana showed that twenty-one typical ranchers still used 94 per cent of their land for grazing. Even so, they were ranch farmers. The extent to which cattlemen adopted ranch or pasture farming depended in part on the size of their holdings and of their herds. Usually, the smaller outfits used less public domain or Forest Reserve. The smaller outfits relied more on feed crops. One survey showed that ranchers with four hundred and fifty or more head used less than 5 per cent of their land for crops. In contrast, ranch farmers with fifty or less head grew crops on 16 per cent of their land. The smaller outfits fenced the range and plowed up the land. In time, pasture farmers competed with ranch farmers much as ranch farmers had competed with range herdsmen. F. A. Welty summed up for the ranch farmers: "So, like the big man of the early days, he must go out of business, and let the cattle be produced by the man who practices diversified farming. . . ."[33]

Pasture farmers naturally depended more on fodder than had their predecessors. On the northern Plains, even as late as 1924, the need for winter feed chiefly spurred cattlemen to adopt pasture farming. By 1924, cattlemen put up one and one-half to two tons of hay for each cow in the winter.

Pasture farmers also increasingly raised other feeds such as sorghums, barley, corn, and oats. Irrigation and dry farming produced these. The smaller operators fed more, fed more nutritiously, and fed to produce gains rather than merely sustain life. Usually, the pasture farmer also lost less when moving cattle from pasture to pasture because he had smaller land-holdings and herds.[34]

Of course, pasture farmers had problems. They had a tendency to run more stock than their land could carry. In addition, their heavy investments in land and stock made them dependent on one crop. In spite of their feed crops, they were peculiarly susceptible to livestock price fluctuations. Many pasture farmers offset these disadvantages by irrigating, and by sometimes producing cash grains. Pasture farmers could often irrigate in ways which ranch farmers could not. Then too, they might, and sometimes did, put dry land in cash grain. If grain prices were low, cattlemen could often profitably feed the grain to livestock.[35]

Naturally, pasture farmers could overdo. In 1925, on the southern Plains, investigators discovered that pasture or ranch farms could be too small. In bad weather cattlemen with large spreads could rely on nature's bounty, and thus they could do better than those who had small spreads and who depended heavily on labor exploitation. Labor exploitation has always been the chief advantage of the small landholder. He exploits his own labor first, of course, and then the labor of his family. Sometimes, however, cattlemen found that their land or stock could be exploited more ruthlessly than their labor. Some scientists thought that this militated against pasture farming, but they were wrong. In moderately good years, ranchers who exploited labor made the greater profits. These profits then carried them across the poorer years.

Anyhow, as Department of Agriculture workers noted, except in highly unfavorable situations, pasture farming gave the best defense against losses. For example, old-style cattlemen who used large amounts of public land also had the larger labor costs. Comparatively unable to exploit labor, the big spreads were more likely to fail. Pasture farmers, in contrast, had the larger investments in land and cattle, but also had the lower costs because the smaller outfits could exploit their family labor force. Careful investigations showed that returns were greater when land and cattle investments were large, and when labor was exploited more than land or stock. Over the long run, the economy favored the pasture farmers.[36]

Several consequences flowed from the evolution of pasture farming. The newer type of cattle farm permitted cattlemen to produce more beef on fewer acres. At marketing, the average weight of cattle increased, but the average age decreased between 1923 and 1925. Three-year-old steers virtually disappeared. Younger cattle produced the greater gains, and so the trend to baby beef gave cattlemen greater and quicker financial returns.[37]

As ranch and pasture farmers appeared and took over they gradually improved water facilities. At first, cattlemen had used dirt tanks, shallow wells, and natural water holes. Cattlemen found these unsatisfactory for intensive cattle raising, however, even though they were less expensive than deep wells. More and more they replaced the primitive storage tanks with steel, concrete, or rock tanks. Where well drilling was expensive, or uncertain of return, some cattlemen built pipelines to fairly distant water sources.[38]

Cattlemen also more closely supervised and cared for calves, which, by 1923, they customarily fed through the winter. The average calf-crop rose when cattle were thus more closely supervised. The increased crop ran about 12 per cent to 14 per cent higher under the newer methods, with obvious profits to pasture and ranch farmers.[39]

Feeding and crop production also evolved. On the northern Plains, cattlemen most commonly grew alfalfa for feed. On 85 per cent of all ranches covered in a study of 1924, alfalfa was used. Cattlemen did not usually put alfalfa into silage, but instead used it primarily as hay. A large percent-age of the alfalfa was grown on irrigated land. In the North, cattlemen usually planted in the spring, and in the South, they planted in summer or early fall.[40]

On irrigated land, alfalfa yielded best of all the feeds, but on dry land, sorghums yielded best. Sorghum acreages con-tinually increased. On the whole, in the early twenties, ranch-ers usually got yields of three tons an acre, but sometimes they got up to six tons.[41] Some scientists and writers kept a sentimental attachment to native Plains grasses, but the various gramas, wheatgrasses, and ryegrasses did not really provide much feed for ranch and pasture farmers. Admit-tedly, statistics are hard to get, but inadequate as they are they clearly show that the imported grasses made the best feeds.[42]

Most cattlemen prepared their fodder as hay. Usually they cured the hay in windrows or stacks. The dryness of the Plains made this practical. Often stockmen left stacks of hay in the fields to cure, or just to store. Hay thus prepared suf-fered some damage, however, and increasingly cattlemen converted fodder crops into silage which spoiled less, and which actually provided more nutrition.[43]

Cattlemen used nearly every plant in making silage, al-though they most commonly used sorghum and corn. In Montana between 1910 and 1920, corn acreage increased 800 per cent, and most of this production went into silage. On the Plains, cattlemen almost always dug pit silos, gen-erally covered with dirt to reduce spoilage of the feed.[44]

Although cattle breeding improved in the early twenties, the southern plainsmen made the greater advances. Appar-ently the southern Plains still fulfilled their old function as a breeding place. The crop of calves and yearlings were then sent to other regions. Because of this business, southern plainsmen seem to have been the more careful breeders, and they also did more to introduce new breeds. They had introduced zebu cattle, and in 1924 enough breeders could be found to form the American Brahman Breeders Association. With this, the Brahmans became unquestionably established in the United States.

In 1923 the new Santa Gertrudis breed became fully established, for in that year the bull Monkey was first used in breeding. From this single bull the Klebergs developed their breed, although it attracted little attention outside Texas in the twenties. On the whole, the status of breeds and breeding remained comparatively unchanged.[45]

As the industry evolved, the number of cattle on the Plains seemed to increase. In spite of rapid turnover, between 1920 and 1925 the number of beef cattle on the Plains rose. In 1920, 17,491,712 beef cattle had run in the Plains states. This number increased 11 per cent by 1925 to 19,433,677. (In comparison, between 1910 and 1920, the number of cattle had only increased 2.5 per cent).[46] Even with this significant increase, it is probable that the wide adoption of pasture and ranch farming would have made possible the carrying of more cattle stock. In 1923 the northern Plains were understocked in places, and possibly other parts of the Plains were also understocked from time to time.[47]

In the United States, the total number of farms decreased between 1920 and 1925. On the Plains, however, the advent of dry farmers, ranch farmers, and pasture farmers all increased the number of farms. Between 1920 and 1925 the number of farms rose from 1,233,847 to 1,264,270. Simultaneously, the average size of the farm decreased throughout the Plains. In 1920 the average Plains farm came to 324.3 acres; in 1925 it came to only 313.2 acres.[48] The figures added up to this: more cattlemen, with fewer acres, produced more cattle, and got more meat from each animal.

Almost all the changes in the cattle industry of the Plains came about because of the growing metropolitan markets for beef. This market grew primarily because transportation made growth possible. The chief transportation of the twenties was still the railroad. The Interstate Commerce Commission was still the chief agency through which cattlemen sought to regulate their transportation facilities. When a few western railroads wanted to ɪaise rates in 1924, cattlemen protested, and the commission kept the rates unchanged. The commission also enforced various regulations ranging from rules requiring cars to be made available, to rules concerning the cleanliness of cars.[49]

Although railroads still served as the most important transport service, trucks began to loom importantly during the early twenties. Losses were much less when cattle were shipped by truck instead of by rail and this alone gave trucks a tremendous advantage. Improved roads and the use of trucks went hand in hand, and tended to change the system of cattle transport. As one cattleman reported laconically: "Hard roads have brought many changes."[50] More were to come. The change to trucks made seasonal marketing less necessary, and cattlemen could also exploit new market outlets. In short, the pasture farmers could get greater returns for their stock with trucks. At the same time, urban consumers paid less for meat. The development of the truck was one of the more significant technical changes for Plains cattlemen.

Meanwhile, cattlemen sought changes in the administration of the public domain. Even though new methods of cattle husbandry evolved on the Plains, individual cattlemen owned very little land. Many ranchers on the northern Plains leased as much as half of their grazing land as late as 1924. In 1924 one study of the northern Plains showed that nearly two-thirds of the cattlemen had less than six sections under control; the remainder of their land was public domain. On the southern Plains in 1925, cattlemen either leased or just used almost three-fourths of their entire land area. Insofar as cattlemen did not own land, their tenure was precarious. In order to assure themselves of ample crop and grazing land, cattlemen wanted to have the public domain more carefully controlled. Their interest in regulation extended beyond federal lands, and where possible, cattlemen secured favorable state legislation.

The American National Livestock Association, meeting in 1923, resolved that the federal government should institute a system of leasing for the public domain. Cattlemen suggested that administration be given to the Forest Service, and interestingly, they suggested that the revenues above administrative costs be used for building highways. In 1924, cattlemen got officials of land grant colleges to petition President Coolidge for laws controlling the public land. In 1925 a Senate Committee held hearings in the West during which the cattlemen of the Plains expressed a desire for some control of the remaining public lands. Changing methods of cattle husbandry united cattlemen in a general request for control of grazing, and removal of land from entry. No legislation resulted, but the agitation had begun.[51]

Most cattlemen wanted the federal government to control the remaining public domain more effectively. At the same time, they continued to be interested in the management of the Forests. In 1923 Congress killed a proposal of Interior Secretary Albert Fall which would have put the Forests under Interior. The cattlemen seemed to approve keeping them in Agriculture. In 1923 the Secretary of Agriculture announced that fees would be raised in 1925, but even this did not alter the pro-Agriculture preference of most cattlemen. As it happened, the cattlemen complained so much that the fee increase was never applied. In the process they also managed to kill their proposal for long-term leases on the Forests. These limited victories of the producers at least maintained the status quo. Meanwhile, the cattlemen continued to press for more supervision of grazing and of farming on the Plains. Some hesitant steps in this direction took place in 1924 when the Clark-McNary Act was passed. The law allowed the Foresters to purchase privately owned lands to be added to the Forests.[52]

In a period when the spirit of free enterprise and self-reliance supposedly dominated the American scene, cattlemen appeared singularly free of any doctrinaire opposition to government aid. Cattlemen not only endured, they actively sought government intervention in their affairs. They wanted federal help in controlling tick fever, and foot-and-mouth disease. When credit was hard to get, cattlemen appealed to the government for help, and when packers threatened, cattlemen once again turned to the government. The federal government did not always respond adequately, but that was not the fault of the cattlemen. On the other hand, the government brought the railroads under fair control for the cattlemen. As trucks became important, cattlemen insisted on federal and state subsidies for road building, that is, subsidies for truck transportation. The plainsmen even demanded more federal supervision of the public domain. In short, the trends of the previous decades continued unabated as cattlemen turned to the government for help.

The trends toward more intensive beef production also continued. Cattlemen changed their operations, and gradually one form of animal husbandry evolved into pasture farming. Cattlemen produced more beef per capita, and more significantly, more beef per acre. They developed water resources, and increased the scope and efficiency of their supplemental feeding. Silage and better bred cattle appeared. All of this transformed the industry between 1923 and 1925.

CHAPTER VIII

The Good Years
1926-1928

In the summer of 1925 the agricultural depression receded. In the years 1926 to 1928, Great Plains cattlemen prospered more than at any time since the war. Prices rose, but per capita beef and veal consumption dropped from an average of 68.5 pounds in 1926, to an average of only 55.2 pounds in 1928. Across the years 1926 to 1928, each American ate an average of only 61.9 pounds of beef and veal.[1] Even so, a steadily rising population consumed the meat produced by the plainsmen.

Between 1926 and 1928, cattle prices rose an average of $3.00 a hundredweight, reaching a high of $10.59 in 1928. Prices of the three years averaged $8.85, compared to the $6.87 of the preceding three years.[2] In 1926 the prices for range cattle rose even faster than the prices for fat cattle. Feeders noticed and complained of this. Although prices averaged less than during the war, they were undeniably high.[3]

American consumers resisted the high beef prices. In December, 1927, popular discontent led to a formal beef boycott in Boston. Lower beef consumption indicated that many Americans participated in some sort of boycott, but the formal Boston effort attracted the most attention. Boston's organized protest temporarily caused prices of dressed beef to fall markedly in January, 1928. The protest movement failed to spread in spite of its success. The Bostonians quieted down, and other consumers just silently decreased their meat purchases. All of this hurt Plains cattlemen who typically blamed newspapers for stimulating urban cupidity. Newspapers got too much credit, for rising prices obviously caused both the protest, and the falling consumption.[4]

Despite this, Plains cattlemen prospered. They had suffered between 1920 and 1925, when most of them had had to pay taxes, interest, and other costs out of their hypothetical wages. This changed between 1926 and 1928. Income from land and stock rose impressively. No other large group of agricultural producers fared as well as the cattlemen. Although some of them continued to liquidate their herds, on the whole they raked in the profits as cattle supplies fell below demand. Great Plains cattlemen who had anticipated a rising beef market were not disappointed. Even so, ranch farmers sometimes got into trouble, and from time to time a ranch went on the block.[5]

Few cattlemen failed, however, as the rate of mortgage foreclosures in western South Dakota suggested. Here, foreclosures declined after 1925 and reached their lowest levels in 1927 and 1928. The high income of pasture ranchers enticed many cattlemen into increasing their herds. H. H. French observed: "Of course there are always some in the business that do not progress, but generally speaking the condition is good."[6] In 1928 cattlemen's income was the highest it had been since 1918. Many a cattleman rejoiced at the ending of the postwar depression. "From a repetition of this latter calamity may the Fates preserve him!"[7] So exclaimed the editor of *The Producer* in early 1929.

The astounding prosperity of cattlemen during the middle twenties immediately caused cattle numbers to decrease, particularly breeding cattle. Ranchers sold everything they could to clean up. In 1927, prices for fat cattle rose, and this stimulated a further depletion of herds. Producers cleaned out many of their older steers. Between 1926 and 1927 the number of cattle on the northern Plains fell roughly 16 per cent. Culling by cattlemen helped shove them over to marketing calves and yearlings. Low-grade cows and bulls also accounted for part of the reduction, which indirectly improved the condition of the herds.[8] The scarcity of cattle was not wholly unfortunate.

As a result of the culling, speculators made more than producers. Irritated cattlemen complained that they suffered from more than their fair share of leeches. Cattlemen not only said so, but they increasingly acted as though they wanted fewer middlemen. While some of the middlemen performed useful services, cattlemen thought many did not; more and more cattlemen shipped directly to feeders or packers in order to cut them out. Producers did not commonly resort to direct selling, but they did it more and more.[9] Meanwhile, the urban consuming center in California grew rapidly. By 1928 the Plains cattlemen shipped appreciable amounts of cattle to California, although this market amounted to little at that time.

Cattle prices continued to rise through 1928, and those cattlemen who had shifted fully to winter feeding profited first. On the northern Plains, for example, gross income from some sixty sample pasture ranches ranged between $3,000 and $25,000. For these cattlemen, this averaged out to a net income of from $1,500 to $19,000 a year between 1926 and 1928. This came to more than a 10 per cent average return on their capital investment, or a very good living.[10]

Good profits brought out eager bankers. For about the first time since the opening of the century, credit shortages did not plague cattlemen. Bankers willingly loaned money as cattle prices rose. Almost anyone could get a loan. Some governmental officials talked about new credit facilities for farmers, but these ideas now won few supporters on the Plains. As one editor remarked: "On the average a producer who is so far gone financially that he cannot pay the 6 per cent is practically hopeless anyway, and the sooner he finds it out the better for himself and his creditors." [11] In 1926, fifty-nine national banks failed in North Dakota, and one hundred and fifteen failed in South Dakota, but these apparently had been brought low by the earlier depression. No considerable number of failures took place in 1927 or 1928. Banking, like the cattle business, was rather profitable.[12]

To add to the cattlemen's joys, the weather generally excelled on the Plains. In 1926, from one end of the Plains to the other, cattlemen reported above-average precipitation and a mild winter. In 1927, the weather was spotty, but generally good. Parts of Oklahoma were wet, while much of Texas was fairly dry. The northern Plains were unusually moist, but some dry spots appeared in western South Dakota.[13] In 1928, observers reported astonishingly similar weather for all parts of the Plains. Abundant rains fell everywhere, from Montana to Texas.[14]

Naturally, Plains grasslands yielded abundantly, but this was not all blessing. Because the grass remained green so long, it did not cure properly and the cattle shrank in transit because their fat and meat were not solid. This did not seem to bother cattlemen much. They preferred abundant feed of any quality, rather than inadequate but nutritious feed. In 1926, from one end of the Plains to the other, observers reported cattle and ranges in splendid condition. Cattlemen had never seen nature so bountiful.[15]

Indeed, pasturage was so good that by late 1926 and early 1927, those plainsmen who normally rented pasture lands faced a shrinking market. Rents fell drastically, and some grazing land actually went unleased. Pasture conditions may have been only partly responsible for the declining need for meadow lands, however, for by 1927 pasture ranching had greatly reduced the plainsmen's need for grass anyway.[16]

By 1928 poor weather had injured plainsmen in a few places. Even so, cattlemen claimed to have done well. They reported both ranges and cattle to be in better than usual condition. On the southern Plains their hay crop fell a bit short in 1928, but a mild winter reduced this problem to negligible size. Cattlemen on the northern Plains apparently had as much grass and hay as they could use. One report from South Dakota even indicated about 10 per cent more fodder than usual. By 1928 the range was actually under-stocked. The wet seasons, good feed, and heavy marketings, all helped produce a relative understocking. Plains cattle-men everywhere rejoiced in the bounteous natural and eco-nomic conditions of 1926 to 1928.[17]

The condition of the grass and of the economy told only part of the story. By 1926 most cattlemen had become pas-ture ranchers and so depended heavily on winter feeds. With high moisture, the supply of supplemental feeds became abundant, so that cattlemen everywhere wished they had more stock to eat up the feed. Cattlemen had seldom been in this position.[18]

As the assaults of weather and the economy declined, other long-standing nuisances became major threats. Be-tween 1926 and 1927, cattle diseases accounted for larger proportions of the losses for cattlemen. Through the twenties, two out of every one hundred cattle died of disease each year. Formerly, starvation losses had submerged and ob-scured disease losses, but now disease attracted widespread attention. No doubt the death rate would have been lower if cattlemen had properly tried to prevent such losses.

In order of importance, the worst killers were: tuberculosis, contagious abortion, anthrax, blackleg, scabies, ticks, and foot-and-mouth. Except for tuberculosis and abortion, cattle-men had preventative measures at hand. For some of the others, simple controls had long been available.[19]

Tuberculosis could only be eradicated through testing and slaughter because neither vaccination nor cure existed for the disease. Although tuberculosis caused greater losses for dairy farmers, breeders of purebred cattle also lost. Eradi-cation programs progressed fairly well through the 1920's, however, and ordinary Plains cattlemen thus benefited di-rectly and indirectly.[20]

Brucellosis, commonly called contagious abortion, not only caused great losses, but threatened to cause more as time went on. The Plains cattlemen suffered from the disease to some extent, but, as with tuberculosis, breeders suffered most. Abortion and tuberculosis thus hindered the improvement of cattle on the Great Plains. In the twenties, however, brucellosis was not the subject of a vigorous eradication campaign.[21]

An effective blackleg vaccine had long been on the market; for years it had even been distributed free. Nevertheless, Plains cattlemen annually suffered large losses from the disease. Blackleg appeared everywhere, and under all conditions. The causal bacteria (*Bacillus chaueaui*) resisted most human efforts to eliminate it, but vaccination almost always prevented the disease. Cattlemen had only to take some interest in vaccination. In the 1920's they began to do so. Probably better control of cattle led to better control of the disease. Blackleg, however, ranked high as a killer through the decade.[22]

Newer methods of husbandry with better supervision of cattle also helped cattlemen reduce the ravages of scabies, sometimes known as mange, scab, or itch. Scabies particularly injured poorly fed or overly exposed cattle. Since pasture ranchers took better care of their cattle than did other cattlemen, losses from the disease automatically decreased. Various mites caused scabies, and so cattle-dips could effectively control the disease. As pasture ranchers increased in numbers on the Plains, dipping became more common. In the 1920's, however, losses from the disease still seriously harmed cattlemen.[23]

Significantly, by 1928, tick fever had dropped to near the bottom of the list of serious diseases. Control measures had been tremendously effective, and the disease rapidly diminished in importance. The chief control continued to be tick eradication by dipping. By 1926, a comparatively ineffective innoculation could be used in areas where the disease was not common. Cattlemen sometimes innoculated cattle going into tick country, but producers rightly placed no great confidence in the medicine.[24]

Foot-and-mouth disease did not break out in the United States between 1926 and 1928; nevertheless, the disease still ranked as a major problem. Cattlemen could treat the disease, and they could effectively vaccinate. Because foot-and-mouth was very contagious, and because it was rare in the United States, government agents and some cattlemen preferred eradication to control.

Screwworms, which had long pestered stockmen, came to excite more interest as the more serious diseases declined in importance. Indeed, as other enemies declined, screwworms increased their ravages, and cattlemen of the southern Plains observed that the attacks of the insect became progressively more serious. Plainsmen could do little to halt the worms in the 1920's, but regular dipping and sanitary precautions helped. The decline of tick fever made anaplasmosis clinically distinctive, and in 1926 Kansans noted major outbreaks of the disease. From then on, scientists tried to find controls for the comparatively new disease.[25]

The last attack on ticks occurred in 1926 when Congress passed the Crisp Act which went into force in 1928. The act forbade all interstate shipments of tick-infested cattle. In 1928 these precautions were applied outside the United States by a sanitary treaty with Mexico. The treaty provided for inspection of animals moving between the two countries in order to prevent the spread of foot-and-mouth disease, rinderpest, and pleuropneumonia. The treaty also provided for quarantine zones where these seemed necessary.[26]

Good prices, good weather, and ever more successful battles against disease were accompanied by more effective control of predacious animals. In 1926, the Bureau of Biological Survey reported that lobo wolves were nearly extinct in the United States, and that only a few crossed over from Mexico each year. As the losses from disease and predators declined, damage by wild horses increased. In 1927 cattlemen noted that state efforts to destroy wild horses had been rather ineffective. Some plainsmen suggested that the federal government act here too. Meanwhile, cattlemen lost an estimated $20 million to $30 million each year to other predators. Bears, coyotes, and mountain lions had to go.

From time to time, in various places, grasshoppers destroyed crops and pastures. Grasshoppers plagued Montana in 1928. These outbreaks clouded the lives of some cattlemen, but the pattern of agricultural specialization remained unchanged. Grasshopper ravages became ever more serious because the newer cattlemen relied so heavily on forage crops. But no new insecticides hit the market, and the grasshopper remained relatively free from control.[27]

Meanwhile, ranch and pasture farmers changed their style of husbandry to take advantage of the exceptionally good markets and weather. Cattlemen devoted themselves to four major management problems: (1) range management, to increase producing capacity (2) feed-crop production, to facilitate range management (3) better care of cattle to intensify production, and (4) more secure land tenure to facilitate range management, feed production, and care of cattle.[28]

By 1926, Plains cattlemen characteristically regulated grazing. Frequently ranchers tried to hold cattle numbers to about what the pasture would sustain in the dry season.[29] Concurrently, cattlemen continued to grow larger proportions of their feed. They did not, however, all make the same changes everywhere. In 1928, for example, about 40 per cent of the Plains land was harvested in crops, with Kansas highest at 55 per cent, and Montana lowest at 19 per cent.[30] Not all of this was cattle feed, but much was.

Winter feed was expensive, especially on the northern Plains, regardless of whether cattlemen grew the feed or bought it. As they intensified their production, however, cattlemen had to winter feed. Feed cost around $9.43 a head in North Dakota, and slightly more in the rest of the northern Plains. On the southern Plains, drouth hazards and the needs of intensive beef production forced cattlemen to produce more supplemental feeds. Southerners also used more cottonseed products.[31]

Meanwhile, cattlemen improved their methods of crop production and made new discoveries about feeding. Slowly, these changes wrought a transformation in the industry. As for crops, cattlemen usually used hay of some sort because, temporarily, the technology seemed to favor it. The gasoline tractor and the newer mowing machinery tremendously reduced the cost and time needed to put up the hay. Even so, baling and stacking were still virtually unsolved problems, and sometimes stockmen mowed and raked more hay than they could store. But just about every year machinery improved, and the tractor became ever more common on cattle ranches.[32]

Simultaneously, cattlemen developed newer cropping practices. Alfalfa, often a useful plant for pasture ranchers, actually yielded best under irrigation. Many ranchers, north and south, thus found it unsuitable. But then, other drouth-resistant crops could be used for hay. Soapweed, for example, grew fairly abundantly on the southern Plains, and proved as good as "some of the poorer hay crops."[33] On the central Plains, a few cattlemen found that sugar beets and mangels made excellent feed. Stockmen customarily stored these in root cellars.[34]

Experiments by scientists and others had left little doubt about the economy of silage. One acre of crops in a silo equalled about two acres of hay or other feed; furthermore, silage was nutritionally superior. Although cattlemen could put almost any plant into a silo, they found that plants adapted to dry farming served best. Sorghum remained unquestionably best, no matter how used and cattlemen used both grain and sugar varieties. They could, and often did, use the whole plant in silage. Corn, although useful, could not be widely grown on the Plains. Sunflowers, however, grew almost anywhere, and they made good silage. Since the crop matured early, it proved useful on the northern Plains where many varieties of sorghum could not be grown. Russian thistles, or tumbleweed, made fair hay for hard-up cattlemen, and could also be converted into silage. Plainsmen sometimes put sweet clover into silage, but most commonly they fed it as hay when they grew it, which was seldom.[35]

Not only crops but feeding patterns changed as cattlemen

shifted to marketing younger cattle. In 1926, experiments showed that calves could be taught to eat at a creep before being weaned. Their fat little carcasses then brought a large profit within a year. Creep feeding of calves marked a fairly new departure in cattle husbandry on the Plains, although nothing much came of it during the twenties.[36]

In spite of changes in management and cropping, some of the same old tasks still had to be done in the same old ways. Cowboys still rode the range, put out salt, cleared cattle off poison-infested land, and buried dead animals. But increasingly they did these jobs more carefully than before.[37]

The obvious evidences of ranch or pasture farming appeared everywhere. More and more cattlemen owned fairly large tracts, put in crops, dug wells, and built better sheds, corrals, and fences. Even the patterns of their domestic life changed. One old timer complained in 1927:

Most of the cow ranches I've seen lately was like a big farm. A bungalow with all modern improvements, a big red barn that holds white-faced bulls an' hornless milk cows. The corrals are full of fancy chickens, there's a big garage filled with all kinds of cars, and at the bunkhouse that sets back where the owner and his family can't see or hear them, are the hands.

You might see a man with a big hat, boots, and spurs— he's the fence rider—but most of them wear bib overalls. The boss wears puttees and a golf cap.

The bungalow, that's got electric lights an' hot and cold water. There's a piana that you play with your feet, and a radio, a Mah Jong set, and a phonograph.[38]

Here was the new Home on the Range.

Typically, these pasture ranches were comparatively small, family-sized outfits, and, as a rule, the cattleman owned a large percentage of his land. Such ownership increased his costs, but also gave him maximum use of his land. With ever-increasing intensity of production, more land ownership became imperative on the northern and southern Plains alike.[39]

The break-up of large outfits, begun on the southern and

central Plains in the early twenties, continued on into the later twenties. As the older cattlemen cleaned out, the newer type came in, although the editor of *The Cattleman* of Fort Worth thought the change went too slowly. In any case, it went on.[40]

From north to south, getting firm control of land was the greatest problem of the new-style cattlemen. Ranchers could buy some land, but few could afford to own all they needed. In 1928, on the northern Plains, cattlemen owned only about one-third of the land they used. Many cattlemen used National Forests, but they hesitated to rely on this. Many others did not have this alternative anyhow. Private and state leases served well enough, but even the best lease provided uncertain tenure. Furthermore, leasing encouraged stockmen to overgraze.[41]

To meet such problems the stockmen turned to the Powell suggestion of cooperative grazing control. The concept of such control was not new, since it had been used by the round-up associations. But the practice of legalized collective tenure of grazing lands was new. The first experiment in this kind of tenure in Montana, and in the nation, originated out of discussions begun in 1926 in the Mizpah-Pumpkin Creek area in Custer County.[42]

Up to 1926, the Mizpah-Pumpkin Creek land had been virtually open range. Railroads owned part of it, private citizens a part, and the federal government a part. In 1926, the cattlemen proposed to get some 95,000 acres of it under ten-year leases. They then wanted to manage it as the Forests were managed. Their plan was hampered by the government which would not lease federal land. Cattlemen finally convinced Senator Thomas J. Walsh that the project would end the era of the tramp herdsman, and would benefit the industry. With Walsh pushing, Congress approved the arrangement in 1928. Montana formally assumed direction of this and similar projects in 1933. This pioneer cooperative grazing district was soon copied in other states after 1928 when the Secretary of Interior was authorized to work out such arrangements.[43]

Cattlemen also tried to secure new ways of handling state land. The federal government had granted huge parcels to the states. Although the states had slightly different policies, they almost all provided for some sort of leasing and selling. Possible sale made the lessors' tenure precarious in spite of varied legal protections. Because the sale prices were usually rather high, few stockmen could buy much. All of these lease and sale arrangements failed to meet the needs of the cattlemen. Leases encouraged overgrazing, and sale provisions left lessors with unstable tenure.

The grazing-control experiments of the Mizpah-Pumpkin Creek area in Montana offered a way around this, but the states only slowly accommodated themselves to the newer ideas on tenure. Still, the concept of cooperative ownership and control was one of the really significant ideas of plainsmen in the twentieth century. Interestingly, they based it on the programs of the abused Forest Service.[44]

As cattlemen intensified production they increasingly relied on Forest lands for grazing, and as usual, they bit the hand that fed them. Generally, those who grazed Forest lands raised hay and silage on their home ranches. The demand for Forest permits constantly rose, but fees remained unchanged. Consequently, the Forests produced less revenue than if they had been leased at prevailing rates. Several people proposed policies to meet the problem. P. V. Woodhead, a Colorado Forest Supervisor, suggested that cattlemen convert hay lands back to grazing lands. No one paid much attention to this idea.

Two investigations of grazing fees, the Ratchford Report, and the Casement Report, both recommended the increasing of grazing fees. This could have been a natural economic response to the growing demand for grazing land, but it did not please Forest users. Dan Casement, a cattleman, suggested that the fees not be raised until 1931. He proposed delay mostly so that cattlemen could be reconciled to the change. Colonel William B. Greeley, Chief Forester, accepted his proposal which Secretary of Agriculture William Jardine, subsequently approved. Rates for cattle were to be advanced from 10.4 to 14.4 cents a head each month.[45]

Asserting their rights as squatters, cattlemen vigorously opposed Forest officers who thus sought to protect the interests of all Americans. The cattlemen complained that the proposed rate changes came just when times were bad, although actually they had seldom been so well off. The more backward cattlemen raised the most fuss because they depended on the Forests more completely than the pasture ranchers. Even the retarded ones quieted after a bit, and shortly their displeasure evaporated before the real disaster of the Great Depression.

In February, 1928, William Greeley resigned as Chief Forester. Few cattlemen regretted the change. Their attitude indicated deep hostility toward the Forest Service in general. The editor of *The Producer* observed:

If the troubled waters of the grazing-fee discussion have lately somewhat subsided, it is not because the justice of the advance is admitted by a majority of stockmen, but rather through realization of the fact that further resistance is useless. Also to some extent, no doubt, it is the result of improved economic conditions. But the wound, nevertheless, is still festering. And Colonel Greeley is the man, in the opinion of many, who not only inflicted it by his stubborn adherence to a wrong principle, but who would have had it within his power to heal it, when he saw the mischief he was doing—and refused.[46]

Oddly enough, in spite of their attitude toward the Forest Service, cattlemen pretty generally agreed that they needed greater federal control of the public domain. In 1926, Senator R. N. Stanfield offered a bill to have most of the domain regulated by the Department of Interior. The Forest Service was to remain in Agriculture. The proposed division of authority partly reflected the personal prejudices of Senator Stanfield. Partly the division showed the attitude of cattlemen who disliked the contemplated fee increase. Anyhow, as of 1926, cattlemen also disliked the open-public-domain policy. They were apparently disappointed when Congress refused to pass the Stanfield Bill in 1926.[47]

As cattlemen urged regulation of the public domain, they discovered a new, alarming force which had entered the scene. Plainsmen objected to "conservationists," a term used to cover "dude outfits," and anyone "who places esthetic and recreational value above utility; who regards trees and wild flowers and game birds as of more importance to the life of the nation than the growing of live stock."[48] Possibly conservationists influenced legislation some, but it is doubtful that they killed the Stanfield Bill as charged. Nonetheless, the conservationists did pose a long-term threat to the cattlemen who now had to share the domain with someone other than a helpless "public." After the failure of the Stanfield Bill, cattlemen again suggested that the government lease the public domain. This was not as good as prohibiting any further settlement by the public, but cattlemen thought it better than nothing.[49]

Although they did not approve of government efforts to raise grazing fees, cattlemen approved of government help, not only in regulating the public domain, but in guaranteeing high beef prices. Plains cattlemen apparently favored the McNary-Haugen Bills. Congressional and administrative attempts to bring in a substitute met with general disapproval. Cattlemen wanted McNary-Haugen, and nothing else, although they supported it half-heartedly. Their attention seemed centered on the domain, and, as usual, on the packers.[50]

On March 19, 1928, the United States Supreme Court upheld the Packers Consent Decree, which the packers had long unilaterally refused to honor. By 1928, cattlemen had some misgivings about the decree because it prevented packers from retailing meat. On the whole, however, cattlemen favored enforcement, primarily because the packers showed no real interest in meat retailing.[51]

Cattlemen endorsed beef grading by the Department of Agriculture. Cattlemen hoped for more intelligent buying by consumers when government-graded beef hit the market in 1927, but no important change resulted.[52]

Ever so subtly, however, methods of cattle transport did change. The truck, which had appeared somewhat tentatively early in the twenties, continued to be used more frequently. During a six-month period in 1928, one observer reported that truck shipments increased 56.1 per cent for cattle, and 89.3 per cent for calves. All markets seem to have experienced about the same phenomenon. Railroads lost, slowly but surely. Meanwhile, cattlemen's associations continued their efforts to halt overcharges and other mistreatment by the railroads. Railroad executives learned little, and forgot most of that. They continued to annoy shippers, even as trucks crowded on the roads.[53]

Between 1926 and 1928, cattlemen profited nicely as prices rose, even though per capita beef consumption fell. The Plains were scoured for cattle, and, in the process, cattlemen culled their herds and raised herd quality. Weather held up well, although both predators and diseases attracted more attention, in part because other problems were less serious. Cattlemen still drove on toward more intensive beef production. Ranch management tended to produce new advances in feeding and breeding patterns; cattlemen tended to live like their city brethren of the golden twenties. Except for their unpleasant attitude toward the Forest Service, cattlemen welcomed government control over grazing land, and also began cooperative grazing attempts. The style of cattle husbandry continued to change in the era of prosperity.

CATTLE AND CATTLEMEN
OF THE GREAT PLAINS

THE OPEN RANGE

W. H. Jackson painting, courtesy Nebraska State Historical Society

Longhorns move north from Texas on the Chis-
holm Trail in the era of the great trail drives
following the Civil War.

Montana State Historical Society

The last great roundup on the gigantic (over 5,000,000 acres) XIT Ranch in Montana in 1908.

Nebraska State Historical Society

Dinner time for a roundup crew in the High Plains country of the Nebraska-South Dakota border about 1900.

TICKS AND GRASSHOPPERS

Oklahoma ranchers dipping cattle to eradicate ticks in 1910. Tick fever once cost the cattlemen millions of dollars in livestock losses annually. The disease has been all but eradicated.

U. S. Department of Agriculture

Grasshoppers often scourged the Plains grasses and cattlemen did battle with a poison bran mix. Montana ranchers in the early 1900's are shown here mixing bran, arsenic, molasses, lemon juice and water in canvas wagon covers.

U. S. Department of Agriculture

FOOD WILL WIN THE WAR

Army R.O.T.C. cadets at the University of Nebraska in 1917 examine beef on the hoof that would help win the war.

Ample forage and high prices stimulated beef production during the 1915–1920 period. Grass-fed cattle in Nebraska's Sandhills are being loaded on waiting cattle cars.

THE DESPERATE YEARS

Ruinously low cattle prices in the 1930 decade were coupled in the Great Plains with the severest drouth of record. Farms and ranches were abandoned by the score when dust covered the grasslands and farmsteads as in South Dakota (above) and Texas (below).

As ten years of almost continuous drouth ravaged the Great Plains range cattle were either purchased by the federal government and condemned and buried as above in Nebraska, or shipped to market labeled "drouth cattle," as below at the Kansas City stockyards.

THE RAINS RETURN

In 1940, rain returns to the Plains and forage supplies for the cattle industry filled silos to the brim.

The Union Pacific Railroad

During World War II cattle flowed to market,
such as these sleek animals in Colorado, to feed
the nation, its allies, and the armed forces.

A SHORT-LIVED DROUTH

The spectre of drouth appeared briefly in the mid 1950's. Again dust drifts appeared in the plains of North Dakota (above), and in an over-grazed range in New Mexico (below).

THE LATE FIFTIES: A PHOTOGRAPHIC ESSAY

The Nebraska Farmer

The long thin line. White faced cattle moving instinctively from the grass hills to a watering trough.

Twenty below. A North Dakota cattle raiser, his dog, and a sled-full of feed. No matter what the weather the herd must be fed.

U. S. Department of Agriculture

Native grass. The marvelous native grasses of the
Plains, when given good management, will adequately support range cattle raising.

Beef factory. In many areas of the Plains where cultivated feed supplies are plentiful, highly integrated feeding operations have literally become "beef factories."

Spectacle. The eye-filling spectacle of a stock show delights the Plains cattlemen. Here a man can show the best of his herd and exult when he comes home a winner.

Pride. The cattleman, surveying his cattle against
the solitude of the far horizon, contemplates a
way of living which has endowed him with great
pride and fierce independence.

CHAPTER IX

The Great Depression
1929-1932

In 1929 depression hit the cattlemen of the Great Plains. Both prices and consumption fell. Between 1929 and 1932, beef prices fell 53 per cent, starting at an average of $10.59 a hundred, and ending at an unbelievable $4.94 a hundred. As prices fell, American urbanites should have eaten more beef. Instead, each year they ate less. In 1929 they consumed an average of 56.0 pounds of beef and veal. In 1932 they consumed an average of only 53.3 pounds. The bottom had not yet fallen out of the cattlemen's universe, but the bottom had fallen out of their beef market.[1]

By 1932, Great Plains cattlemen found themselves in the worst depression in their history. To make matters worse, the cattlemen could do little to correct the situation. The depression originated in the urban-industrial complex of the society, well beyond the control of the plainsmen. Between 1929 and 1933, average personal disposable income fell from $678 a year to $360.[2] Still, cattlemen accommodated as best they could.

During the depression, beef exports fell to nearly nothing.[3] Cattlemen achieved a so-called independence of foreign markets, but this independence hurt cattlemen, because it made them dependent on the American market. Americans suffered from the Great Depression more than any other people in the world. Cattlemen who depended on the domestic market leaned on a frail reed. At first, cattlemen attributed the drop in meat eating to a change in consumer food preferences. In a sense their analysis was sound because depression forced urbanites to cut back on their beef consumption. Cattlemen sturdily refused to believe in an urban depression until the later thirties.

The stock-market crash came in October, 1929. For most Americans, however, the depression had begun before then. As early as June, 1929, the cattle market slumped, and for a while, slaughterers stopped buying. In time, market experts discovered "an irresistible depreciation force." [4] Meanwhile, urban employment dropped. In 1929, the unemployed numbered 3.2 per cent of the labor force, in 1930 they numbered 8.7 per cent. In 1932 the unemployed figure rose to an unbelievable 23.6 per cent of the available workers. In spite of the clearest contrary evidence, writers and public prophets forecast a quick recovery for Plains cattlemen. They did not recover. Instead, between 1928 and 1931, gross returns to cattlemen fell about 66 per cent.[5] But the decline occurred rather slowly.

Cattlemen came out fairly well in 1929. Everywhere plainsmen generally prospered if they owed little and owned much. One study for 1929 showed that Montana cattlemen received the rather high net return of $8.86 for each animal unit. Cattlemen received progressively lower returns, however, and in 1932 cattle prices fell to their lowest point in twenty-two years. Few costs fell that far. Over-all, between 1922 and 1932, cattle prices fell, but taxes, interest, and other charges remained stable. In their dilemma, when cattlemen could, they borrowed money to survive. Usually this expedient of borrowing only delayed their failure. Still, bad as their condition was, in 1932 cattlemen appeared to be better off than the dry farmers.[6]

In 1929, even before their sources of credit had dried up entirely, cattlemen found credit harder to get than before. By 1931, however, bankers had stopped lending, and the federal government had to advance feed loans to plainsmen. Before they would lend, government officials placed a lien on the cattle. Consequently, stockmen could borrow only if other creditors agreed to share the risk, and not many creditors appeared willing to do this. Shortly, for most plainsmen, interest charges not only became a major expense, but a nearly unbearable expense. By 1932, the depression had become so bad that bankers generally refused to lend, even with security.

No banker felt any confidence that he would ever see his money again. . . . A few banks had tried to foreclose and take over such security, but farmers conspired to make the foreclosure sales a mockery. Someone bid one dollar on the land. As the auctioneer labored for a higher bid, the farmers stood grimly silent with clenched fists and there would be no more bids. The banker received the dollar.

Banks quit lending money. Only the government dared lend money.[7]

Clenched fists or no, foreclosures increased on the Plains.[8]

Many cattlemen who had just managed to weather the postwar depression (1919–1923) went bankrupt between 1929 and 1932 as cattle prices continued to skid. "Much of this calamity was abnormal industrial, financial and economic conditions, a combination constituting an irresistable [sic] force."[9] Cattlemen wondered what had gone wrong with the law of supply and demand. Surely something had gone wrong, because in 1930 cattlemen marketed fewer head than in any year on record, and yet prices continued to fall. Tariffs remained high, and production declined, but still prices fell another 50 per cent just between 1930 and 1932. A marketing specialist remarked: "What all this means is anybody's guess. Constant reiteration of reviving prosperity is absurd." The universe was cracking up.[10]

One bright spot did appear although it went virtually unnoticed at the time. The submetropolitan markets of California grew. Because Californians ate large amounts of hamburger, they used the lower-quality Plains cattle. The appearance of a beef deficit in California indirectly influenced the prices of Plains cattle. At the time, however, the Great Depression obscured the development.[11]

The depression grew worse, and as it did, plainsmen

looked for culprits. Packers were readily at hand, and furthermore, they had behaved oddly, and sometimes badly, in the past. In 1928, for example, although the United States Supreme Court had validated the Consent Decree of 1920, the packers continued to resist. In May, 1929, the Court once again declared the decree in force. For nine years the packers had ignored the law and the courts, and so few cattlemen expected the processors to obey the decision of 1929. Anyway, by 1929 many cattlemen hoped that the packers would retail meat, and that the decree would not be fully enforced. Consequently, although cattlemen felt misused, they also sometimes doubted the usefulness of the decree. In October, 1930, the packers appealed to the Court of the District of Columbia for a dissolution of the decree. By then the depression had hit hard, and cattlemen supported their former opponents. The editor of the *Kansas Stockman* explained: "If the packing companies were permitted to establish retail markets it would reflect higher prices back to the producers, is the general belief among stockmen." [12] Events shortly disillusioned them.

On January 5, 1931, the Court of the District of Columbia set aside many parts of the Consent Decree, but to the disgust of cattlemen, the court still forbade packers to retail meat. Cattlemen felt the packers had not seriously tried to have this part of the decree revised. [13] They may have been right. There the matter stood.

While the battle of the decree went on, conflicts arose between packers and chain stores. Chain stores' processing of meat increased and furthermore, some twelve thousand chain stores (or about 14 per cent of the total meat outlets) sold meat. Economists did not know the chain stores' share of total sales, but they assumed it to be more than 14 per cent. Although cattlemen seemed to hope that the chain stores might somehow bring them higher prices, they did not place much confidence in any retailers. [14]

Indeed, during the depression, cattlemen came to be thoroughly disenchanted with all meat dealers. In 1930, when cattle and wholesale beef prices dropped sharply, retailers cut prices scarcely any. This irritated cattlemen. Retailer behavior partly explained why cattlemen supported the packers in the Consent Decree wrangle. By 1932 at the latest, cattlemen firmly believed that retailers were engaged in sharp and shoddy trade practices which caused meat consumption to decline. Accordingly, cattlemen tried to make people eat meat by reprimanding retailers. In short, as the depression grew worse, cattlemen pounced on victims as helpless as themselves.[15] Cattlemen still did not believe there was a national depression.

The battle with middlemen went on. In a decision of February 24, 1930, the United States Supreme Court upheld the right of the Secretary of Agriculture to determine just and reasonable charges by market agencies at stockyards. The Court also decided that the charges then set were reasonable. The law and the courts thus forced more middlemen into line, but without much benefit to Plains cattlemen. The Great Depression continued in full fury.[16]

Out on the Plains, depression went hand in hand with natural disaster. Small local drouths began in 1929. Generally, however, the Plains received enough moisture.[17] The next year, 1930, an early drouth damaged the grass, and reduced the hay crop on all the northern Plains, and also in Colorado and New Mexico. In late summer the drouth expanded into Kansas, Texas, and Oklahoma. In the fall of 1930, however, rains rescued most of the central and northern Plains. Then came the blizzards. By 1930, however, cattlemen could survive even severe winters.[18]

Winter had nearly ended when a surprise blizzard swept through Kansas in March, 1931. The toll surpassed that of any previous storm. Perhaps as many as fifteen thousand cattle perished from this rather localized blizzard. After this, another drouth struck the northern Plains, particularly Montana and the Dakotas. On the southern Plains, in contrast, a heavy rainfall broke the drouth there.[19] On the northern Plains, however, a bit of hell seeped through in the summer of 1931. George Reeves, of South Dakota, recalled:

I looked at the spring-fed water holes and saw that they were stagnant, that when riled they turned black with the sediments of blue shale.

"All right," I said, "we'll corral at night and hold them on water at the wells." . . .

The next day a forest fire broke out in the Black Hills to the West. . . .

That night my well coughed and spit blue mud. It was dry.

The following morning, while a pall of acrid smoke concealed the countryside, I went to town and bought a wagon tank to fit my truck, and began to truck water eight miles from city mains.[20]

Hot, dry weather continued through the summer of 1931. Desperate cattlemen sent stock out of Montana and the Dakotas, although they scarcely knew where to ship. Plainsmen generally saw their first hay crop fall short.[21] Then, early in 1932, the weather just about reversed on the Plains. Cattlemen of Montana and the Dakotas reported satisfactory moisture. Although northerners thought they might come through all right, southerners in their turn looked on burned pastures and dying crops. Still, the drouth hit rather spottily.[22] It could have been worse.

Cattle diseases continued to decline in importance; ticks, for example, had been virtually eradicated on the Plains. Cattlemen benefited not only by losing less, but also by being able to move cattle freely out of drouth areas. Furthermore, those who wanted to restock could import without hindrance.

Successful control measures for other diseases also facilitated cattle mobility. In 1929, foot-and-mouth disease broke out in California. A vigorous program of slaughter eradicated the disease, and thereafter cattlemen of the United States were not threatened by it.[23] In 1930, scientists of the Department of Agriculture developed a fairly effective brucellosis vaccine called Strain 19. Although Strain 19 did not produce complete immunity in all cattle, it effectively brought the disease under control. One more battle neared an end.

Meanwhile, the war against tuberculosis continued, but this went less smoothly than before. Eradication required slaughter, and even compensated slaughter proved expensive for the producers. So, in the 1930's Plains cattlemen began resisting tuberculin testing. They fought almost as viciously as dairymen had fought a decade earlier. The Department of Agriculture moved more slowly with the plainsmen than they had with dairymen, however. In 1932 federal officers began checking packer's records to see if the disease was as rare on the Plains as stockmen insisted. Officials considered a tuberculosis quarantine, but they did not impose one, and so cattle mobility continued unimpaired.[24]

As all these troubles beset the cattlemen, they turned, as usual, to the federal government. Between 1929 and 1932, their requests for help developed along four major lines: (1) price supports and tariffs (2) credit assistance (3) regulation of land use, and (4) scientific research and education.

To begin with, the McNary-Haugen Bill was dead; President Hoover saw to that. In its place, Hoover supported the Agricultural Marketing Act, passed in 1929. The act set up a Federal Farm Board which was: (1) to assist farmers and ranchers to control marketing through cooperatives and (2) to establish stabilization corporations which might buy surplus commodities in order to support prices. No one ever seriously suggested a purchase program for animals. Possibly because of this, cattlemen distrusted the act from its beginning. The editor of *The Producer* warned: "Failure of the bill, after a fair trial, to produce the desired benefits will once again bring to the front schemes which have for the present been discarded." [25] He meant the now ignored McNary-Haugen Bill.

The Farm Board did not do too well. Its chairman (Alexander Legge, of International Harvester) almost immediately accused farmers and ranchers of blind greed, and so he quickly fell from their favor. In addition, just as Legge began demanding that farmers suffer a little, his International Harvester raised its prices. The events, in conjunction, did not improve farmer response to the act. When Legge quit, few cattlemen regretted his resignation.

The cooperatives founded under the Agricultural Marketing Act did not fill the needs of most ranchers. Ultimately the act collapsed under the attacks of urbanites, cattlemen, and farmers. The election of Franklin D. Roosevelt killed it altogether. Cattlemen had not wanted the act in the first place. Whatever they thought of Roosevelt, they at least approved the end of the old support policy.[26]

Along with support, cattlemen wanted more protection from foreign beef producers, particularly those of Argentina and Australia. Cattlemen received the help they wanted with the passage of the Hawley-Smoot Tariff in 1930. One section of the tariff prohibited anyone from importing meat from countries afflicted with foot-and-mouth disease. This provision effectively excluded Argentine beef. When importers tried to introduce frozen beef, the Chief of the Bureau of Animal Industry stopped it. He held that freezing did not make the meat edible. On the whole, the tariff satisfied cattlemen, but it did not solve their problems.[27]

As for credit, the federal government attacked this problem directly by setting up the Reconstruction Finance Corporation in 1932. The RFC could lend to other agencies in pump-priming efforts. Cattlemen received their greatest help when the RFC established the Regional Agricultural Credit Corporation.[28] The Regional Agricultural Credit Corporation loaned money on livestock, and supplied some credit to stockmen when they could not obtain it otherwise. The corporation gave only temporary relief, but even so, it was "the best livestock relief agency ever inaugurated up to that time." [29]

In almost every line of endeavor, cattlemen implored the federal government to do something. When it came to grazing fees, however, stockmen insisted that the government do nothing. In early 1929, hostility between cattlemen and the

Foresters had temporarily ended.[30] One year later, however, cattlemen were restless, if not hostile, because the Foresters went ahead with their planned fee increases. No later than 1931, cattlemen began petitioning the Forest Service to suspend fee collections, and some users even suggested reducing fees. The Foresters held that reductions would discriminate against those who did not use the Forests. Pressure increased, however, and in 1932 the Forest Service reduced fees 50 per cent. Almost immediately cattlemen called for more and greater reductions, but these did not come at once. Cattlemen complained because government officials acted slowly, but the most prompt, and the most extreme action, would not have helped the distressed producers much.[31]

Whatever cattlemen said of fees, they knew that the grass on the Forests was greener than that on the public domain. Cattlemen and others again asked that the domain be more carefully supervised. Instead of offering control, in 1929 the Secretary of Interior suggested that the public lands be turned over to the states. At the time, this grab suggestion, resurrected from a distant past, appealed to cattlemen. Apparently they favored the plan because it was at least a plan. They came rather uniformly to support the idea during the early thirties, even though surrender to the states would not have achieved much. As the editor of *The Producer* pointed out: "state lines in many cases are not natural boundaries . . . and to some extent makes impracticable application of any plan by individual states." [32]

No matter, pressure for the giveaway mounted. In April, 1930, Congress approved the appointment of a Public Lands Commission, which reported in March, 1931. The commission advocated giving the public domain to the states, but before anybody acted, Franklin D. Roosevelt won an election. The New Dealers took a different approach to the public domain.[33]

In the meantime, two areas of scientific research especially interested cattlemen: food technology, and farm technology. Food technology interested a few cattlemen primarily because they believed that by the use of science, meat could be better merchandised and consumption raised. Cattlemen endorsed anyone's effort to sell more beef. Several new technical innovations tended in this direction.

In 1929, quick-frozen meat came on the market. It came in limited quantity, to be sure, but it came as packaged cuts of meat, sold at retail from freezing compartments. Some producers hoped this quick freezing would increase meat consumption. Others thought the process might level out market fluctuations by enabling processors to hold meat in times of glut. In 1929, the chief impediment to wide use appeared to be shipping. Then, late in 1930, western railroads introduced mechanically refrigerated cars. The only remaining problem was mechanical refrigeration for trucks. The new process promised to change the whole packing business, but immediate results were unimpressive.[34]

Along with this development, cattle and meat transport had shifted even more rapidly to trucks. By 1932, producers sent more than half of all their livestock to market in trucks. The percentage was destined to grow and so also was the volume of meat shipped by trucks. Because of the increasing importance of trucks, their lack of refrigeration seriously hampered the distribution of frozen meats.[35]

Of course, some technological changes hurt cattlemen. Before 1914, oleomargarine had contained only 40 per cent vegetable oils, but by 1930, oleomargarine contained over 75 per cent vegetable oils. As a result, animals fats were diverted to less profitable uses. Not later than 1932, therefore, cattlemen came to demand heavier duties on cocoanut and other vegetable oils. In this campaign they joined the dairymen who had long been engaged in an anti-oleo campaign.[36]

Under the pressure of depression and drouth, cattlemen not only asked for government help, but also changed their operations. Their accommodations to the needs of the metropolis came unevenly, but certainly. In general, however, the evolution merely continued and accentuated older patterns. On the whole, the changes they instituted tended toward ever-greater intensification of beef production.

Intense production forced them to rely heavily on feeds. Of the several feed crops, sorghum most directly and frequently entered the stockmen's operations. Southern plainsmen also used more cottonseed cake as feed. As of 1929, northern cattlemen still relied chiefly on alfalfa and other hays. All cattlemen fed their stock some, and as a rule, plainsmen raised more of their feed than ever before. Indeed, the old cattle ranch was fast disappearing. As Marion Clawson noted for 1929: "The striking thing about ranches, statistically, is their comparative scarcity." [37]

In contrast, the striking thing about dry farms was their comparative ubiquity. Dry farming reached its peak in the 1920's. Wheat acreage expanded from 33,714,000 acres in 1924, to 41,418,000 acres in 1929, an increase of 22.8 per cent.[38] But wheat was already proving unattractive to many farmers on the Plains, although, as late as 1933, crops came through all right in some places. Still, drouth rather generally wrecked the dry farmers, and those who remained began the expected shift to some sort of cattle farm. They shifted more rapidly after 1932.[39]

In time, drouth and depression made life unbearable for most dry farmers. Hard as life was, however, as of 1930 settlers still continued to move onto the Plains. Between 1925 and 1930, farms and ranches on the Plains increased 3.6 per cent, rising from 1,264,270 units to 1,310,853 units. Simultaneously, ranches and farms increased in size from an average of 312.2 acres to 345.7 acres.[40]

The size of the ranches varied greatly. Between 1929 and 1932, family-sized ranches on the northern Plains ran around 2,700 acres, while on the southern Plains they averaged about 6,300 acres. Of course, averages are fictional, but even so, landholdings grew in spite of the depression.[41] Large-scale cattle farms formed a large percentage of all cattle farms; more so, proportionately, than large-scale farms formed of all types of farms. In 1930, large cattle outfits made up 2.6 per cent of the total cattle ranches. In contrast, large-scale farms made up only one-tenth of one per cent of all farms in the United States. Cattlemen, rather than dry farmers, accounted for increased acreage in Plains farms.[42]

While ranch and pasture farmers increased their holdings, they decreased the number of cattle they ran. On the northern Plains, for example, the number of cattle on family ranches fell from an average of 140.8 in 1930, to 132.0 in 1932. On the Great Plains, beef cattle decreased 3.9 per cent between 1925 and 1930. Cattlemen had 19,433,677 beef cattle on the ten Plains states in 1925, but only 18,677,007 in 1930.[43] The depression decrease in cattle stood out most sharply when compared to the 11 per cent increase between 1920 and 1925. The later decrease reflected drouth and depression. In short, plainsmen accommodated to disaster in three ways: (1) they increased the size of their ranches and farms (2) they reduced the number of cattle they carried, and (3) they made heavier use of supplemental feeds.

Their responses arose, in part, from their competition for land with dry farmers. By 1929, dry farming had advanced to such an extent that over 60 per cent of the income of plainsmen came from cash crops. Much of these crops, however, ultimately went to feed livestock. The census of 1930 recognized this when it considered any farm an "animal specialty" enterprise if 40 per cent of the farmer's cash income came from livestock. In the Dakotas particularly, stockmen bought a lot of feed from dry farmers. As dry farmers failed, however, cattlemen had to, and did, raise more of their own feed crops.[44]

As they moved toward general diversification, cattlemen became more interested in dude ranches. Only a few ranchers started them, but once undertaken, they provided fairly secure income. Dude ranches called for capital outlay, of course, and not many cattlemen could afford that;[45] nevertheless, this new institution slowly arose on the Great Plains.

As cattlemen carried out their major accommodations,

grazing naturally decreased in importance. As early as 1930, in eleven western states, supplemental feeds accounted for 20 per cent or more of all livestock feed and almost no change had taken place between 1920 and 1930. Instead, the changes which counted most had occurred in quality and methods, rather than in quantity of feeds produced.

Human survival on the Plains depended on cattle and feed. Since range pastures deteriorated steadily between 1929 and 1932, cattlemen were forced into ever-greater reliance on supplementary feeds. In early 1929, range grasses were only fair; by late 1929, grasses were in poor shape. By 1931, the ranges had seriously deteriorated, although they could still carry some cattle. In 1932, pastures improved in most places, although northern Plains cattlemen reported poor grazing.[46] In spite of their ruined pastures, cattlemen kept their stock in good condition through the early days of the depression. In an earlier day they would have been wiped out. Pasture ranching had changed that.[47]

In 1929, as before, sorghum appeared to be the leading forage crop used by southern plainsmen, although on irrigated patches they preferred alfalfa. For northern plainsmen, hay, corn silage, and browse led in importance. There, cattlemen favored oats for hay, when it could be grown. By 1930, southern cattlemen had increased their reliance on sorghum and silage. For northerners, Russian thistles became more important as drouth continued.[48]

Stockmen of the northern and central Plains used increasing amounts of silage, although not all cattlemen had silos by any means. The poor crop year of 1931 caused feed costs to rise on the northern Plains, but some cattlemen cut their costs by using thistles. Between 1931 and 1932, cattlemen in some places also seriously considered reseeding or conserving native grasses.[49] This effort clearly reflected their desperation, since native grasses yielded poorly in good years, and were worth considering only in bad.

Probably the most important change in feeding, virtually unrecognized at the time, was the initiation of contract feeding. (A later generation dignified the practice with the name "vertical integration.") Contract feeding first began in large volume in 1930. The number of farmers and cattle involved rose through 1932, and then declined after 1934. A temporary spot of good weather and fair prices seemed to cause the decline. Initially, at least, cattlemen adopted the practice because of the depression.[50]

Meanwhile, better-bred cattle showed up on the Plains. New breeds made little impression on the ranchers, however, even though the tariff of 1930 allowed cattle to be imported for breeding purposes. Under the new law, Africander cattle entered the country in 1931, but this was all. Furthermore, this new zebu breed only slightly influenced the Brahman cattle breeders. More importantly for southern cattlemen, the Santa Gertrudis continued on its hesitant way. The great sire, Monkey, died in 1932, but he had by then firmly fixed the breed in America.[51]

Under various pressures, haphazard methods of cattle handling gradually disappeared. By 1929, chutes for holding animals while segregating, dehorning, castrating, and marketing had become rather common. On pasture ranches, standard equipment included corrals, windbreaks, and even sheds for cattle. Stockmen dehorned more consistently in an effort to keep cattle from injuring each other. As cattle transport increasingly depended on trucks, ranchers more frequently installed loading docks for trucks. Many pasture ranchers used automobiles for transportation, and sometimes they used them for herding and fence riding as well.[52]

Throughout all this history of change, the 4-H Clubs assumed tremendous importance. Club members not only learned for themselves, but more importantly, they also taught their parents and neighbors. Time after time, the quality of cattle in a community improved, sometimes spectacularly, as 4-H Club work got under way. Feeding and other practices improved too, under the impetus of 4-H work. Stubborn old-timers could, or would, learn only from their children and grandchildren. More importantly, 4-H

Clubs helped develop a type of cattleman who accepted change as the ordinary circumstance of life, and who welcomed progress as a good, not merely as an unpleasant necessity.[53] The depression helped bring the change, for often the clearest lesson taught by the 4-H was that the son made a profit while his father did not.

The depression struck with unexpected severity between 1929 and 1932. Cattlemen turned in several directions seeking a way out of their dilemmas of falling prices and falling consumption. As prices fell, costs remained unaltered, and shortly, loans became nearly impossible to get. At the same time, drouth injured the industry. In response, cattlemen increased the size of their ranches, but decreased the size of their herds. They also sought aid from the government through price supports, credit, regulation of land use, and scientific research. Most notably, cattlemen were clearly at the mercy of the metropolitan economy, although they usually refused to recognize their dependence. They faced economic and natural disasters by altering operations, and by asking for, and sometimes getting, aid from the federal government. But the help brought regulation, and regulation the cattlemen could not abide. The depression grew worse, and the old problems remained.

CHAPTER X

The First New Deal

1933-1935

The frightful depression lingered on. In 1933, the number of unemployed came to a staggering 12,830,000 persons, or to 24.9 per cent of the work force. Employment fell to the lowest level in American history. In 1934, conditions improved some; only 11,340,000 people were unemployed. In 1935, only 10,610,000 Americans could not find work. At least the percentage of unemployed fell, but on the other hand, a total of 20.1 per cent of the work force, still unemployed in 1935, meant misery and concern for most Americans.[1]

The level of per capita income in the United States explained part of the misery too. In 1929, the average employed American received an insignificant $703. The income of this average American dropped to $376 in 1933, and then rose a bit to $473 in 1935. Even the employed could not afford much beef; the unemployed ate less. Simultaneously, businessmen recorded a net loss in inventories of $1.6 billion in 1933, and yet another $1.4 billion in 1934. Only in 1935 did their inventories rise, and then only by a modest $9 million.[2] The figures inadequately mirrored pressing human problems, for literally millions of people lived hand-to-mouth, and many of them hovered on the edge of starvation. For cattlemen of the Great Plains, nothing counted for as much in their lives as the Great Depression.

In 1933, each American ate an average of 58.6 pounds of beef and veal. Americans would have eaten even less if the federal government had not furnished beef for people on relief. Cattle prices fell to unbelievably low levels. Producers received an average of $4.14 a hundredweight. For plainsmen, cattle prices fell as much as 25 per cent below the already low levels of 1932. As 1933 began, many cattlemen had already become insolvent, and most of them produced cattle at a loss.[3]

At the same time, the weather got worse. In 1933, moisture shortages appeared all over the Plains, and near-drouth hit Texas, Oklahoma, and the Dakotas. Bluestem pastures in Kansas filled fully and quickly as southern cattlemen sent their cattle north. Colorado and Montana received enough moisture through 1933, but as the year progressed, severe drouth struck the rest of the Plains. Feeders, meanwhile, postponed buying while they waited to see how low distress-selling would push cattle prices. Then too, feeders also suffered from drouth in the Mississippi, Missouri, and Ohio Valleys. Soon cattle piled up in the market centers. Prices fell ever lower.[4] In late 1933, prolonged drouth produced new disasters.

In South Dakota, November 11, 1933, the farms first began to blow away.

By mid-morning a gale was blowing, cold and black. By noon it was blacker than night and this was an opaque black. It was a wall of dirt. . . .

When the wind died and the sun shone forth again, it was on a different world. There were no fields, only sand drifting into mounds and eddies that swirled in what was now but an autumn breeze. There was no longer a sectionline road fifty feet from the front door. It was obliterated. In the farmyard, fences, machinery, and trees were gone, buried. The roofs of sheds stuck out through drifts deeper than a man is tall.[5]

Along with the dust storms came the grasshoppers. In 1933, the insects hit Montana especially hard. These wandering hordes devoured feed supplies, and often destroyed what drouth had missed.[6]

On all fronts, cattlemen faced disaster, and as usual, they

wanted the government to help them. The New Dealers did what they could without hurting the general public.

To begin, the federal government attacked soil erosion, and other drouth-related problems. In March, 1933, Congress passed an Emergency Soil Conservation Act which aimed to control not only erosion, but fires, insects, diseases, and floods. At the same time, the act provided some employment too. The act applied mostly to federal and state lands, but private lands also benefited.[7]

Next, New Dealers tried to relieve the money shortage. The Congress set up the Farm Credit Administration which undertook several major enterprises such as the Federal Land Banks, the Intermediate Credit Banks, and the Production Credit Corporations. The Credit Corporations helped cattlemen by providing them with feed loans in the drouth-distressed areas. The Credit Corporations concentrated on areas where dust storms had damaged early crops.[8]

Meanwhile, Congress took up laws to assist all farmers by raising prices. At length, in May of 1933, Congress passed the first Agricultural Adjustment Act. Before Congress acted, most cattlemen opposed all efforts to have cattle included as a basic commodity. Plainsmen asserted that the proposed production limits were unsound because lower beef output would only force consumers to use other kinds of meat. Apparently, most cattlemen believed this. They wanted help, but not controls; they hankered after a handout without regulation. Anyhow, at first cattlemen lobbied for their traditional programs: (1) higher tariffs on beef, fats, and hides (2) lower interest rates (3) lower freight rates, and (4) agencies for more orderly marketing and advertising.

Plains stockmen probably took these positions simply because, as of early 1933, they had not yet been thoroughly crushed by the depression. As drouth and depression continued with renewed fury, Plains cattlemen came to reconsider their position. By then, however, they could do little more than try to reach price agreements with packers. These efforts proved futile.[9] By November, spokesmen for the range cattlemen had revised their earlier ideas. F. E. Mollin, Secretary of the American National Livestock Association, observed:

In discussing the agricultural adjustment program from the standpoint of western cattle-producers, it seems only fair to state that when the domestic allotment bill was first under consideration, with the large surpluses of wheat and cotton in the limelight, the great majority of cattlemen voiced active opposition to any such program being applied to live stock. . . .

Taking stock of our own situation in the light of these [more recent] conditions, we must face the fact that the steady gain in cattle census figures since 1928—even though much of it is in dairy animals—cannot long continue without creating a major surplus problem, and it behooves us determinedly to set about to check the rather alarming increase at the earliest possible moment.[10]

Cattlemen finally got the help they wanted on November 10, 1933, when the Federal Surplus Relief Corporation began to buy beef. The corporation tried to cut down production, as well as to feed the poor, and so chiefly bought young cows. Cattlemen approved the program which they had asked for.[11]

The surplus beef went to the Federal Emergency Relief Administration which used it to feed some 15 million people in 1933. At first, the FERA ordered 15 million pounds of beef, but then it continued the program. Additional orders came to about eight pounds of beef each month for every family on relief. Cattlemen gleefully approved the FERA policy of paying fairly high prices as a support measure.[12]

Erosion control, credit assistance, and relief buying did not exhaust cattlemen's programs for federal assistance. Forest users, for example, wanted lower grazing fees. The Foresters had increased fees as contemplated in 1927, and by 1933 they had raised them to the maximum of 14.5 cents per head per month. Cattlemen now begged that fees be based on current cattle prices. Secretary Henry A. Wallace agreed to consider the matter for the second half of 1933. In May the Foresters announced that the Secretary would use the price formula proposed by the cattlemen.[13]

The fee changes, when they came, disappointed the cattlemen. In a letter of May 30, 1933, Assistant Forester C. E. Ratchford told F. E. Mollin that: "Accordingly, a plan for adjusting fees in harmony with market prices, to be fair, should result in an average grazing fee for cattle of 14.5 cents over a representative period of years."[14] In short, grazing fees remained unchanged for 1933.

These grazing fees were about the only remaining issue between cattlemen and Foresters. Other complaints sank to insignificance, since by 1933 all plainsmen could see that the Foresters had indeed preserved the grass. As of 1933, cattlemen still suggested that grazing control be extended to all of the public domain. The cattlemen got some unexpected action on their request for real control of the domain. Once again, however, cattlemen became victims of some cosmic irony when Secretary of the Interior Harold Ickes, using a law of 1885, insisted that all fences be removed from the public lands. Plainsmen protested most piteously. After all (they came close to saying), they had defied the law for so long that they could not reform immediately. Ickes remained adamant, however, and the fences ultimately came down. Before they did, though, protest meetings sent in a heavy number of denunciations.[15]

In other ways federal acts influenced the lives of Plains cattlemen. Most significantly, the Congress created the Division of Subsistence Homesteads in the Department of Interior. This agency tried to put families on homesteads where they might farm part-time and work part-time. Congress also set up the Rural Rehabilitation Division which loaned money to farmers who could not find credit elsewhere. At the same time, the Farm Credit Administration sought to have businessmen readjust the debts of farmers. All these agencies helped the bedeviled cattlemen keep their land and their cattle.[16]

Even so, critics of the New Deal protested that the program produced no long-run successes. John Maynard Keynes once observed: "In the long run, we are all dead." In the short run, the New Deal did accomplish something. Per capita beef consumption rose startlingly from 58.6 pounds in 1933 to 73.2 pounds in 1934. A footnote to the statistical table noted: "Includes production and consumption for Government emergency programs." [17] Seldom has so much been summed up so briefly. Government emergency programs literally saved the cattlemen.

Nevertheless, the critics had a point, for the Great Depression continued. The average price of cattle rose slightly in 1934 to an unimpressive $4.55 a hundred.[18] The economic life of the time appeared in the comment of one editor who described this trivial increase as "showing decided strength." Even this slight advance did not help Plains cattlemen much. They generally failed to get maximum returns because of their higher transportation costs.[19]

Meanwhile, the fiercest drouth in all history hit the Plains in 1934. Hell moved west. No bright spots appeared anywhere. Grasshoppers and rodents struck savagely, and devoured what little food they could find. Springs and streams dried up. Wheat dried up, corn failed to sprout, the wild-hay crop never materialized, and by May, the alfalfa crop was lost. Almost everywhere, stockmen watered cattle only by pumping. When they could, stockmen moved cattle off the Plains, and so swelled an already glutted market.[20]

Early in June the water holes gave up. Three weeks later the wells quit. I hauled water, working sixteen hours a day on hot days in an effort to keep the troughs full, but never could I really haul enough.

Meanwhile the panic was on. Cattlemen, who knew by now that there would be no haystacks for winter, and fearful of their dwindling water, began to ship to market in increasing numbers.[21]

At Froid, Montana, a little less than five inches of rain fell in 1934. North and south, over the Plains, the drouth continued.

Then came the dust storms. The worst began in the northern Plains in 1934.[22] From Fargo, North Dakota, came the report: "Dust has been so bad in part of North Dakota that street lights have been turned on in the daytime." [23] No doubt about it, by 1934, dust storms and soil erosion had become the most dramatic of all the problems facing the plainsmen. On one 47,000-acre field in Texas, winds blew out the entire wheat crop. The federal government set up a demonstration area at that place to show how the land might be saved and brought back to production. Similar projects were begun other places on the Plains.

Simultaneously, the federal government began having windbreaks of trees planted on the Plains. Federal authorities hoped these shelter-belts would break the sweep of erosive winds, and the projects gave people some work. The shelter-belt idea worked fairly well. It might have worked better had it been pursued long and vigorously enough. In other places, government officials tried to halt erosion by having the Plains reseeded with native grasses. This program did not work too well, however, because the grasses did not seed well naturally. Furthermore, plainsmen could seldom get good clean seed. Nevertheless, somebody or other tried all these programs in 1934, and all accomplished something.[24]

Nothing could stop the drouth, however. It continued through 1934 and threatened to destroy countless herds. In 1933 the Jones-Connally Act had made cattle a basic commodity, and had also provided for support purchases up to $50 million. These small purchases, however, hardly solved anything. Officials of the AAA, the FERA, and the FCA, all "watched with growing apprehension the increasing severity of the drought and made tentative plans to cope with its effects." [25]

Then, in June, 1934, government officials announced a federal drouth-relief buying program. Cattlemen selling to the government had to agree to any future production-control plans which might be started. On June 8, Rexford G. Tugwell began the purchasing plan as part of the Drought Relief Service. By June 16, some 445,820 cattle had been bought by the government, and in addition, emergency feed loans had been made. By July 23, over 1,363,000 head of cattle had been purchased. This came to an average of thirteen head for each farm involved; about 10 per cent of these cattle were slaughtered on the farms and the meat destroyed. By the end of 1934, the federal government had purchased some 8 million cattle. The prices paid were not high, but then, the alternative for the cattlemen had been total loss. By late October, the government had spent nearly $525 million in a single year to save cattlemen from ruin and starvation. For this salvation, many cattlemen never forgave the government. Large numbers of them resented the help.[26] Wrote one:

When an actual cattle-buying program was announced the rattling of chains could be heard in it. Wallace was not ready to say how many cattle we should keep and how many we should sell. He didn't know yet how many cattle he wanted in the United States. So a form had been prepared for this contingency. In it the seller agreed to agree to any future agreement submitted by the Secretary of Agriculture.[27]

The form also asked how many cattle the plainsmen had on hand. Local committeemen suggested that each signer inflate the figure a little for the future. With astonishing candor, the perpetrator of fraud continued:

With my tongue in my cheek, I signed the agreement to agree, and in due course of time received a check which was double the amount the cattle would have brought at market.[28]

Instead of seeing their fellow citizens as saviors, many cattlemen saw the people as suckers.

The moral of this experience wasn't lost on me. Government, no matter how hairy-chested it might appear to be, had a blind side. I saw that the planning of the Planners was another of the hazards of agriculture that could be avoided by any private planner who had eyes. There was nothing in my rule book that prevented me from taking this sucker's money.[29]

Apparently not everyone reached this ethical level. The editor of the *Montana Stockgrower* complained of the gratitude of some plainsmen!

But now on every hand one finds ranchers who are only grateful to a Government which lent them a helping hand. . . . This purchase program is not an unmixed blessing—it only fulfills the need of the moment, and for every hour we live beyond that moment we will see more clearly the error of "selling our birthright for a mess of pottage" because we were so hungry.[30]

Well, it wasn't that bad, after all. Although the condition of cattlemen remained desperate, government programs reduced the number of beef cattle by 17 per cent. Among other things, this not only improved the market, but brought a better balance between feed and cattle.

Altogether, 8.3 million head were purchased in 1934. The rewards in human survival and dignity far outbalanced the costs of administration and the loss of some meat. "Many of the cattle sold to the government would not have been marketed at all if not taken over that way." [31] On the whole, cattlemen seemed to have wanted the government purchase programs. When these seemed about to be ended, they protested. The memory of a Texas cattleman still remained green many years later. Said he: "If it hadn't been for government help, I never would have come through. . . ." [32]

Observers thought the program and the drouth caused many cattlemen to become more responsible in their attitudes. They learned that rugged individualism was outmoded. They learned of the need for conservation, and for improved methods of farming. They learned about the pre-eminent rights of the people of the United States. These lessons were not insignificant, and they were learned as cattlemen discovered their helplessness.[33]

Of all national legislation passed in 1934, nothing endured so well as the Taylor Grazing Act. In 1934, cattlemen in various areas apparently held several views on what they wanted done with the public domain. Almost all seemed to agree that the land should be removed from entry. They also seemed to agree that the Forest Service should not be put in charge. Soon, Congress and the administration abandoned any idea of extending the Forests. Here and there, some cattlemen wanted to turn the domain over to the states, but those who wanted this represented only a minority. Late in 1933, Secretary Ickes expressed his views on the public domain, and in January, 1934, Representative Edward T. Taylor, of Colorado, offered a bill along these lines. Immediately, cattlemen's organizations throughout the Plains announced support of the Taylor bill; on June 27, 1934, Congress passed it.[34]

Edward T. Taylor had long advocated giving the land to the states. He gave this up, however, when Congress refused to do this. He then fervently embraced his grazing act which put most of the domain under the Department of Interior. House and Senate committees greatly altered the bill, chiefly through amendments presented by Senator Patrick McCarran of Nevada. The bill survived his assaults, however, and President Roosevelt signed the law on June 28, 1934. By executive orders issued November 26, 1934, and February 5, 1935, Roosevelt withdrew from entry practically all unreserved and unappropriated public domain.[35]

The act allowed the Secretary of Interior to administer 143 million acres of public domain. He could establish grazing districts on 80 million acres of this land. He could also grant permits to cattlemen for ten years for grazing specified numbers of animals at certain seasons, on payment of grazing fees. Preference in granting permits was given to those near or in the districts, and local customs were respected, particularly range rights. Grazing districts were to be formed only after hearings and notice.[36] Details still had to be worked out, as of 1934, but as the editor of *The Producer* remarked: "Anyway, this puts an end to many years' turmoil, and the matter should now be allowed to rest. . . ." [37]

Assistant Secretary of Interior Oscar Chapman, held hearings all over the West as he started putting the law into effect. Most cattlemen cooperated well, and they generally approved Chapman's administrative methods. F. R. Carpenter, of Hayden, Colorado, became the first Director of Grazing, and in his first year he got along famously with the notoriously cantankerous cattlemen. Part of the good will may have derived from the grazing fee of five cents a head each month. This came to nine cents less than the Forest fee.[38]

Programs and policies which cattlemen had discussed with increasing fervor since the 1880's at last ended with the Taylor Act. For the first time in history, someone really managed the public domain. For the first time in history, cattlemen could reasonably estimate the amount of land they might expect to use. This certainty probably helped cattlemen take a renewed interest in range management.

Meanwhile, Forest grazing fees declined. Beginning in 1934, the Service adjusted rates to the average prices received by stockmen in eleven western states. Halfhearted efforts to have the Forest Service removed from the Department of Agriculture failed because cattlemen disapproved of the change.[39]

Cattlemen wanted more, however, and in particular they wanted more tariff protection. Good as it was, they felt more would be better, and they especially viewed with alarm the possibility of reindeer meat competition. Unfortunately for them, Alaska was not a foreign country.[40]

Cattle diseases continued to bother cattlemen. Congress continued the battles by paying for animals destroyed in brucellosis and tuberculosis eradication campaigns. In 1934, some 11.5 per cent of all cattle suffered from brucellosis. Furthermore, as the range became progressively less open, bovine tuberculosis reportedly increased here and there on the Plains. The war against these killers picked up speed as time went on.[41]

Few changes and little relief appeared in 1935. The government apparently reduced its beef purchases in 1935, because each American ate less beef in 1935 than in 1934. Per capita consumption fell to 61.7 pounds in 1935. The average price of beef rose to $6.54 per hundred, which was the highest since 1930. In truth, "The price rainbow was reappearing." [42]

Still, the drouth continued, and cattle starved to death all over the Plains. Some perished simply for want of feed, some starved because of dust on the feed, and not surprisingly, some died because moneylenders would not let cattlemen get federal feed loans. Drouth undoubtedly caused the principal shortage of feed, and the consequent destruction of cattle. The western Plains suffered most, but all the Plains felt the effects.[43]

The dust storms had begun on the northern Plains in 1933, and southerners seemed to think they had little to fear from dust. Indeed, 1935 began well enough. In early spring, however, clouds of dust rose on the central and southern Plains, and stockmen had to move cattle out. Western Kansas, eastern Colorado, eastern New Mexico, and the plains of Oklahoma, and Texas suffered especially. In many places "pasture and grass land are practically covered with a sheet of dust." [44] An anonymous minor poet declared:

> Out in the West where men are men,
> It hasn't rained since God knows when.[45]

He was right, but that wasn't all. Back when the depression had begun, the federal government had reduced predator control work, much to the advantage of bears, wolves, and lions. In 1935, however, the Bureau of Biological Survey, with funds from the Emergency Relief Administration, once again took up predator control, but as a part of work relief. As relief the program no doubt did some good; as control it worked an overdue miracle. The 1935 catch turned out to be the greatest in history to that time.[46]

In spite of self-help and federal help, the economic plight of the cattlemen continued. Consequently several of the older emergency programs had to be kept in force through 1935. The Farm Credit Administration continued to lend money for feed, but only enough to keep animals alive. The federal government also continued to buy livestock in drouth distress areas. These food relief purchases fed the poor, prevented cattle from dying of starvation, and allowed cattlemen to take better care of the remaining stock. Viewed any way, the feed and purchase programs succeeded. One editor noted that the program "saved many ranchers from complete ruin this year." [47]

When the drouth-relief program had been started, some cattlemen had been alarmed at the possible controls they had been required to agree to. By 1935, however, well over eight million cattle had been bought and slaughtered, and the need for cattle production controls disappeared. No one imposed controls, for controls were not needed. Drouth, dust, and purchase ended the problem of overproduction.[48]

At the same time, the federal government began or continued several long-term projects on the Plains. The shelterbelt programs continued as before, as did the reseeding projects.[49] In 1935, the Congress and the President established the Resettlement Administration to: (1) take over the already existing relief and rehabilitation programs and (2) begin new measures for rural relief. A Land Utilization Division continued the purchase of submarginal land, a Resettlement Division continued to develop homestead and community projects, and the Rehabilitation Division continued the relief activities of the old FERA. The Resettlement Administration directed the three new Divisions, which replaced other earlier agencies.[50]

Entering its second year, the Taylor Grazing Act seemed

to work rather well. By 1935, some thirty grazing districts
had been set up, and a total of 14,653 licenses had been
granted. Cattlemen, although reluctant to cooperate, did
come to take more interest in forming grazing districts and
cooperatives. They also took greater interest in range conservation.[51]

Other old projects continued dear to the hearts of plains-
men. For years cattlemen had sought higher tariffs. In 1935
the administration threatened them with less protection.
Early in 1935 one of the most prolonged disputes involving
Plains cattlemen began when Secretary of State Cordell
Hull negotiated a series of treaties under the Reciprocal
Trade Act. On May 24, 1935, the Secretary signed a Sanitary
Convention with Argentina which would have allowed Argentine beef into America. The cattlemen most vehemently
opposed ratification by the Senate. Senator Connally of Texas
headed the Foreign Relations Committee, and largely because of his heavy hand, the treaty lay in committee where
it remained poised as a threat to the industry.[52] Nothing
ever came of it, however.

Other older programs got further. In 1935, Congress expanded the activities of the Civilian Conservation Corps.
The Corps thus continued its soil, water, and forest conservation work on the Great Plains. They worked for the enduring
advantage of plainsmen, and of all Americans. For cattlemen,
the greatest achievements seemed to come from those camps
assigned to the Division of Grazing.[53]

As usual, however, cattlemen still tied into the Foresters.
In 1935 Forest Service troubles took a new form. The linking
of grazing fees to cattle prices came to be resented by those
many cattlemen who could not use the Forests. The Foresters held firmly to their program, however, and as drouth
continued, they even forced cattlemen to reduce the numbers
of cattle grazed on the Forests. In 1934, the Foresters forced
a 24 per cent reduction, and in 1935, an additional 30 per
cent. Some cattlemen who still preferred to ruin the ranges,
demanded a change in policy. The Foresters ignored them,

however, mostly because the Forest Service policies had general public support.[54]

Looking at the whole picture, how did it all appear for the years 1933 to 1935? Well, for one thing, the best efforts of government and of individuals could not save all the residents of the Plains. Between 1930 and 1935, an estimated 150,000 persons moved off the Plains. Almost all of the emigrants came from the northern Plains: South Dakota, North Dakota, Montana, Nebraska, and Kansas. The southern Plains states, however, gained in population. Although the bulk of these immigrants did not move to the Plains, the population of all Plains states rose from 15,087,000 in 1930 to 15,401,000 in 1935. The rate of growth came to 2 per cent, compared to 3.2 per cent for the United States as a whole.[55] The actual decline in the North, and the relative decline in the South, came mostly from the migration of dry farmers.

Several interesting things happened to the dry farmers. In the first place, their yields per acre fell sharply. They averaged 12.8 bushels of wheat an acre between 1928 and 1932, but this fell to 8.8 bushels an acre between 1933 and 1935. The figures counted only harvested acres. Total production also fell sharply. Dry farmers harvested an average of 539,608,000 bushels annually between 1928 and 1932, but harvested only 250,648,000 bushels annually between 1933 and 1935. Dry farmers also cropped fewer acres. In part this decline represented land they abandoned, and in part it represented land that simply failed to produce any crop at all. Between 1928 and 1932, farmers grew some 42,106,000 acres of wheat annually. Between 1933 and 1935 this acreage fell to a yearly average of 28,607,000 acres of wheat. For the most part, the differences between the two periods resulted from abandoned or ruined land.[56] This was what the depression did.

The stories of farmers on the Plains varied in detail, but all accounts showed about the same depressing picture. For one farmer, production fell from 14,000 bushels of wheat in 1930—to 600 bushels in 1933—to nothing at all in 1935.

His experience may not have been typical, but it did illus-
trate the steady downward trend on the Plains. As crop
yields declined, farmers recklessly grazed the land. They
grazed not only their own, but anything at hand. They also
depleted the already scant water supplies. If farmers had
no stock, they accomplished the same destruction by leasing
to those who did. Here and there they seeded and took care
of pastures, but not many bothered.[57]

In 1938, a study of the unsuccessful dry farmers on the
northern Great Plains showed the failures had rather similar
characteristics. Dry farmers who failed apparently lacked
adequate capital from the beginning. They owned little
machinery, had inadequate buildings, and notably, had inadequate water resources. Most importantly, they did not
follow the best dry-farming methods, and also quite significantly, they owned very little livestock. Instead, they
depended almost exclusively on wheat, the sure route to
destruction, as earlier generations had discovered.

A few livestock farmers failed, but they usually had raised
very little feed. The most successful farmers combined their
enterprises, or else concentrated on livestock, with some
wheat on the side. The failures most often had come to the
Plains between 1908 and 1918. They were the last remnants
of an earlier horde, most of whom had already been cleaned
out. In short, ranch and pasture farmers most often succeeded; dry farmers and herdsmen failed.[58]

And so the tale went around again. As the defeated farmers left, the cattlemen came to take over, but the newcomers
came as ranch or pasture farmers, not herdsmen. The change
appeared in the average size of farms and ranches on the
Great Plains. On the northern Plains, for example, the average family-sized ranch rose from 2,624 acres in 1933, to
2,661 acres in 1935, but more to the point, the amount of
land owned increased from 966 acres to 972 acres.[59] In time
of depression, it would seem that cattlemen would be unlikely to increase their land holdings, and on the southern
Plains they apparently didn't. In 1930, the average Plains

farm came to 345.7 acres; in 1935 it came to only 332.3 acres.[60] Still, land in farms actually increased in some Plains states: South Dakota, Nebraska, Texas, Montana, Wyoming, Colorado, and New Mexico.[61]

By 1935, however, other indexes could be used to show the change to pasture farming. In 1935, cattlemen relied on the range for only 71 per cent of their feed. This compared to 80 per cent as late as 1930. Cattlemen on the Plains had become much less dependent on pasture, and more dependent on grown feeds. During depression they could not easily increase their land holdings, and so they increased their crops.[62] At the same time, ranch and pasture farming continued to change. Cattlemen found that cattle fed primarily on grass brought lower returns than those fed on grains and silage. Meanwhile, new varieties of sorghum appeared and moved northward to the central Plains.[63] All these changes worked. South Dakota investigators discovered that: "While the ranch-farms fed more roughage they carried relatively larger feed reserves, which apparently were sufficient to carry the roughage consuming stock through the drought year of 1934. . . ."[64]

Ranch farmers learned to use silos more. In Texas alone the number of trench silos rose from twelve in 1930 to four thousand in 1935. All over the Plains, silos appeared more frequently. Generally, cattlemen favored the inexpensive trench silo. Drouth especially accelerated this shift because a crop injured by drouth often made some sort of silage, even though it was otherwise useless.[65]

But none of this mattered if the cattle could not be moved economically. The story of transport during the thirties was simple: trucks. One Texas cattleman shipped by rail and by truck; the rail shipment took twenty-four hours, the truck shipment nine hours, and the cattle sent by truck arrived in better condition. Cattlemen all over the Plains had about the same experience. Furthermore, the trucks hauled at lower rates. Refrigerated trucks also appeared, and this, as much as anything, helped break the strangle hold of the big packers. Trucks also helped lessen the hold of the railroads with their refrigerated cars. No matter where, the number of cattle shipped by truck steadily rose, much to the advantage of the stockmen.[66]

Well, after all, just how important was the cattle industry of the Great Plains? In fifteen years the total number of beef cattle on the Plains declined markedly from 43 million head in 1920 to only 31 million head in 1935. Cattle numbers had fallen, and yet Plains cattlemen had actually increased their share of the total in the United States. In 1920, 44.6 per cent of all beef cattle in the country came from the Great Plains. In 1935, 45.3 per cent of all beef cattle came from the Plains.[67] The Plains were important as beef country for urban Americans.

CHAPTER XI

The Second New Deal
1936-1939

The unemployed came to 16.9 per cent of the total labor force in 1936; rose to 19.0 per cent in 1938; and then fell slightly to 17.2 per cent in 1939. The depression had receded since 1935, but not much.[1] The New Dealers had begun to think less in terms of emergency, and more in terms of long-range improvement. Most of the newer programs required the cattlemen to do something, rather than just have something done for them. Naturally, they seldom accepted these new policies gracefully.

Nonemployment and less beef eating went together; in each succeeding year Americans ate less beef and veal. Only in 1939 did average consumption rise slightly. Each American ate 68.9 pounds of beef and veal in 1936, but only 62.3 pounds in 1939. In 1936, federal relief purchases ended, and the "blessings" of a free economy showed up in the years thereafter.

Prices improved, however, although not evenly. Cattlemen received $6.26 a hundred in 1936, and $7.76 a hundred in 1939. By 1939 cattlemen were on the edge of prosperity, although they really recovered only in 1942.[2] Of course, not all Plains cattlemen got average prices, and of course, their net returns also depended on their costs. To increase their returns, Plains cattlemen increased their sales through local auction markets. These seem to have worked, sometimes. Cattle prices rose above parity levels for some cattlemen in 1937. Those cattlemen who benefited most marketed comparatively young feeder stock. The grass-fed steer had become unprofitable, and nearly obsolete.[3]

As prices rose, some urban Americans objected, especially union members. In 1937 the United Automobile Workers joined certain metropolitan papers in leading consumers in resisting the high meat prices. Cattlemen deprecated the "No Meat Weeks" campaigns, but consumer efforts did seem to halt the price increases. The UAW continued the campaign through 1938. After 1938, urban consumers apparently accepted the rising cost of living, probably because of returning prosperity.[4]

Plainsmen, however, could not see much recovery, for their income consistently remained low in spite of higher cattle prices. For one thing, plainsmen had no outside jobs. Throughout the United States, off-the-farm jobs already produced sizable income for farmers, but not on the Plains. In the extreme case of North Dakota, 92 per cent of all families derived their living only from farming. Well, only from farming in a manner of speaking. Actually, relief payments of one kind or another supported a sizable number of farmers and cattlemen. In 1936, on the northern and central Plains, most people had incomes below $1,000 a year, and some even ended up in the hole. In South Dakota, Montana, and Colorado, at least 63 per cent of the families got less than $1,000. In Kansas and North Dakota proportionately more families received less than this minimum of $1,000.[5]

Studies for New Mexico and Montana for 1938 showed about the same levels of income for cattle raisers. For the whole period, about two-thirds of all Plains cattlemen received below the $1,000 a year which economists regarded as the necessary minimum. All of these income computations included the value of farm food, and the farm dwelling. On the whole, cattlemen seemed less well off in these things than the dry farmers.[6]

If the weather had improved along with prices, cattlemen might have fared better. As it happened, the weather did not improve, and sometimes it grew worse. Severe blizzards on the northern Plains opened the year 1936. "We had seen storms like this last three or four days, but we had never seen one last six weeks, and we had never heard of fifty-two below." [7]

At first, the northern Plains suffered most from the drouth. The year 1934 still held the records, but 1936 came close almost everywhere. In some ways 1936 hurt more because dust residue from previous storms smothered grass which might have grown otherwise. In July, the central Plains still had barely enough water, but the northern Plains were in deep trouble. On the southern Plains, feed crops did poorly in July, and by November had been nearly ruined. Cattlemen reduced their herds even further, managed their lands more carefully, and still barely kept going. The dust storms took up again in the fall and winter, and more cattle left the Plains in distress selling.

The winter of 1936–1937 did not hurt the Plains at once, but the light snowfall intensified the drouth. By 1937, drouth had come to be regarded as ordinary. Rancher Greely Hughes reported from Wyoming: "We have not had any range grass here in three years. The drought has about cleaned out all the cattle in this section. These are the facts about this section." [8] In Montana, cattlemen sold from 50 per cent to 75 per cent of all their livestock in 1937. Although the weather apparently improved in the South, Texans stocked lightly. By the end of 1937, however, most places reported the range in satisfactory condition. Cattle reductions, plus some rain, helped improve things.

More moisture came by the end of 1938. As early as April, southern Plainsmen reported vastly improved conditions. The central Plains improved a bit by March, and by November had just about recovered. Records on the northern Plains indicated more, but not enough rainfall. As nature started to let up, cattlemen took hope, and some took the offensive. A few even advanced the astounding proposition that the range had never been overgrazed, but that drouth alone had caused all the trouble on the Plains. [9]

The return of moisture, which began in 1938, continued in 1939, and the ranges came back fast, mostly because of low cattle numbers. Reports from all over told of the advent of moisture. "The sagebrush even has the old familiar smell." [10] Throughout the year, grass became better and better, and cattlemen strove to restock. Late in the year, however, drouth hit again on the southern Plains, particularly in Texas and Oklahoma. To prevent heavy death losses, cattlemen shipped stock out, but in 1939 they at least had some place to ship them to. Otherwise, 1939 ended in blissful moistness.[11]

The hot, dry weather suited grasshoppers perfectly. From 1936 to 1939, hordes of the insects ravaged the Plains. They came in huge swarms and ate everything that grew. Feed crops and grasses all disappeared. In 1936 they first attacked Montana, and later all the northern Plains. By midyear, the central Plains saw the invasion, and in the emergency, Congress appropriated $260,000 for control of the insects.[12]

Grasshoppers came again in 1937. As usual, the insects just ate the best parts of the plants. "A single hopper could destroy ten times what he actually consumed." Control worked only when all farmers and cattlemen cooperated, and they did not always do that. In spite of the best efforts of the Bureau of Entomology, defenses could not be perfected.

Except for the ravages of grasshoppers, 1938 would have been a prosperous year for cattlemen. The insects destroyed extensively, especially on the northern and central Plains. The destruction incidentally nudged quite a few crop farmers in the direction of cattle husbandry, because hoppers hurt cattlemen less than dry farmers. Plainsmen of the North discovered that grasshoppers wouldn't eat sorghum. Sorghum, however, could be used for little except cattle feed. In sorghum and cattle, then, lay salvation, as many a Plains farmer discovered.[13] The grasshoppers continued their forays through 1939, but they did less damage than before. Wet weather cut down on their raids, although they remained a serious pest in some places. They did not, however, halt the hesitantly returning prosperity.[14]

Undoubtedly, the Taylor Grazing Act alleviated some of the effects of depression and drouth. The act gave stockmen about all they wanted, except that they had comparatively little land available for grazing. This low acreage forced the number of stock down, and helped solve all manner of problems, and so, the policy was roundly attacked by the cattlemen. Not that the cattlemen opposed the Taylor Act, for as Secretary F. E. Mollin of the American National Livestock Association correctly noted, the cattlemen had suggested some control of the public domain for many years. No doubt too, as his report observed: "Erosion there has always been; erosion there will always be."

The return of rain brought fairly rapid recovery of the grasslands. Still, the recovery would not have been possible if the number of stock had not been drastically reduced. The argument that rain, not regulation, brought recovery, ignored three decades of ever-increasing ranch and pasture farming. These new methods had measurably reduced the use of range grass. The cattlemen had a point, of course, because overgrazing had not caused all of the trouble. Nevertheless, this could not be properly advanced as an argument against regulated grazing.

In 1936 Ding Darling suggested in *Successful Farming* that the whole public domain be closed to grazing. Spokesmen for the industry vigorously denounced Darling for his suggestion which, incidentally, would have benefited the Corn Belt directly, and the public indirectly. Instead of reducing the amount of grazing land, cattlemen had it increased to the full 143 million acres. To administer the act, Congress created a Director of Grazing, to be appointed by the President. The law also provided that grazing fees from all lands should be split fifty-fifty between the federal government and the state where the domain was located. In short, the law went rather far toward granting the wishes of cattlemen, but even so, it kept the principle of control.[15]

By 1936, observers noted that the Taylor Act favored the big cattlemen, that it had no teeth, and that grazing officials based cattle allotments on the amount of hay the stockman raised. In favoring the ranch farmer, the act also favored the larger operators. However that may be, more and more grazing districts came into being, and more and more permits were issued. By 1937 more than 17,000 licenses covering 110,000,000 acres had been issued for some 1,800,000 cattle, and 7,800,000 sheep. The fees came far below those charged by private owners and the Forest Service.[16]

In 1938, cattlemen received another boon when Congress passed the Pierce Act. This law let the Secretary of Interior lease state, county, and private land which lay within federal grazing districts. Thus Congress put about ten million acres potentially in the control of the Secretary of Interior who could then sublease. The Secretary used the act for the first time in 1940, and then only for tax-delinquent land. The rent paid and received was set by the Department of Interior which turned it over to the landowner. The United States could not charge less than it paid. Ostensibly, the act promoted orderly use of the land. By 1941 over one million acres had been leased under this provision which actually gave cattlemen even greater control of their range.

The Department of Interior's absurdly low rates of 1934 continued in force through 1938. The chief administrative change in 1938 occurred when Secretary Ickes dismissed Farrington R. Carpenter as Director of Grazing, and replaced him with Richard H. Rutledge. Cattlemen rather liked both men, but Ickes got rid of Carpenter because of his political views, an action which many thought unnecessary, and unworthy of the Secretary. Considering the political disposition of the plainsmen, they came off better than they might have.[17]

Belatedly, in 1939, the Department of Interior decided to stop people from illegally grazing the public domain. Probably some 44 million acres were grazed without lease. Well, better late than never. In the same year, Congress provided that each grazing district should have a local advisory board of from five to twelve members to offer advice on administration of the Taylor Act. Cattlemen thus came ever closer to control of what they persisted in considering *their* range.[18]

At the same time, Forest-users forced concessions from the Forest Service. Ten-year grazing permits expired in 1934, and in 1935 the Foresters decided to issue only annual permits. Cattlemen protested, and so in 1936, the Foresters agreed to issue ten-year permits again. Cattlemen then insisted that private irrigated meadows should be considered when the Foresters judged the carrying capacity of the range. The Foresters agreed to this too, although not as enthusiastically as the cattlemen wished.

Conflicts between Foresters and stockmen arose partly because many cattlemen did not yet grasp the principles of range management. Furthermore, the cattlemen felt they had a vested interest in the Forests, while the Foresters thought all the people had an interest. Naturally, conflicts over policy developed.

At one time, cattlemen had insisted that fees fluctuate with the price of cattle. Ironically, some users, by 1936, complained that fees fluctuated too much. Of course, they only objected to the rises, but fees rose in 1936 to 13.05 cents each month for each head, and cattlemen discovered their fee-setting rules had backfired. Then too, from time to time, the Foresters forced cattlemen to run fewer head on the range. This issue came up in 1936, and again in 1937. Cattlemen protested, for apparently any program for preserving Forest range roused their resentment.[19]

And Foresters feared resentment because, as an Idaho stockman explained: "There never was a time when we could get so much out of the Forest Service as now, since they are competing with the Taylor Grazing Act." [20] This farsighted, public-spirited attitude apparently appeared often on the Plains, and made the work of the Foresters more difficult than usual. With Foresters currying favor, they did well to save any grass at all.

In general, in 1936, federal conservation and relief measures entered a new and more permanent phase. Oddly enough, the changes began when the United States Supreme Court destroyed the First Agricultural Adjustment Act in January, 1936. Congress immediately passed new legislation to replace the ruined law. The Court had left marketing agreements untouched, and so several avenues for control and relief remained open. As part of the Soil Conservation and Domestic Allotment Act, on September 29, 1936, Congress set up a range-conservation program. Under what many called the "new AAA," the Secretary of Agriculture paid cattlemen for developing water resources, and undertaking other conservation measures.[21] Not all cattlemen favored conservation. The editor of the *American Cattle Producer* grumbled:

The program which the Agricultural Adjustment Administration is now putting into effect throughout the range territory can by no stretch of the imagination be considered the livestock men's program. The record in this matter should be kept straight. It should show that individually and through their organizations the great majority of live-stock producers clearly indicated that they did not want a government program, believing it to be the first step in regimentation of their industry.[22]

The editor may have been mistaken, for, on the other hand, Forest officials believed that the program had good support from the cattlemen. Foresters explained that in some parts of the Plains cattlemen delayed starting the program because of their greater interest in price supports. More succinctly, many cattlemen welcomed anything that gave them money, but objected to doing anything to get it.

By 1937, the conservation program had definitely caught on, and complaints virtually disappeared. The general program continued as before. Plainsmen probably profited most by the payments for natural reseeding through deferred grazing. This bounty came to 35 cents for each animal unit kept off the grass for each full month in 1937. Other payments ranged from $1 for a linear foot of wells dug, to 10 cents for every 100 linear feet of ridging on the range. The only really new suggestion came from Colorado cattlemen who wanted payment for converting hay land to range. Allen S. Peck, Forester in Denver, supported the idea because "hay production is one of the biggest causes of overstocking of pastures and ranges in the west." [23]

The programs for 1938 and 1939 differed little from those of previous years, except that in 1939 Congress set a limit of $10,000 on payments to any one farmer. In 1938 the Executive Committee of the American National Livestock Association recommended the end of the conservation program. They noted that it had saved a good many cattlemen, but they also noted that it had subsidized producers. Apparently no one paid much attention to the Executive Committee. Plainsmen generally rather welcomed the subsidy, with or without complying with the rules. One study in New Mexico showed that some cattlemen cheated. Some actually increased their herds while taking payments for reducing them. More significantly, some cattlemen actually did as they agreed, and anyhow, almost all took their subsidy without complaining.[24]

Meanwhile, Congress and the administration changed some of the earlier emergency measures which affected the Plains. Late in 1936, an Executive order transferred the Resettlement Administration to the Department of Agriculture. On September 1, 1937, the administration was reorganized as the Farm Security Administration. The Land Utilization Division of the old Resettlement Administration went to the Bureau of Agricultural Economics.[25]

While it existed, the Resettlement Administration undertook a modest program on the Plains. By 1936, the administration had purchased four million acres on the northern Plains, and had created forty-one projects for controlled grazing. The administrators hoped that the projects would form the basis for a permanent cattle industry. Meanwhile, the WPA worked on the Plains, chiefly on demonstration farms, roads, dams, and gully-erosion projects.

The WPA thus supplemented the Civilian Conservation

Corps. In 1935, seven CCC camps had been assigned to the Division of Grazing. By 1936 these had been increased to forty-five camps. In 1938, forty-five more camps were assigned to the division, distributed across the Plains according to the number of cattle grazed on public lands. By late 1939, the CCC accomplishments came to an impressive list of: "358 spring developments; 143 wells with storage facilities; 780 earth reservoirs; 7,300,000 acres of rodent control; 1,950 miles of range fences; 225 corrals . . . ," and on, and on, and on. Men from eighteen to twenty-five, later, seventeen to twenty-three, could enlist in the CCC. They received $30 a month, most of which had to be sent home. Cattlemen benefited greatly from the activities of the CCC, as most of them realized.[26]

In order to encourage good ranch-farming practices, the Department of Agriculture continued to set up demonstration farms. Those on the Plains showed clearly what good practices could do to preserve grass and soil. The Soil Conservation Service, created in 1935, directed most of the work. They dammed streams and gullies, and planted grass to replace wheat. Contour plowing and ridging showed how moisture could be conserved. In many cases, some variety of sorghum was the first crop to hold the soil successfully.

Most clearly, the service showed what deferred grazing and contour ridging could do. The SCS worked with little capital, during the driest years on record. Cattlemen drove as many as four hundred miles, or more, to see the projects; ranchers and farmers did not emulate immediately, but they could not but be impressed.

The most improbable, least appreciated, and ultimately one of the most useful of the New Deal projects was the Plains shelter-belt project. The program began as a new formal administration in 1935, and continued under various guises through 1939. Between 1935 and 1939, more than 11,000 miles of trees were planted as shelter-belts on 20,000 farms on the Plains.[27]

Because of drouth and depression, the federal government

purchased beef. Cattlemen's associations had protested cattle buying in the country, partly because they felt the government paid too little. So, in 1936, the government bought beef cattle at terminal markets. Altogether somewhat less than four thousand head were bought at a total cost of $108,-000. Some $5 million had been appropriated, but distress selling apparently did not damage the market as much as federal officials had feared. The purchases of 1936 ended support buying of cattle until the 1950's.[28]

Cattlemen also had a few projects of their own. Pasture farming, growing steadily across the century, began in the late thirties to get support from all federal agencies. Briefly, plainsmen proposed to base their economy on grass, feed, and livestock. Cattle kings and dry farmers alike no longer made suitable residents for most of the Plains. At the same time, nature and the economy forced wider adoption of the techniques. Specifically, more and more ranch farmers sought to improve the range rather than just grow more feed.

One of the many difficulties of pasture farmers arose from the dust covering of pastures. On the southern Great Plains, few pastures escaped dust damage, and relatively few escaped in the north either. Bringing the pastures back into production took time, and general improvement seemed to be noted only in 1939. At the same time, cattlemen seemed to have increased their herds enough to need more pasture lands, and the pastures of Kansas and Oklahoma began to find renewed use as leased grazing land. Cattlemen relied heavily on grazing. Throughout Region 6 of the Forest Service (on the southern Plains) out of some 97 million acres available, pasture accounted for some 65 million acres as late as 1939. Attitudes had changed over the years, however, and in 1939 cattlemen tended to treat the grassland as "pasture," not just as "range."

Still, they fed more too. The principal crops on the northern Plains continued to be alfalfa, clover, and small-grain hay. For both North and South, cottonseed cake continued as a major feed for many stockmen, but in the thirties they often bought according to the protein content of the cake. In New Mexico (where cattlemen seldom had to winter feed) one survey showed that some seventy-five per cent of all cattle received feed for thirty to one hundred and twenty days each year. Throughout the Plains, increased crop production and feeding accomplished more than did new methods.[29]

Nevertheless, new methods did appear. Some cattlemen, for example, burned the spines off cactus to get feed in 1936, but the land then tended to blow away, so they stopped the practice. The use of large quantities of cottonseed cake in the North apparently dated from around the drouth of 1936. In Texas, some cattlemen began hesitantly feeding for market, using the readily available cottonseed cake. Over in New Mexico, irrigated patches supplied fair quantities of alfalfa hay, some of which the ranchers shipped out.

By 1939 feed supplies on the Plains proved more abundant, and reportedly rose well above 1938 levels in that year. In most years, however, cattlemen had to buy some feed, and this cost them dearly. In 1936 Montana cattlemen paid $15 a ton for alfalfa hay, and in New Mexico in 1938, feed costs made up 34.3 per cent of all cash expenses for cattlemen.[30] Because of the relatively high costs, Plains cattlemen had rather noticeably reduced their feeding operations by 1939. Simultaneously, they tended to hold cattle, particularly in the North, to build up herds again.

Of all the crops, none did as well as sorghum. It resisted drouth, defied grasshoppers, and grew when nothing else would. Cattlemen all over the southern Plains raised it extensively. It also began to move to the North—tentatively at first, but more rapidly as grasshoppers hit the range. Sorghum ranked third in volume and value in Texas in 1937, but more than that, it ranked first in reliable yield. Texans favored Dwarf Yellow Milo; Kansans just favored sorghum, and the acreage in the crop continued to rise. R. W. McBurney of Kansas discovered an incidental value of sorghum when he noted that it effectively smothered bindweed. It also proved astonishingly effective in halting wind erosion, especially on depleted soils. Glenn Rule noted in 1939:

For years these camels of the plant family have demonstrated their ability to take punishment in the form of drought. . . . But it has only been in recent years that the sorghums, in a broad way, have had an opportunity to demonstrate their usefulness in protecting the soil. As long as there was sufficient organic matter in the soil partially to offset the effect of limited supply of rainfall during drought years so that wheat could be raised, few farmers paid much attention to any crop which they thought to be less remunerative. With the humus supply depleted and with repeated failures of wheat to afford cover for the land the sorghums have taken on an increased importance as a crop barrier against the wind.[31]

Technically, the greatest advance between 1936 and 1939 centered on the proven advantages of contour ridging and furrowing. Furrows or ridges for pastures measurably increased the moisture in the ground by causing water to penetrate a foot or more further at the furrows than in the spaces between. By using furrows, cattlemen vastly reduced the need for supplementary crops. This was just as well, for the land furrowed might well be range unsuitable for anything else. Further, the ridges and furrows also broke the surface winds and so cut down on dust blowing. The first pasture furrows on the Plains, in 1935, were spaced twenty to forty feet apart, but by 1939, experience had shown that ten to twelve feet worked better. In any case, Plains cattlemen found contour work on pastures to be nearly the most important development of the thirties.[32]

Meanwhile, battles against diseases changed, but never ended. Anthrax broke out in South Dakota which required a temporary quarantine to keep the disease within the state. The effort succeeded, and the disease finally subsided. Less dramatically, veterinary scientists made new discoveries. In 1938 scientists of the Bureau of Animal Industry began work on better diagnostic tests for brucellosis, and they managed to find one. Beginning in 1938, the bureau also discovered the value of phenothiazine as a worm killer for livestock. Around 1939, officers of the United States Department of Agriculture began seriously urging calf vaccination as a preventive for brucellosis. They aimed at eventual eradication of the disease. Scientists and cattlemen had pretty largely brought the major diseases of the past under control, except for brucellosis. The most persistent pests of the new era were insect and worm parasites.[33]

Another kind of parasite—rustlers—grew bolder during the last days of the depression. In Kansas alone, cattlemen lost an estimated $100,000 worth of cattle to thieves each year. In 1939, in New Mexico, seventeen cases of rustling came before the first district court alone. These cases represented only a part of the violations. The problem became so serious that cattlemen appealed to their old savior, the federal government. Plainsmen wanted interstate rustling made a federal offense. Senator Pat McCarran of Nevada introduced such a bill which passed Congress, but President Roosevelt vetoed it on the ground that it would extend federal jurisdiction to petty larceny. There the matter stood in 1939.

Through the early thirties, the number of cattle on the Plains fell. After hitting a low in 1937, however, the count steadily rose. On the northern Plains, the average number of cattle for the family-sized ranch increased from 124.2 in 1937, to 134.2 in 1939. The decreases up to 1937 probably reflected drouth; thereafter, the slow increase mostly reflected depression. Given the economic situation of the times, the Plains supplied as much beef as the American consumers could eat.[34]

Simultaneously, cattlemen continuously increased the size of their farms. They learned the lesson of the depression which taught that families on relief had smaller farms than did nonrelief families. And so, ranchers increased the size of the family ranch. On the northern Plains, the family ranch increased from an average of 2,890 acres in 1936, to 3,408 acres in 1939. The amount of land owned rose, but not as impressively. Approximately the same changes took place on the southern Plains.

If the very small operators failed to make out, very large ones did not do well either. Now and then a ranch went bankrupt, but these failures generally occurred on the southern or central Plains, and even then were not typical. Most failures, however, resulted from too-small outfits.[35]

Dry farmers sometimes made out a bit better than in earlier periods, but generally they did not do well. Most reports told about the same story: "These people are far from self-supporting. In 1936, 73.3 percent of the total money income was advanced by the Federal Government." [36]

Price supports and relief reduced human misery, but unfortunately they did not halt soil erosion. And dry farmers most conspicuously caused erosion. George Reeves saw the motion picture, *The Plow That Broke the Plains,* and went home mad, but mad or not, the picture told the truth. On the other hand, strip cropping, sorghums, lister plowing, and other techniques reduced the damage of dry land farming. Meanwhile, although wheat farms fell on hard times, more and more land went into cotton on the southern Plains. The advance of cotton accelerated through 1939.

For most of the Plains, however, cattle supplemented crops. On the ten Plains states, harvested wheat acreage came to 46,529,000 acres in 1938, but fell dramatically to 34,990,000 acres in 1939.[37] People moved off the Plains, thus emphasizing the disaster. Actually, between 1936 and 1939, Plains population rose slightly from 15,425,000 to 15,572,000. Population increased far less rapidly than in the rest of the United States, however, and in several states the number of people actually declined. Population fell in North Dakota, South Dakota, Nebraska, Kansas, and Oklahoma. Significantly, the declines took place in states raising wheat by predominantly dry-farming methods.[38]

The plainsmen stood at the beginning of the meat business, and the urban consumers stood at the end. In between, processing and transporting showed more progress than almost any other aspect of the industry. Cattlemen wanted meat inspection laws more rigidly and widely enforced, and in 1938 Congress limited the exceptions to the meat inspection law of 1907. Continual decentralization of the packing industry, and the smaller volume handled by the giants, inspired the law.[39]

Trucks for cattle transport developed rapidly and astoundingly. In 1936, nearly half of all stock going to public stockyards went in trucks. Trucks brought 54.8 per cent of the cattle, and 57.5 per cent of the calves. This proportion rose through 1937, and by 1938 came to far more than half of all cattle. Meanwhile, the railroads had learned nothing, or less. In 1938 cattlemen fought a railroad effort to raise freight charges 15 per cent. Cattlemen thought the proposed increases particularly mistimed because of the drouth. What the railroaders could not lose through competition, they seemed determined to lose through misjudgment.

Simultaneously, quick freezing of meat became more important, and made some impact on the plainsmen. Between 1936 and 1938, frozen-food production in the United States more than doubled, and meat accounted for a sizable amount of the increase. Consumers apparently reacted favorably to frozen beef, and cattlemen took what comfort they could from the potential sales of the future. In the thirties, however, frozen beef hardly dented the market.[40]

On another front, cattlemen struggled to hold their domestic market. The unconfirmed Argentinian treaty caused them the greatest concern, for at any time the treaty might have been ratified by the Senate. Senator Connally of Texas kept it bottled up. Ostensibly cattlemen objected to Argentine beef because of foot-and-mouth disease on the Pampas. From time to time, however, cattlemen and their spokesmen also expressed disapproval of trade agreements in general. As of 1939, however, the Sanitary Convention with Argentina remained unconfirmed.[41]

Drouth relief and soil conservation programs still loomed

large as the cattlemen began to come out of the depression. At the same time, contour ridging and furrowing, combined with greater reliance on ranch farming, produced a new aspect in the old industry. All that cattlemen really hankered after was higher prices, and the Second World War brought those.

CHAPTER XII

The War and the Plains
1940-1945

The Second World War began September 3, 1939. By early 1940 war had begun to boost the American economy through European purchases, and through domestic preparations for war. Lend-Lease began in March, 1941, and further boosted the industrial economy. Then, on December 7, 1941, the United States was suddenly and grimly at war and a period of unprecedented inflation began. The nation quickly mobilized all its resources. First came price controls, and then rationing; still, beef prices and consumption rose. Plains cattlemen entered an era of unparalleled prosperity.

The number of people employed in industry rose. In 1940, only 85.4 per cent of the labor force was employed; by 1945, 99.1 per cent of the labor force had jobs. Weekly earnings boomed. Wage income rose about 50 per cent during the war, but prices rose only about 30 per cent. More and more people could afford beef. Even those outside the Armed Forces ate better than before. The rate of urbanization accelerated, while farm population rapidly declined. The great migration to the cities produced an increasing number of prosperous urban beef-eaters.[1]

Unquestionably, income levels influenced total beef consumption. Even in the prosperous twenties, beef consumption (but not pork and chicken) had risen and fallen with income levels. As income rose in the forties, producers could barely satisfy the demand for meat. The United States government also was buying large quantities for the growing military forces. Total commercial slaughter rose constantly

169

year by year from 1940 to 1945, although civilian beef consumption did not go up in 1943, probably because of rationing. Still, each American ate an average of nine pounds more beef and veal in 1945 than in 1940. Consumption rose from an average of 62.3 to 71.3 pounds.

Full employment combined with wartime fiscal policies soon threatened America with wild inflation. Congress and the administration had to act promptly to halt inflation, "the cruelest tax of all." Their efforts took two forms: price controls, and rationing. First came price controls, for almost at once meat shortages had caused a rise in the cost of living. Between May and October of 1942, agricultural prices rose 4.6 per cent. In one real sense, the plainsmen simply did not meet demand, for "The truth of the matter is that our consuming population had never had all the meat it needed and wanted." Plains cattlemen could not fill the deficit on short order.

The beef shortage of 1942 caused a heavy slaughtering of unfinished, light cattle. Thus everyone got less beef from each carcass. Mostly, however, the beef shortage came from a "sharp increase in consumer buying power due to heavy concentration of laborers in war production plants." [2] A further drain on beef supplies developed in 1943 when the beef-consuming public was increased by the seven or eight million men who entered the Armed Forces. For the first time in their lives most of these men came to be well fed. They had been around before, but as civilians they had apparently eaten less than half the meat they wanted. Cattlemen could not produce enough beef, and prices shot up.

Rising prices forced Congress to pass the Emergency Price Control Act in January, 1942. Under the General Maximum Price Regulation, vendors had to sell all commodities and services (unless specifically excluded) at a price not higher than their highest price of March, 1942. This simple law proved rather difficult to enforce. Under the act, agricultural products had both a minimum and a maximum ceiling. These ranged from 85 per cent to 110 per cent of parity.[3] At first the minimum delighted cattlemen who had no reason, at the time, to complain about the maximum. Their attitude changed as prices rose and came closer to the maximum.

Prices did rise. So much so that on April 27, 1942, President Roosevelt asked Congress to reduce the maximum ceiling below 110 per cent of parity. He wanted prices set at about the level they had then reached. Congress moved slowly, but the President imposed price ceilings by Executive Order on May 18. Evidently most Americans approved this action. In September, 1942, Roosevelt again asked Congress to hold prices at parity. He also wanted authority to stabilize wages and salaries. Congress granted the authority in general, although some farm representatives protested. On October 2, 1942, Congress passed a new Stabilization Act, and the next day the OPA placed ceilings on various foods, including beef. Cattlemen complained a little because the ceilings failed to account for variations in the grades of beef. On the other hand, they welcomed ceilings on other agricultural commodities, especially the controls on feed grains.[4]

Price controls worked rather well. The cost of living continued to rise from November, 1942, to February, 1943, but at an infinitesimal rate. Then, between February and April, 1943, the cost of living advanced alarmingly. Urban workers grew restive because of wage controls. On April 8, 1943, the President ordered the Price Administrator not to allow any further price increases, and to stop "adjustments." As a result of the President's action, prices rose only 2 per cent between 1943 and 1945. This came to one-sixth the rate of increase from 1941 to 1942. By 1945 food prices had actually declined at retail by more than 4 per cent. None of this hurt the cattlemen. In 1943, for example, they received about 107 per cent of parity for beef.

Of course, some cattlemen objected to price regulations. In 1944, a few plainsmen thought they saw a beef surplus. They insisted that restrictions should be removed. Fortunately for the other producers, the War Food Board denied the request. Consequently, no beef deficit developed in 1945.

Some stockmen also complained about the black markets in feeds, particularly in cottonseed cake. Considering the size of the OPA operations, and the difficulty of administering the acts, the infractions appear insignificant.[5]

Throughout the war, beef prices fluctuated in response to demand, and price regulations. In 1940, average prices stood at $7.95 a hundred. Prices rose continuously to $12.22 a hundred in 1943, and then declined slightly in 1944. In 1945, the average price rose to $12.41, which, all things considered, amounted to a gouge of the urban consumer. Plainsmen profited handsomely from the war. They had not seen such prices since 1918.[6]

Price controls kept the cost of living down, but also made beef harder to get. In order to distribute the meat fairly, the federal government slowly moved toward rationing. At first, most Americans had expected rationing only for scarce industrial materials. Early in 1941, for example, Congress gave the President power to allocate scarce materials in the national interest. In August, 1941, "the President delegated this authority to the Office of Production Management, later renamed the War Production Board." The WPB in turn redelegated this power to other agencies for particular commodities. The board did not redelegate food rationing, however, until April, 1943. In that year the WPB established the War Food Administration. Congress had only indirectly granted authority to use the Office of Price Administration in rationing in January, 1942.

Cattlemen did not much like the idea of rationing, but they preferred it to the "meatless days" of World War I. At first the government attempted a "share the meat" program, but like most voluntary programs in war, it did not work. The creation of new industries compounded the difficulties of meat distribution by swelling the urban population.[7]

By the time of the meat crisis of 1943, the OPA had already begun food rationing. Ration books had been distributed in May, 1942. Everything was ready to go, therefore, when meat rationing began in March, 1943. Meats, butter, fats, and oils developed into the second largest rationing program, surpassed only by gasoline rationing. Each consumer received an allotment of ration stamps worth forty-eight total points each month, and from time to time the OPA declared the point value of various commodities. The consumers then had to distribute their forty-eight points, in almost any combination, across the rationed items.

Cattlemen did not protest very much against this governmental invasion of food distribution because before rationing began, black markets in meat had already appeared. These not only threatened quality, but more importantly, they irritated consumers. Plainsmen apparently hoped that rationing would cause more equitable distribution, and thus build good will and markets. Anyhow, rationing did not affect producers much personally because farm families could consume any meats raised on their farms without using ration points. They could do this even though they did not slaughter for themselves.[8] Cattlemen and farmers also received special treatment on certain rationed items such as batteries, grain scoops, drills, pails, tubs, and a host of other things. In the fall of 1943, the OPA allowed the manufacture of more than fifty of these items, in specific quantities, especially for farmers.[9] The officials of the OPA managed to administer this monumental system with few serious breakdowns.

On the whole, meat production rose through 1944. The need for rationing steadily declined. On May 4, 1944, the War Food Administrator stopped rationing all meat except beefsteaks and roasts. OPA officials protested that they could not really administer such a small program. They wanted to ration all meats some, but the War Food Administrator thought that slaughter of swine and other animals should be encouraged. In the great surge of meat consumption of 1944, beef fell behind. Cattlemen had some misgivings about this. Most of them seemed to think that beef should have been unrationed. In retrospect, however, the WFA policy of 1944 seems to have been premature, because the OPA had to begin meat rationing again in 1945. Cattlemen avoided these ups and downs.

In a way, cattlemen benefited from their exclusion from the boom of 1944. Indeed, they profited when, in 1945, total meat supplies fell 20 per cent below the corresponding period of 1944. Only consumers suffered. The shortage affected the bigger packers rather more than the small local ones. Consequently, consumers in urban centers could not obtain the meat to which they were theoretically entitled. This hurt other meat producers, but not cattlemen. The free-meat policy of 1944 also broke the control machinery of the OPA which never again achieved control of meat on quite the same scale as before. Widespread counterfeiting of ration stamps broke out in 1945, partly as a result of their temporary loss of control.[10]

But, for cattlemen, rationing and the later fiasco proved beneficial. In October, 1945, the editor of the *American Cattle Producer* summed up:

Rationing during the war was a necessity. Perhaps it was even a help to the industry. It gave the widest possible distribution to the product. It introduced meat to many people for the first time. They learned the value of meat through the precious little red [rationing] points. But rationing did not come to us without evils. When you try to see that everyone gets a share of a scarce article you invite trouble. Rationing brought black markets and they thrive on sky-high prices.

At that, under the tension of war, rationing succeeded. Most people respected the rules. But will they continue to abide by them now that the war is over? [11]

Obviously they would not, for lawbreaking reached alarming proportions even before the end of the war. So, by order of Secretary of Agriculture Clinton P. Anderson, meat rationing ended Friday morning, November 23, 1945. Most cattlemen agreed that the program had worked, and now they looked forward to a postwar boom.[12]

Through all this government regulation of marketing, two results stood out fairly clearly: (1) the system worked well in properly distributing meat, and in keeping prices down; and (2) cattlemen accepted the government intervention with little complaint. The specter of "paternalism" apparently could not frighten men who had just passed through the depression, especially when the specter produced such handsome profits.

Meanwhile, the number of markets increased, the terminal markets declined in importance, and chain stores grew in their function as packers and distributors. At the same time, a greater percentage of Plains cattle went to the West Coast to feed the burgeoning population. Of course, most Plains cattle still moved eastward, but the line of balance between east and west cattle movements steadily shifted.

By 1940 it was roughly along the Continental Divide, swinging farther eastward in New Mexico. The greater eastward movement of the southern end of this line, than of the northern end, is due to the greater growth of population in California, especially southern California.[13]

Concentration of the Armed Forces on the West Coast, along with ceiling price differentials and freight-rate differences, all caused a further tendency of plainsmen to sell to the West.

A method of dehydrating and compressing meat marked the chief innovation in processing. The technique helped feed troops in war, and saved both time and shipping space. Although the innovation helped win the war, it seemed to have little peacetime use.[14]

Although war dominated the lives of cattlemen in the forties, some of the New Deal programs continued in effect. Range and soil conservation programs continued, at least in some fashion. Even without incentive payments, some cattlemen continued to defer grazing. In this they received aid and encouragement from the Division of Grazing and the Forest Service. On badly eroded or hilly land, terraces and contours appeared.

Furthermore, the Department of Agriculture paid cattle-men for certain conservation practices, and at least through 1941, the number of cooperating cattlemen steadily increased. So also did the practices for which payments were made. After 1941, however, the cattlemen turned most of their attention to the war, and anyway, wet years reduced the pressing need for conservation. The programs continued, but cattlemen stressed them less.[15]

On the other hand, the Civilian Conservation Corps kept at its work until disbanded on June 30, 1943. The CCC worked on rodent control, check dams, insect control, and a nearly inexhaustible list of other activities. The corps did much of its work under the direction of the Division of Grazing. Its projects vastly improved the grazing capacity of the public domain at virtually no expense to the cattlemen. Cattlemen benefited, and the public picked up the tab.[16]

Other federal range improvement programs went forward in spite of the war. In 1941, and again in 1942, the Department of Interior reseeded sizable acreages of range. Other millions of low-producing acres needed reseeding, and so the department planned to work through the forties. The Soil Conservation Service also continued work on the Plains. The Service bought low-grade range and retired it from use. By and large, however, these efforts ended by 1940, and the service thereafter concentrated on education. They continued their demonstration projects which proved fairly effective in showing cattlemen the virtues of pasture and ranch farming.[17]

Meanwhile, the Taylor Grazing Act and the Division of Grazing tried to protect the range. Overgrazing diminished on the domain, and, at the same time, more of the public range came under the act. By 1941, federal range programs embraced about 93 per cent of the 143 million acres set aside by the Taylor Act. Sometimes, however, the Division of Grazing tended to continue range rights which were attached to inferior private land. In the view of one authority, the division should have been allowed to revise its allotments from time to time. So long as ranchers only made policy, they tended to perpetuate an inefficient and outmoded form of cattle husbandry.[18]

A controversy over fees arose in the Division of Grazing. The division split the fees; one-half to the states where the land was located, one-fourth to the division for range improvements and land purchase, and one-fourth to the National Treasury. In 1940, the fees produced only $800,000. After distribution, the fees brought in rather markedly less than the cost of administration. From 1941 on through 1945, Congress debated raising the fees. Ranchers and their congressmen opposed any increase. Congress finally curtailed services, and reorganized the division. There the matter stood at stalemate in 1945. Spokesmen for the stockmen rather reluctantly agreed to a future fee increase, but they wanted it delayed until after the war.

On the Forests, cattlemen had, by 1940, pretty well reconciled themselves to the fees then charged. These fees had long been determined by ability to pay as indicated by the price of cattle. By 1945 Forest fees had risen to twenty-four and eight-tenths cents a month, compared to the five cents charged by the Division of Grazing. No one seemed to see any point in complaining about this. Instead, cattlemen wanted the rules changed so they could run more heavily on the Forests. The Foresters showed that greater productivity resulted from moderate use of the grass, and thus successfully resisted pressures to increase cattle numbers. For some reason cattlemen showed less fight than they had in the past.[19]

Several New Deal price supports and other aids continued through the war. Cattlemen also benefited from these older programs. The Farm Security Administration, for example, continued an active, if uncertain career. In 1942 Congress lumped the administration with other agencies to form the Food Production Administration, and then in 1943 put all of these agencies under the War Food Administration. The Farm Security Administration became an independent agency within the Department of Agriculture on June 29, 1945.

Through resettlement programs the administration saved many plainsmen from ruin, and then later, as prices rose, the administration emphasized the very best ranch farming techniques. Southern plainsmen particularly seemed to benefit from these activities, which were essentially long-range programs. They were also intended for the less fortunate farmers. Not surprisingly, some big operators looked on the administration with distaste.[20]

Resettlement under the Farm Security Administration officially ended in 1942, but liquidation was completed only in 1948. Meanwhile, the Resettlement Division had constructed camps for migratory labor. During the war these camps became centers for farm labor, and so continued a useful function on the Plains. During the war, the camps came under the Office of Labor in the War Food Administration.

Plainsmen also received various cash subsidies. Supports fell into two general categories: (1) beef subsidies to take up the slack in a "roll back" order in 1943, and (2) feed grain subsidies under the AAA.

In spite of some protests from cattlemen and others, on June 1, 1943, the OPA rolled back prices for certain foods to their former levels. In order to benefit consumers, but not penalize stockmen, Congress had the Commodity Credit Corporation subsidize meat producers at the old high prices, while consumers paid the lower prices. Objectors, such as there were, criticized the effort to aid urbanites: "Consequently, while this proposed roll back is clearly a consumer subsidy, it will be advertised as a producer subsidy in order to comply with the law." [21] At the end of the fiscal year, 1944, some $462 million had been paid to packers to maintain prices. Once again critics attacked the law because it subsidized consumers, and urbanites allegedly did not pay fair prices for food. Well, anyhow, cattlemen profited.

In 1945, Congress granted special bounties to encourage feeders to finish cattle, and to avoid price increases for consumers. The feeder subsidy of fifty cents a live hundred did not go to the Plains cattlemen as a rule, but they benefited anyhow. They sold their cattle to feeders at comparatively high prices, and they remained aloof from certain market uncertainties. As one cattleman put it: "My headache has been taken over by an Iowa feeder and I'm satisfied for this season." [22]

Through depressions and wars, cattlemen held fast to one solution to all problems: raise the tariff. Or, after the Reciprocal Trade Agreements Act: stop reducing the tariff. In 1940 the cattlemen returned to their fight. The Texas and Southwestern Cattle Raisers Association unanimously resolved that the Reciprocal Trade Act be ended or amended. Others joined the Texans, but in May, 1940, the editor of the *American Cattle Producer* mournfully reported defeat.

Across the years, the duty on beef and cattle had been steadily eroded by use of the "favored nation" clause. The United States had "favored nation" treaties with many countries. The clause provided that the nation involved would pay duties as low as the most favored nation, whichever that might be. Thus a reciprocal agreement with Canada that lowered beef tariffs automatically lowered it for most other nations. In this fashion, most rates had been cut 25 per cent or more below the level of the 1930 tariff. By 1945, cattlemen lamented that the policy not only injured them, but that it seemed destined to continue forever.[23]

Cattlemen did have some reason for concern. Well before America entered the war, beef imports rose spectacularly. After all, Americans could afford the meat, and they wanted more than the domestic cattlemen produced. In 1939 the United States imported only 2,354,000 pounds of beef, but in 1940 this rose to 12,559,000 pounds. This rate of expansion exceeded that of any other period in our history up to that time, but imports went even higher. In 1945, the United States imported 127 million pounds of beef. Placed beside a domestic production of 10,270 million pounds, however, the imports looked trivial.[24]

In retrospect, protests about beef imports seem a bit silly. Not so the fear of the weather. In 1940 the drouth of the thirties continued, only on a smaller scale. From Wyoming, B. W. Bridges reported: "It is worse than last. I don't know what in the world is the matter, but it can't rain any more." [25] In the forties, drouth caused slight loss because of the generally good economic conditions. In 1941, beef prices rose, and simultaneously the weather improved. Indeed, a series of wet seasons began in 1941. Texas had a few dry spots in 1942, as did some other southern Plains states, but the rest of the Plains had plenty of moisture, feed, and grass.

The southwestern drouth grew worse in 1943. Texas reported the worst weather since 1917. Large parts of Texas, Kansas, and Oklahoma were declared disaster areas. The War Food Administration sent in quantities of soybeans and hay to rescue the stricken ranchers. The government did not buy cattle, however, because the drouth was not that serious.

In the North, the winter of 1942–1943 caused distress. Northerners who survived the winter came into a fairly lush year in 1943. Southerners, in contrast, had to feed heavily because of drouth. Cattlemen accommodated rather easily. In 1944 and 1945, rains fell abundantly all over the Plains. The northern Plains seemed especially blessed, but the South also recovered.[26]

Wet weather provided stock water, and as this happened, the long-term water developments of the New Deal paid off. Reservoirs and ponds impounded water which in an earlier day might have run off. Some ranchers even held some water for the next year.

Although the weather proved good, cattlemen still suffered from various natural pests. Grasshoppers, because of wet weather, threatened only a few places during the war. Prairie dogs, however, destroyed appreciable quantities of range forage, particularly on the southern Plains. Cattlemen continued their war against the dogs, without much prospect of victory.

In dealing with predators, cattlemen struck on two fronts:

(1) they cooperated with the Fish and Wildlife service in employing professional trappers, and (2) they offered county bounties. The bounties sometimes encouraged fraud and seldom produced useful results. Wolves and coyotes destroyed the most stock in the 1940's, although advancing civilization seemed to restrict their range and activity.[27]

Disease control took several forms. By 1940 the tick had just about vanished. Early in the year, the last remaining counties in Texas were removed from quarantine. But other troubles remained. Shipping fever still cursed cattlemen, and until around 1940, no really effective cure had been found. Antibiotics proved effective, however, and came to be used frequently during the 1940's. Meanwhile, brucellosis control campaigns moved forward. In 1940 new tube and plate antigens became available for diagnosis. In 1941, the Colorado Stock Growers and Feeders Association began statewide, voluntary control of brucellosis in range cattle. The plan called for only calf vaccination, and proved only moderately effective. It was at least a start toward eradication.[28]

Stockmen lost heavily to internal cattle parasites, although apparently few cattlemen grasped the extent of their losses. By 1940, scientists had developed an effective antiworm drug, phenothiazine. During the war, veterinarians used the drug as fairly standard treatment for parasites. The great use of the drug came after the war, however. In the forties, the most serious parasite was the screwworm grub. Against it, scientists of the Department of Agriculture evolved a new treatment of spraying cattle with insecticides. The treatment apparently worked well enough. By 1945 one observer estimated that one million Kansas cattle had been sprayed, and that the treatment would produce at least $5 million in additional income.[29]

Although scientists discovered new treatments, and cattlemen tried some of the remedies, the greatest application of science against disease came after the war. Nevertheless, the whole approach to veterinary medicine changed during the war because scientists and cattlemen already had the big killers fairly well under control. Ticks, for example, no longer seriously menaced the industry, and the fight against ticks had been a fight for survival. Grubs, although serious, did not quite fall in the same class.

In every way, cattlemen had stumbled into a newer era. They did what they could to adjust. With government ever more in the industry, with a wartime economy booming along, with weather favorable, and nature benign, cattlemen could and did devote themselves to rather sophisticated problems of economic philosophy. The newer problems of the age demanded penetrating thought, and complex solutions. The cattlemen did well in handling their problems.

For one thing, they had to solve the increasingly complex problems of finding land for cattle husbandry. After the Taylor Act, state land remained about the only large parcels left for purchase or lease. State practice apparently did not meet the needs of cattlemen, for state agents usually tried to get maximum revenue, which meant that the land generally went to speculators. Small operators found it difficult to expand. Furthermore, the Tenant Purchase Division, created in 1937, had by 1946 been changed in objectives. It became a rural lending agency of limited value on the Plains. For cattlemen the problem appeared clearer than the solution, but intensified production seemed to be their only way out.[30]

So, they intensified. They introduced more and greater changes in production methods. They innovated little, but did apply more of the old ideas and devices. Ranch and pasture farming gained impressively during the war; probably more than at any other period in history.

For one thing, alfalfa production expanded. Once, plainsmen had considered alfalfa a blessing because of its drouth resistance and feed value. In the 1940's, ranch farmers increasingly prized alfalfa as a soil-building legume. Cattlemen with irrigated lands particularly grew alfalfa to build fertility. In New Mexico, for example, they used between 20 and 25 per cent of all irrigated land for alfalfa. Meanwhile, acreages in crested wheatgrass increased. Part of the expansion resulted from the ever-growing appreciation of grassland farming.[31]

Grassland farmers grew tame grasses as their basic crop. Grassland farming differed markedly from a simple reliance on range grasses. Through the forties, Kansans grew more acres of tame grass, and rather less of grain crops. Simultaneously, fewer grassland farmers leased grazing land as the forties progressed. Instead, they ran their own cattle. In wheat country farmers began running cattle in the stubble. This sometimes led these farmers to shift over to cattle. The federal government speeded the change somewhat by furnishing grass seed, and by even providing the planting machinery.

As grassland farming developed, many crop farmers changed to animal husbandry, or else sold out at high land prices. As a result, farms grew larger, and high-risk cropland tended to go into grass. In seriously arid places on the northern Plains, grassland occupied some 85 per cent of the land in 1944, although most of it could not really be considered pasture.[32]

All cattlemen depended on feeds other than grass. In dry seasons and hard winters, they still relied on sorghum. During the forties, they used sorghum more as silage. Sorghum made an excellent long-keeping silage which surpassed corn for palatability. Furthermore, some Plains cattlemen found that surplus sorghum could be used to feed to a finish. The discovery did not threaten Corn-Belt feeders, but plainsmen did have an auxiliary enterprise in time of good yields. Still, experiences varied. During the war, Texas cattlemen usually found full feeding unprofitable, but some Kansas stockmen made money by finishing. The comparative nearness of Kansas to sources of corn and soybeans apparently made the difference. On most of the Plains, feeding failed economically. Repeated exhortations of feeding enthusiasts could not change the facts. On the other hand, because of silage and sorghum, occasional dry years in the forties did not force cattlemen to cut herds seriously.[33]

At first, farmers increasingly combined dry farming with animal husbandry. All over the Plains farms went into ranches. In South Dakota, for example, livestock accounted for 75 per cent of the state's farm income by 1940. Impressive changes were noted elsewhere. Then the war placed a premium on wheat, and dry wheat-farming expanded. This forced cattlemen to more intensive husbandry. Intensity by irrigation they found impossible, however, because sprinkler-irrigation had not yet reached the Plains. The Bureau of Reclamation, acting under the Newlands Act of 1902, had produced works which had been socially useful, but for the most part, economically unrewarding. As of 1945, irrigation, combined with animal husbandry, still could not usually yield satisfactory returns.[34]

In spite of expanding wheat acreages during the war, the number of cattle increased, and farmers relied on stock more rather than less. This dual economy resulted entirely from the use of ranch and pasture farming techniques. Part of this revolution centered on breeds and breeding. For the first time in several decades, startling advances took place. The Santa Gertrudis breed, resistant to insect pests, resistant to great heat, and meaty of frame, now began to expand well beyond its point of origin. In 1940, the Bureau of Animal Industry officially recognized it as separate and distinct. The improvement of older breeds continued apace, but the old Herefords still retained their position of dominance. They were ever more intensive producers, however.[35]

War, pasture farming, and grassland farming, all produced clearly marked changes in cattle husbandry, and these, in turn, appeared in the changing sizes of Plains ranches and farms. The total number of farms on the Plains decreased 8.1 per cent between 1940 and 1945, from a total of 1,163,876 farms, to 1,069,036 farms. At the same time, the average size of each farm increased considerably. Percentages varied, but the trend was roughly the same all over. A survey of typical ranches on the northern Plains showed year-by-year variations, but also showed a movement toward greater acreages. In 1940, the average typical ranch ran around 3,559 acres; in 1945, the same average ranch had 3,667 acres. The increases were, on the whole, more pronounced than for any earlier period.[36]

Throughout their long history, cattlemen had never been entirely free of rustlers. In the 1930's, losses to rustlers mounted, and from 1937 on, various associations sought a federal law against cattle stealing. Roosevelt vetoed such a law in the later thirties, but a federal law finally cleared Congress and the Executive in 1941. The results were not impressive. Indeed, with the development of black markets, rustling apparently increased. Wyoming and Montana cattlemen, at least, discovered that state law enforcement was about the only sure way of ending rustling. Federal marshals were no longer effective, if indeed they ever had been. The end of the war, and the end of the black market did as much as anything to reduce the volume of rustling.[37]

Through prosperous years cattlemen bore the inconveniences of price controls and rationing with fairly good humor. Grassland farming marked the era technically, good weather told the story of nature, and socially, the decline in the number of units reflected greater intensity in production and growing urbanization of the population.

CHAPTER XIII

Reconversion with Stability
1946-1949

When peace returned, Americans insisted that price and consumption controls end. Vainly the Truman administration tried to retain some controls in the face of mounting public disapproval. The whole effort failed, largely because people resented meat shortages. Many vociferous citizens who demanded the end of price controls and rationing, supposed, erroneously, that this would give them more beef at once. In spite of all administration efforts, the people soon got a comparatively free market in almost everything. Few foresaw inflation and its problems.

Unquestionably, cattlemen and others intentionally created a meat shortage before controls ended. Producers held their cattle off the market as they waited for the end of controls; when controls did cease, they expected prices to shoot up. They were right, and they did not have to wait long. In October, 1946, all meat controls ended, and prices immediately rose. Stimulated by price incentives, producers sold all they could, but they could not market enough beef to satisfy consumers. The postwar inflation had begun.

Anyone could have predicted both the shortage and the inflation, and yet the sequence of events took packers and producers rather by surprise. Speculators and cattlemen did well, for as one observer noted: "a rising market . . . made it possible for a man to buy a dogie in the morning and sell it in the afternoon for enough profit to pay for his dinner and perhaps a few drinks." [1]

Cattle prices rose from $14.66 a hundred in 1946, to $18.88

a hundred in 1947. In 1948 prices reached $23.29. Never since the beginning of the Republic had prices reached this level. In 1949 cattle fell slightly to $20.74, and cattlemen complained about the terrible decline. Even at this lower price, beef cattle still brought 115 per cent of parity. In four years (1946 to 1949) most cattlemen saved more than they might ordinarily have accumulated in a lifetime.[2]

The boom stemmed from: (1) full urban employment (2) the highest wage levels in history, and (3) an urbanite inclination to eat meat. Americans spent a larger percentage of their incomes for meat than ever before. They ate an average of 71.6 pounds of beef and veal in 1946, but they ate 80.4 pounds in 1947. Then the people had to cut back to 72.6 pounds in 1948, and 72.8 pounds in 1949. As prices rose, people couldn't afford to eat much meat, and some of them resented their enforced abstinence. In 1948 some women consumers struck against high meat prices. The strike, denounced as ineffective, may have spurred the decline of meat prices in 1949. Possibly too, the threat of price controls had something to do with returning sanity.

Costs rose for Plains cattlemen, but prices rose faster and more. A Montana study showed that between 1940 and 1948, gross income for cattlemen rose 144 per cent, while total costs rose only 96 per cent. In short, net cash income for Montanans rose 188 per cent between 1940 and 1948. For all plainsmen, their *net* income for 1948 exceeded their average *gross* income for the years 1935 to 1939.[3]

Most cattlemen apparently paid off their debts while they had the money. Furthermore, many of them took care not to contract serious new debts. For short-term loans, cattlemen sometimes turned to the Farmers Home Administration. This agency, created in 1946, succeeded the Farm Security Administration. In 1949 the Farmers Home Administration took over the work of the Farm Credit Administration. The FHA provided emergency credit, but few cattlemen needed the service until the blizzard of 1948.

Labor costs for cattlemen continually rose during and after

the war because of a shortage of workers. Even so, high wages did not greatly reduce the income of cattlemen. Labor costs hurt only on odd-sized ranch farms where one man could not operate alone, and yet could not really use a full-time hand. On the Plains, as elsewhere, wages lagged behind inflating profits. For the time, cattlemen stopped complaining about high wages.[4]

Because of their unusual prosperity cattlemen needed no subsidies, and so rejected them. Plains cattlemen watched with equanimity as the feeder subsidy disappeared in 1946. The prosperity of the cattlemen probably explained their opposition to the Brannan Plan of 1949. The Brannan Plan would have subsidized producers directly, while the product reached a price level on a free market. Secretary Charles Brannan thus hoped to help both consumers and producers. Prosperous cattlemen could but view the assistance as superfluous at best, and paternalism at worst. In May, 1949, the Texas and Southwestern Cattle Raisers Association announced: "We are opposed to Secretary Brannan's program in so far as it relates to beef cattle and beef. We want no part of it."[5] The Brannan Plan proposed to subsidize food costs for urban workers. Consequently, the plan failed to appeal to farmers or ranchers. By the end of 1949, Brannan's plan had died as a piece of legislation, although his idea lived on, and from time to time excited comment.

Plainsmen reveled in such wealth that they not only opposed price supports, but they even reduced their complaints about packers and merchants. On the northern Plains, cattlemen continued to turn more to local buyers and local auction markets, but they did so without rancor. Central markets consistently lost ground as cattlemen sought, and found, the highest prices possible. Packers and buyers set prices, but no one seemed able to stop them. In various ways packers cheated producers, in spite of federal and state regulations. Cattlemen put up with it all, however, because excellent prices took the sting from shady and illegal practices.

Anyhow, the Packers and Stockyards Division of the Department of Agriculture maintained some honesty in the market. By 1947, over 4,700 dealers and packers had come under control, and had been required, among other things, to submit bonds to assure performance of their financial obligations. Chain-store officials argued that the Packers Consent Decree of 1920 did not apply to them. Their assumed exemption became a matter of controversy as they became more involved in meat buying and packing. No decision was reached on the subject in the 1940's.

On the other hand, in 1946, the Agricultural Marketing Act brought chain stores, and other packers, under new regulations. The act prohibited the sale of bad meat, and also regulated the class, quality, and condition of products shipped between states. The Secretary of Agriculture received broad powers to enforce the law. The law helped protect producers from fraud, and assured consumers a comparatively safe commodity. No audible voices could be heard from the Plains protesting this invasion of free enterprise.[6]

Meanwhile, the population of the submetropolis on the Pacific Coast continued to grow. By 1949, at least 10 per cent of the nation's people lived on the Pacific Coast. The increasing consumers offered an ever more profitable market for Plains cattlemen. Those of the northern Plains felt the pull less than those in other places. Consequently, the effects of the Pacific market on Montana stockmen showed just how important the Coast had come to be for all plainsmen. In 1946, brand inspection records showed that Californians had become the largest group of consumers of Montana cattle. Feeders and packers in Illinois and Iowa came second and third as buyers, but those of Washington came fourth. The Pacific metropolitan market increased fantastically, not only during the war, but thereafter. More and more, Plains cattlemen sold to these consumers. Plains traffic alone could not have called forth the necessary network of railroads and roads, but the through traffic from the East to the Pacific provided the transportation the cattlemen needed.

Throughout the twentieth century, cattlemen had tended

to sell younger cattle. Baby-beef marketing stopped during the war, however, because federal price regulations did not provide for differentials in favor of younger cattle. But around 1946, cattlemen shifted back toward selling young cattle. Cattlemen explained that they did this because young cattle brought higher prices. Furthermore, young cattle gained faster on less feed, and so produced more meat for each unit of fixed cost. On the ranch farms, the quantity of beef for each animal rose throughout the forties. Early selling meant heavy turnover, which then meant more meat from each acre. Cattlemen received higher profits, and consumers got more meat.[7]

They got it only if someone brought it to them. Transport had always been crucial to Plains cattlemen. Their lives depended on it, but railroaders did not depend on the cattlemen. The railroads existed primarily for shipping across the Plains. Although the trains carried a lot of cattle and meat, the railroaders rather consistently considered this traffic as only incidental. Railroad officials seldom followed policies designed for the specific needs of cattlemen. For example, variations in rates per ton mile still tended to penalize plainsmen, sometimes strikingly. High rates on feeds sometimes actually encouraged cattlemen to raise more feed in order to avoid shipping charges. If, as sometimes happened, cattlemen could not economically grow the feed, they suffered some losses through railroad policies. Increasingly, therefore, cattlemen relied on trucks.

Truck-shipping for part of the journey had developed in the 1920's and 1930's, but in the later 1940's cattlemen used trucks more and more for long-distance hauling. Stockmen found that trucks cost less for intermediate shipping. They also found that shippers could reduce costs more by not transferring to rail, but by shipping all the way by truck. Gasoline and tire rationing had prevented a full development of truck transportation during the war. After 1945, and the end of rationing, trucks rapidly moved into first place as cattle carriers. As cattlemen shifted to trucks they incidentally developed some new outlets, particularly local and Pacific Coast markets. Railroaders did little to halt the change.[8]

Meanwhile, the larger cattle outfits slowly but surely shrank, or disappeared altogether. As in years past, the largest concerns showed the least staying power, probably because of their wage competition with other industries. By 1949, large outfits had become so unstable that some people wondered why any remained at all. For the most part, they survived through the will power of their owners, and little else, other than oil royalties. As Marion Clawson suggested, the feudal labor system may well have explained why owners of big spreads even kept on trying. Clawson declared:

Ownership and management of this type of enterprise appeal to certain types of men, and it seems probable that many large-scale ranchers have been willing to follow this type of life for much lower financial rewards than they might have obtained elsewhere. The inheritance and family nature of some of the better known large-scale ranches are other resemblance to the feudal prototypes.[9]

When cattle and then land prices shot up, many big operators hurried to get out on top. Most ranch barons had always been land speculators on the side anyway. The big boys went for their killing when they could, and in the forties they could. The Swan Land and Cattle Company of Wyoming disposed of its holdings, and so did the Bell Ranch of New Mexico. The Matador Land and Cattle Company and the King Ranch of Texas both chopped off large parcels of land and sold them. So did several others. Land prices continued to rise. In time, ranch farmers commonly had from $150 to $500 invested in land for each head of cattle they carried. An investment of this size probably represented at least a 50 per cent inflation in the true grazing value of the land. Prosperity on the Plains thus built up trouble, and also caused an increase in the number of smaller holdings. On the other hand, family-sized units decreased in acreage slightly.

On the whole, changes in the size and number of ranches probably reflected an effort on the part of cattlemen to find the optimum holding for family operation. Basically, the problem came down to finding the size of ranch which suited a certain size herd in a given locality. Probably a 200-head herd suited those who had to winter-feed, and about a 400-head herd those who did not usually winter-feed. Ranch farms of the proper size called for little or no extra labor force, and yielded high returns to the owner.[10]

On most of the Plains, cattlemen followed a general ranch farming pattern. They raised all ages of cattle. Here and there, however, cattlemen engaged in specialized enterprises. On the steer ranch, for example, the cattlemen bought steers at the beginning of the grazing season and sold them at the end. In the Flint Hills of east central Kansas and Oklahoma and the bluestem pastures, cattlemen generally followed this system. Cattlemen in these areas sometimes leased part of their range, but in any case, they seldom fed much. Steer cattlemen usually operated under unfavorable price conditions and they profited only in occasional windfall years.

In the dry Southwest, most cattlemen concentrated on cow and calf husbandry. In the South, animals bred well, but fattened slowly and inadequately. Southern cow and calf ranchers sold calves primarily. They sent the animals north to fatten, as in the days of the long drive. The cow and calf raisers seldom followed any systematic breeding program. Consequently, calving mostly occurred in the late winter and early spring, and the marketing was seasonal with its natural price fluctuations. Neither steer, nor cow-calf outfits typified the Plains cattle industry.[11]

Large outfits did not dominate the Plains cattle industry either. The number of cattle on the Plains increased largely because of the further development of ranch and pasture farming. Some areas showed a high density of comparatively small, family-sized ranch farms. Parts of Texas, Montana, Wyoming, South Dakota, Nebraska, and New Mexico had a very high density of small outfits. The few large ranches survived mostly because of the unusual sacrifices of their owners. Lewis Corey pointed out in 1950:

The King Ranch, however, seems to be kept going more by the will of its master than by economic necessity, for the production of beef is becoming more closely linked with general farming and with dairying, where, by and large, closer observation and more individual attention can be given to the job.[12]

As the demand for meat rose after 1945, the number of cattle declined on the Plains. They did not, however, decline as much as certain spokesmen for the industry liked to believe. Between 1946 and 1949, the greatest yearly differential came to rather less than one million head. In 1945 the Plains states accounted for 24,505,000 head of beef cattle, and by 1949 they carried 24,082,000. A study for the northern Plains showed that except for 1948, the number of cattle on ranches and farms either increased, or decreased but slightly. Cattlemen supplied consumers by being more efficient and by marketing cattle at an earlier age. Stockmen did not greatly cut into their breeding herds.

The large numbers of cattle on the Plains resulted somewhat from the excellent weather which permitted cattlemen to stock heavily. Only in 1948 did drouth threaten. Some dry spots in the Southwest only emphasized the abundance of moisture elsewhere. Range grasses, crops, and cattle all flourished on the Plains. Kansas pastures did a brisk business, and almost every place, cattle appeared sleek and fat. Even in the Southwest in 1948, cattle apparently prospered in spite of the drouth.[13]

Then, in 1948 and 1949, the plainsmen suffered the worst blizzard since the disaster of 1886 and 1887. In the first blast, "cattle drifted as far as 40 miles from their home range, and scattered badly, making it difficult to locate and feed them after the storm subsided." [14] Some went for days without feed, and death took a dreadful toll. Congress appropriated $200,000 for immediate relief. By March, 1949, the Department of Agriculture estimated losses at more than 81,000 head of cattle. But no one had had time to count all the carcasses. Many more cattle would have died if the Forest Service and the Bureau of Land Management had not given prompt aid. Road-clearing equipment, provided by these departments, greatly reduced losses by allowing feed to be delivered to isolated places. By April, dead animals totaled over 200,000 head. Calves born during the blizzard accounted for the greatest group of losses.

An extension service agent reported: "The causes of cattle losses were reported as starvation, freezing, and pile-ups both from drifting and in sheds—in the order named." Truck trains moved behind bulldozers and brought in feed and other supplies. Often a return path had to be cleared, so persistently did the snow fall and blow. The melting snow subsequently helped both range and crops, and in 1949 most plainsmen reported cattle in better condition than in 1948.[15]

Wet weather and good prices seemed to encourage cattlemen to relax their conservation work. They did a little, but not much. They planted legumes to rebuild the soil, and they did some contour ridging, but that was about all. Sportsmen fussed around about their own peculiar sort of conservation, but cattlemen resolutely held to their view that cattle properly belonged on the land; wildlife could fit in where it found room. Cattlemen generally felt that federal conservation efforts should be relaxed rather than increased. For most of them, the thirties had receded into dim memory.[16]

The memory of the thirties had faded some, but cattlemen remembered enough to provide emergency supplies of feed. In the forties, cattlemen kept more stock than usual on the range, but they kept them fairly well fed, and in pretty good shape. Generally, stockmen raised as little feed as possible because of the expense, but they almost always raised enough to hold cattle off the range until rather late in the season.

Usually scientists recommended that cattlemen run only

65 per cent of the cattle which a ranch farm could support in an average year. Almost all cattlemen carried far more stock than this suggested maximum. Indeed, the meat consumer would have been short of beef if cattlemen had carried conservatively. The blizzard of 1949 showed, however, that a sizable number of cattlemen did not have adequate feed reserves. Just the same, the cattlemen who survived the blizzard not only had feed, but they also kept routes open to their cattle. Closed routes, rather than feed shortages, caused much, and perhaps most, of the misery and loss.

As it happened, cattlemen not only raised feed, but they even worried about its vitamin content. In one more way science had come to the Plains. Feed reserves sometimes accumulated into feed surpluses. When this happened, some plainsmen tried to feed to a finish, generally with good results. But only when they used surplus feeds. When plainsmen tried to fatten cattle by growing feed to do it, they simply did not make out, except for very limited local markets. The Plains had not yet become the Corn Belt.[17]

Still, by 1946 most Plains stockmen produced about as much feed as they possibly could, given their climate and skills. Improved plants, and better irrigation offered the most obvious routes to greater production. Scientists had by no means reached the ultimate in plant breeding, nor had cattlemen adopted every new variety. Stockmen progressed, however, as the expanded use of crested wheatgrass on the northern Plains illustrated. Everywhere cattlemen used more legumes and legume silage. They increasingly seeded more black grama grass in pastures, as they strove to restore the grasslands. Black grama yielded well for southern plainsmen who could not use the then current varieties of crested wheatgrass.[18]

In the heroic age of the industry (1850–1900) the grass of the northern Plains had produced fatter cattle than had the grass of the southern Plains. This remained true in the twentieth century. Although the Plains altogether accounted for only a little more than a third of the nation's range land, they carried half, and possibly two-thirds of all range live-stock. In spite of expanded crop acreages, pasture grass still provided most of the feed for these cattle. A 1948 study in Montana showed Plains ranchers used 96 per cent of their land for grazing. This may have been exceptional. Anyway, that 96 per cent of the land most certainly did not provide that percentage of the total fodder. Still, grass took little care, and it had to be used up because most of it deteriorated quickly. Ranchers either grazed, or else lost the grass.[19]

Meanwhile, danger threatened from Mexico. In 1945, Mexican officials allowed some importers to introduce over one hundred Brahma bulls from Brazil. (This violated a treaty of March 28, 1928, between the United States and Mexico.) Nothing much happened, and so the Mexicans imported more cattle from Brazil. By the spring of 1947, foot-and-mouth disease had spread to ten Mexican states. The United States closed the border to cattle from diseased areas, and officers of the Department of Agriculture went to Mexico to assist in eradication. The United States also helped replace slaughtered cattle with mules. Late in 1947 slaughter gave way to quarantine and vaccination.[20]

Slaughter programs brought terrible economic distress to Mexican farmers, but on the other hand, vaccination took time. Not until 1955 did the threat end in Mexico. As the battle went on in Mexico, the United States took further steps toward control of the disease. In 1948 Congress established a research laboratory for foot-and-mouth, and for other highly contagious animal diseases. The Department of Agriculture placed the facility on a coastal island.[21]

Ox warbles, or grubs, had long injured cattle, and cattlemen had for centuries lost money because of the insects. They continued to lose money, for no effective treatment had been discovered. In 1945, for example, approximately one-third of all cattle slaughtered had been infected by grubs. Grubs perforated the skins of infected animals, the hides of which consequently sold at discount when they could be sold at all. Under the grub holes a mass of yellowish, gelatinous, inedible matter would be found. This sickening mess had to be trimmed off. Economically, grub-infected cattle produced less, and had inferior meat. This in turn reduced the returns of their owners. The losses of 1945 alone amounted to about 12 million pounds of meat and tallow. Furthermore, the heel fly (the adult ox warble) so irritated cattle that they frequently lost weight during the fly season. No one knew the exact losses from cattle discontent, but all authorities believed them to be considerable. The life cycle of grub and fly could be broken if the flies could be killed before they laid eggs. Scientists tried DDT spraying experiments in 1945, but spraying failed to eradicate the grubs. Apparently the attack had to be made directly on the parasites. Unfortunately, by the time the grubs could be removed from the hide, they had already made their holes by boring from the inside out.

As late as 1947, therefore, DDT attacks on the flies seemed to be the only feasible control measure. Interested cattlemen supplied the insecticides, and the federal government loaned the spraying trucks. The cooperators then sprayed whole neighborhoods, with uneven results. Even if the attack did not eradicate the grubs, it cut down on the flies and gave the cattle some relief. In 1946, for example, a Kansas entomologist found that treated cattle gained one-half pound a day more than untreated cattle. By 1947, Kansans had entered their third year of fly control, and had managed to get gains of around sixty additional pounds for sprayed cattle. Soon commercial sprayers entered the business. In places, some cattlemen bought spraying equipment out of their very considerable profits. By 1949 the four-year DDT control program had gradually, but noticeably, cut into the fly and grub population. Still, the insects had not been eradicated.[22]

Other afflictions also bedeviled the cattlemen. From 1941 on, cattle had been increasingly injured with the frequently fatal X-disease. In 1948 cattlemen of fifteen states reported nine hundred and ninety-one cases. As of 1949, no one knew the cause or cure for the disease. Then, in 1949 vesicular stomatitis swept across the United States. The sudden eruption caused huge losses which no one knew how to stop. Fortunately, the plague subsided after a while. About the only significant advance by veterinary scientists came with the greater use of phenothiazine against internal worms. This turned out to be a real step forward, but full effects made their impress in the next decade.[23]

Cattlemen also contended with crop pests as well as animal pests. Grasshoppers again proved troublesome throughout the later forties. Northern and southern plainsmen suffered some in 1948. In 1949 experts correctly predicted one of the worst infestations in history. Crop-dusting planes went aloft to control the insects, but the chief weapon, DDT, did not work very well. Northern cattlemen often shipped stock out because grasshoppers had destroyed both grass and crops. Some ranchers spread poison bait, but bait only killed the first waves of the ravaging hordes. In 1947 entomologists began using chlordane compounds as insecticides for grasshoppers. Chlordane failed to live up to its advance billing. In 1949, plainsmen brought grasshopper ravages under uncertain control only by baiting. Here and there insect devastation reached alarming proportions. Nowhere did plainsmen profit by the outbreak, although they mostly managed to profit in spite of it. Grasshopper control still remained only a hope for the future.[24]

Cattlemen fared better in their battle against predators. Buzzards, however, had become increasingly destructive. The scavenger birds apparently became predators because animals, such as wolves, had been greatly reduced in numbers. The buzzards had to make their own carion. Mainly, they killed newborn calves. The birds were even protected by law in some places. By the 1940's buzzards had become a serious menace. A few cattlemen tried to kill them. Following their ancient traditions, however, most cattlemen put off action until the problem should become more serious.[25]

During the drouths of the thirties, weeds and mesquite had proliferated and luxuriated, and by the forties had become so common and persistent that most cattlemen accepted them as a normal burden of life. Suddenly, several herbicides hit the market. In 1946 scientists began testing 2, 4-D as a weed and sagebrush killer. By 1948 some few plainsmen had undertaken intensive weed eradication programs. Here and there they achieved 80 per cent effectiveness. In 1948 scientists successfully employed TCA to kill pricklypear cactus. TCA also killed grass, but if used carefully, in spot treatment, it generally only inhibited grasses for a few weeks. Unfortunately, neither 2, 4-D nor TCA cleaned out mesquite. As late as 1949, ranchers had to eradicate mechanically.[26]

In the forties some hostile cattlemen demanded the end of federal land ownership in the West. After 1946 resolutions from cattlemen's associations proliferated. Usually these resolves demanded that the Forest Service keep range allotments high, and that the Division of Land Management and the Forest Service turn their land over to private owners by "a method that would specifically safeguard the economy of the present users." A congressional investigating committee offered every opportunity for certain cattlemen to complain about the Bureau of Land Management and the Forest Service. The Congress apparently didn't take the committee too seriously. The land remained in federal control.

Meanwhile, the Foresters cut down on the number of cattle which could be grazed on the Forests. In 1948, big operators (and their helpers) claimed they found a lot of wasted forage. The waste, they said, ranged from 70 per cent to 90 per cent of the several grasses. The secretary of the National Wool Growers Association even claimed that the Foresters' policy reduced the amount of meat, and increased its cost to the consumers. Forest users protested allotment decreases on into 1949, but they had been protesting so long about so much, that hardly anyone paid any attention.

More to the point, users observed that for years the Forest Service had not been able to improve its range because of the stinginess of Congress. For twenty-three years the service had not received any appropriations for range improvements. The lack of money may have helped force the service to reduce allotments. In 1947 Congress gave the service some $500,000 for reseeding, although the Foresters needed much more. Well, anyhow, Congress had done something.[27]

On the whole, the Forest Service had less trouble with Congress than did the Bureau of Land Management. The fees set by the Bureau had never covered costs. In 1946 congressional committees insisted the Bureau charge higher fees. Cattlemen successfully blocked the raise, and so Congress reduced the services provided by the Bureau in 1946. In 1947 cattlemen saw the light. They let fees be raised to eight cents per animal unit. The fees still did not cover expenses, but all the people bore the remaining costs because everyone had a general interest in range preservation. Out of the increase, two cents went for range improvement, and of the remaining six cents, three went to the counties containing the land. As a result of the changes, Congress agreed to appropriate more money for the Bureau in 1947 and 1948. Actually, most plainsmen had little direct interest in the dispute since the Plains contained only about 10 per cent federal land, not counting Indian reservations.[28]

Overall, two other agencies did more for the protection of the range: (1) the Soil Conservation Districts, and (2) the Cooperative Grazing Districts. The Soil Conservation Districts, authorized by an act of 1935, could be set up under state charter. Cattlemen could thus band together and prevent the use of land by tramp herdsmen, and by speculative grain growers. Although they began in the thirties, conservation districts became more prominent during the forties. The grazing districts had begun as early as the twenties, and they also solved some problems of land tenure. Both kinds of districts could lease federal land and avoid some of the problems of federal ownership. Cattlemen found, however, that allotting land to their members presented them with as many difficulties as they had when federal officers allotted the land. Generally, Cooperative Grazing Districts flourished only where patterns of land ownership made any other approach more difficult.[29]

For the most part, however, cattlemen owned their land. Often cattlemen secured land by purchase from unsuccessful dry-land homesteaders. Some stockmen bought directly from the farmers, and some bought from counties which had taken the land for unpaid taxes. These transfer processes, common enough throughout the twentieth century, accelerated greatly between 1940 and 1948. In those years, cattlemen had money, and homesteaders saw their long-awaited chance to get out. Consequently, the leasing of state land fell off during the later forties, while private ownership increased. By 1949, individuals owned almost all of the land of the Plains.[30]

Ranch farmers also intensified their production, although they introduced few new methods of cattle husbandry. Cattlemen in some areas used more crops harvested from irrigated farms. Some cattlemen purchased feeds such as cottonseed cake, sugar beets, alfalfa, and corn grown by farmers. In general, ranch and pasture farmers became impressively common, almost to the exclusion of other kinds of animal raisers. As a result, the blizzard of 1948 and 1949 hurt only a few plainsmen.

The record showed clearly that the ranch farmers survived winters with only a little inconvenience. In contrast, those who depended mostly on range either failed, or lost heavily. Furthermore, converted dry farmers, if otherwise inexperienced, suffered heavily even though they relied on stock. Southerners who had come north also lost because they had no experience with northern winters. Ranch farming with feed cropping expanded rapidly. As one result of this, the amount of meat per animal unit rose through the forties.

So far as can be determined, cattlemen merged crop production with more careful pasture-range management. They developed water resources, and deferred grazing. Range reseeding, however, proved too expensive for most grazing land. By the late forties, much of the land which could be economically reseeded had been. Even some that couldn't be reseeded had been. In range management, plainsmen progressed mostly just by increasing their use of good practices. The new herbicides did, however, open new technical possibilities for the future.[31]

Cattlemen also improved their stock-breeding practices some. Generally, cattlemen infrequently segregated cows and bulls, and consequently they seldom achieved a continuing calf-crop. Instead, stockmen usually ran all animals together. As a result, they had heavy breeding at some seasons, and little at others. Usually, they had their greatest calf-crops in the winter.

Not all of their breeding practices were backward. All over the Plains, for example, cattlemen kept high-quality bulls. As in the past, they favored Herefords. They preferred Herefords, in part, because, in the haphazard breeding system they employed, Herefords bred more readily and produced better calf-crops. More and more cattlemen used private pastures, and so segregated the cattle of the several owners. This alone led to an increase in the calf-crop. In 1949 the average calf-crop ran around 84 per cent of the breeding cows, compared to 74 per cent in 1939.[32]

With the effective death of the New Deal, cattleman no longer feared competition from good neighbors. In May, 1947, the *American Cattle Producer* gleefully announced:

The Argentine sanitary treaty is now dead. It was withdrawn from a congressional committee a few days ago. Proposed in May, 1935, and set for a hearing which never came to pass, it has been resting in committee all this time.[33]

Almost alone, cattlemen had saved the nation from destruction, and had rescued the Republic from its gravest peril. No Argentine beef had legally entered the country.

The whole story, briefly told, came to this: prosperity deadened all pain, and few cattlemen felt any pain anyhow. Trends begun before the war continued after. Trucks entered cattle transport to stay, and biochemistry made inroads on disease, insects, and weeds. Readjustment to peace left cattlemen with little energy for technical innovations. In the immediate postwar period they set the stage for the future as they recovered ground they had lost during the depression and during the war.

CHAPTER XIV

The Korean War and After
1950-1955

Americans fought in Korea from June, 1950, until June, 1953. The Korean War accelerated inflation, and the cost of living rose consistently then and thereafter. It would have risen more if food prices had not fallen between 1953 and 1955. Before the decline, food prices had advanced, but not as much as the prices of other commodities. On an average, farmers got 101 per cent of parity in 1950, but only 84 per cent in 1955. The real wages of urbanites, however, rose enough to offset the inflation. Meanwhile, urban population rose from 96,468,000 in 1950, to an estimated 103,631,000 in 1956. More people, with more disposable income, ate more beef.[1]

Consumption of beef rose steadily from 1951 to 1955. Even in 1950, Americans ate 6 per cent more protein, on an average, than they had between 1935 and 1939. Americans continued to prefer light red meat from young animals. The trend actually helped most cattlemen because they found it cheaper and easier to produce young animals of around nine hundred pounds. Pasture and feeds produced twice as much gain for young animals as for old ones.[2]

In 1950 Americans ate an average of 71.4 pounds of beef and veal, but inflation apparently cut their buying power, and in 1951 they ate only 62.7 pounds. Thereafter, people ate more and more beef and veal. In 1953 average consumption reached a new high of 87.1 pounds, and in 1955 each American ate an average of 91.4 pounds of beef. This gastronomical feat came close to the fantastic.

Cattlemen received lower prices than they wanted. In 1950 cattle prices averaged $24.06 a hundred, then moved up in 1951 to an all time high of $29.69, or 146 per cent of parity. Cattlemen had never seen prices like these before, and were unlikely to see them again. After 1951 prices fell, although the 1952 price of $25.71 a hundred came in second in all American history. In 1953, the first year of the Eisenhower administration, prices fell sharply to an average of $17.66. In 1955 prices declined to $16.92. Cattlemen thus experienced the same falling prices which had earlier hit other food producers.[3]

When the Korean War began in June, 1950, prices shot up. Congress acted promptly to restrain inflation by allowing the Office of Price Stabilization to place ceilings on meat, and other commodities. Congress, however, ordered that producers be allowed a "reasonable margin of profit." By February, 1951, prices for hides had been rolled back 15 per cent, but meat prices had not been rolled back. The American National Livestock Association opposed any efforts to roll prices back. Indeed, they objected to any price controls. Between congressional obstruction and public disinterest, the OPS found regulation difficult, but not impossible. In May, 1951, after prices had reached astronomical heights, the OPS set beef prices 9 per cent below the then current level. The office also established retail and restaurant price ceilings. Once again the American National objected in the name of all cattlemen. Cattlemen probably agreed with the American National because the order would have wiped out $700 million in inventory values of cattle.[4]

The control order came out on April 28, 1951. Almost immediately cattle prices declined. In June Congress stopped rollbacks in beef prices. No matter, the OPS had attained its objective and prices began to decline to reasonable levels. After 1951 the administration managed to keep prices in line by periodically threatening stronger price controls. Although this did not work as well as controls, it did keep the market steady and prices low. Retail prices went low enough in 1952 to end the threat of meat price-inflation. Congress took no chances, however, and controls continued. In the middle of 1953 price control legislation expired, but by then the war had nearly ended, and the gravest inflation threat had disappeared.[5]

For some time cattle marketing had been changing as producers shifted to shipping by truck. In the fifties, however, pickup trucks began to influence the industry in many ways. With pickups cattlemen more readily moved cattle around the ranch, and they also transported cattle more easily to major shipping points. Many cattlemen shipped to auction markets. In 1952 economists estimated the number of auction markets in the United States at no less than two thousand two hundred. Of these, at least five hundred were big enough to come under the control of the Packers and Stockyards Act. Although some auction markets failed, the others grew bigger. Trucks, including pickups, eliminated the need for many auction markets. Cattle were often shipped from one part of the Plains to another before ending up at feedlots in the Corn Belt. These movements took advantage of feed surpluses where they appeared, and were certainly facilitated by truck transport.[6]

Meanwhile, all costs rose. Of these costs, taxes had become increasingly significant over the years. In the fifties, however, some cattlemen received a little tax relief. In January, 1951, the U.S. Court of Appeals ruled that cattlemen could count receipts for culled cattle as capital gains rather than as income. The Treasury Department reluctantly accepted the decision, and later agreed to allow capital gains for the sale of draft, breeding, or dairy cattle, provided the cattle had been held for twelve months. Congress inserted this last decision into the revenue law of November, 1951. Not until 1954, however, did the courts clearly rule that the law allowed capital gains on *any* breeding stock. Government assistance, it turned out, could take many forms beside direct subsidy.[7]

Tax reductions were one thing, but direct subsidies were

another. The more prosperous cattlemen did not need subsidies, and they objected to others getting them. They continued to oppose the Brannan Plan. Members of the Kansas
Livestock Association, for example, resolved that all "patriotic Americans" should denounce "socialism," and should
"work energetically and courageously for the re-establish-
ment and maintenance of free competitive enterprise and
the restoration of the Republic." Two years later, during
the drouth, they demanded government help.

As early as 1953 a few cattlemen had toyed with the idea
of seeking government relief. Most of them, however, seemed
not to like the idea of asking for help. In March, 1953, the
Department of Agriculture began buying beef in order to
support prices. In July the department announced it would
increase its purchases to about 200 million pounds of canned
beef and gravy, mostly for school lunch programs. As usual,
the cattlemen accepted the help but stoutly opposed any
production controls. In Colorado a convention vote ran five
to one against production controls, but the convention did
not vote against government purchases. The government
continued buying on through December of 1953, and thus
held up a sagging market. In November, it appeared that no
purchases had in fact been made before October, even
though they had been authorized for July.[8] Said the editor
of the *Kansas Stockman:* "It is a little hard for us to under-
stand how cows bought during October, November, and
December will benefit the poor devil who was forced to sell
last July and August." [9]

The poor devils were poor in part because localized but
severe drouths forced them to dump stock on the market.
Stockmen began cutting herds in the Southwest as early as
1952. By July, 1953, Texas, Oklahoma, and Colorado had
been declared disaster areas by Secretary Ezra T. Benson,
and $8 million had been set aside for drouth relief. By Sep-
tember only $4,777,000 had been used, although requests for
more had come in. In 1954 the disaster area was increased.
In August, 1954, the Farmers Home Administration took

over most of the drouth-relief program which by that time had reached huge proportions.[10]

At the start of the decade the weather was good. In 1950, reports indicated abundant rains, fine grass, and fat cattle. Kansas and Nebraska seemed especially well off. Early in 1951 Texan cattlemen felt the first shock of drouth which then hit the northern Plains briefly in the fall, but it did not cause acute distress.[11] The drouth became worse in the Southwest. Early in 1952 grass in the Flint Hills leased at high prices. Moisture shortages appeared over the Plains, but many cattlemen had some feed reserves and so managed to come through without loss. But they used up their hay and silage, and so ran short when the real drouth hit in 1953. Many southerners moved cattle north where the drouth had not been severe. The southern plainsmen suffered greatly, even though the government offered a little help. Montana and the Dakotas reported good rainfall and adequate feed.[12]

In 1954 everything got worse on the scorched southern Plains. The hay crop fell well below needs, and in some spots cattlemen hauled water on a scale to equal their efforts of the thirties. Dust storms arose in Kansas and other places; drouth struck all over the Plains. About two-thirds of all cattle were affected by the drouth of that year. Grasshoppers returned as they invariably did during dry spells, but in 1954 cattlemen kept the pests fairly well under control. Many plainsmen left a strip of alfalfa on the edge of their fields and sprayed it with Chlordane, Toxaphene, and Aldrin. The treatment seemed to do the job.

The drouth continued into 1955. By April, more than 13 million acres had been damaged by dust storms. Another 19 million dry and naked acres were set to blow away. The greatest dust damage occurred on the Plains of Colorado, Kansas, Oklahoma, Texas, and New Mexico. Wyoming and Nebraska suffered some. Later in the year rain fell in many of these places, but not on the southernmost Plains. Farther north crops came along fine, although many cattlemen still had to haul water. By August, farmers and stockmen began to harvest bumper feed crops, and the future looked bright. On the other hand, a rash of advertisements for the sale of ranch properties suggested that some cattlemen had been done in.[13]

Drouth inspired cattlemen on the southern Plains to take more interest in fertilizing and in using legumes. Long experience had shown that highly fertile soil withstood drouth better than exhausted soil. As more cattlemen planted legumes and applied fertilizer, the water-holding capacity of the soil increased, sometimes spectacularly. Cattlemen also discovered that fertilizers contributed to good animal nutrition. Montana scientists showed that cattle which grazed on worn soil suffered from various nutritional deficiencies, made lower gains, and more often died too soon. Oklahoma scientists found that fertilized grasslands could boost gains 58 per cent. Even as late as 1955, however, few farmers fertilized their pastures; more fertilizing was done with crops. Still, some did something to their grass, and more were to do so.[14]

Drouth also brought irrigation to the attention of more cattlemen. Cattlemen who had before paid little attention to irrigation began to consider it carefully in the fifties. How much more they irrigated is uncertain, but they did increase their irrigation of crop and pasture lands. In 1952 the Extension Service of Montana conducted a survey to find what farmers and ranchers considered their most pressing problems. The responses indicated the ways society and ranching were changing. Ranchers indicated primary concern in about the following order: (1) irrigated pastures (2) brucellosis control, and (3) livestock on irrigated farms. Interestingly, the Extension Service had not given any priority to the irrigation items.[15] Irrigation allowed greater intensification, and produced a changing pattern of social life, with both more stability and more flexibility.

Technology influenced the development of irrigation. Pipe and sprinklers were cheap and this greatly facilitated the growth of irrigation and the stability and prosperity of the cattle industry. The advantages of irrigation were particularly apparent during times of drouth, of course. Irrigators also received a bonus return in grass seeds, particularly native grasses, which could be grown commercially as a side line. Not that everything moved smoothly. Often irrigation farmers feared that range conservation would reduce the water supply because the grasses would use up the water. This fear was not only unfounded, but as experience showed, was quite the reverse of the truth. But it took time to get all cattlemen and irrigators to realize that a flourishing grass-cover caused ground water and stream water to increase. Then too, irrigation encouraged cattle congestion, and as a result, the problems of parasites and diseases became greater. New advances brought new problems.[16]

Drouth brought dust storms; soil erosion received the attention which the experience of the thirties had shown useful. Soil Conservation Districts multiplied, cattlemen allowed sorghum and other stubble to stand, and barren lands were reseeded to grasses. Pitting, or digging small holes at regular intervals to catch water marked one of the more important technological innovations of the fifties. This newer version of the older contour furrowing could be more widely used on grasslands, and could be done with a disk plow with the disks set off center. The Soil Conservation Service also urged greater use of new varieties of crested wheatgrass which could be grown on the southern Plains. Finally, plainsmen let grass take over some of the land which had been plowed during the wheat craze of the Second World War. Even so, on the southern Plains scientists estimated that at least six million acres, which should have been in grass, continued in cultivation.[17]

The herdsmen of old had turned grass into beef, and so did the new grassland farmers and ranchers. The similarities ended there. Grassland farming only remotely resembled the old open range. All over the Plains, scientists worked to find newer varieties of grass, and even stockmen bred and crossbred grasses to find useful hybrids. Crested wheatgrass, because of its limited range, was replaced to some extent by a new variety called Siberian wheatgrass. In some places in the South, Siberian wheatgrass produced remarkable yields of hay, silage, and forage. Grassland advances could not be limited to plainsmen, however, and some experts wondered what would happen when all American farmers turned to grassland agriculture. During the fifties farmers everywhere did become aware of the advantages of grassland farming.[18]

On the southern Plains, experimenters successfully introduced crested wheatgrass. Wheatgrass resisted drouth, remained dormant during periods of water shortage, and yielded well in most years once it had grown to a stand. In common with other xerophytes it did not yield well in time of great moisture, but excessive rainfall was hardly a problem on the southern Plains. Northern cattlemen benefited from scientific advance in 1954 when the Department of Agriculture and the North Dakota Experiment Station released a superior variety of wheatgrass named Nordan. Nordan, a pure strain, not a hybrid, grew especially well in the first year even during the severe northern winters.[19]

Scientific work with sorghum also continued. By 1955 various scientists had crossed sorghum with Johnson grass, thus combining the perennial growth of Johnson grass with the high feed-values of sorghum. Their achievement promised to be one of the more significant advances of the fifties. Sorghum had great feed-value, but it also proved especially useful in covering and holding naked land so that other grasses could grow. Interest in sorghum grew as drouth moved onto the Plains. As in earlier years, cattlemen tried to regrass land which had been senselessly plowed. Charles Petit of the Flat Top Ranch successfully regrassed some two thousand four hundred acres of abandoned cropland. Many others did much the same on the southern Plains.[20]

Grassland farmers on the Plains used silage in their operations. Cattlemen who had been caught short of feed in the thirties particularly took precautions in the fifties. Those who had reserves survived nicely. They sometimes had to hold large silage reserves, but they found that even nine-year-old silage could be fed with advantage. Silos changed little. On the northern Plains, for example, concrete-block and trench silos continued to be more popular than towers. Silage helped cattlemen reduce hay losses. Silage did not always produce the greatest gains, especially on the central Plains. The certainty of the feed supply, however, more than compensated for some deficiency in quality. Stockmen still favored alfalfa for ensilage. In 1953 scientists improved grass-silage technology by introducing a powdered preservative called sodium metabisulfate. The preservative kept carotene content high, and also made the silage more palatable for cattle. It cost less and was easier to handle than sulfur dioxide which had been used before.[21]

Animal husbandry had changed greatly across the half century. As the Montana Extension Service reported: "Little strictly range work is done any more by the livestock specialists but pasture work is increasing rapidly." Supplemental feeding increased along with grassland farming. Many cattlemen relied on nearby farmers to produce part of the cattle feed, not only for emergencies, but for all the year. As before, some cattlemen tried to finish as well as raise cattle, but plainsmen seldom found this profitable. They did not find it very profitable to bypass the corn-feeding lots either. In the fifties about 85 per cent of all steers slaughtered had been fattened, and the remainder almost never graded choice or prime.[22]

Taking the Plains as a whole, cattle raisers carried on a vast variety of enterprises. Often ranchers combined cattle raising and sheep raising. Mixed farming and ranching, however, predominated. Many cattlemen kept part of their calf-crop about nineteen months, and fed them corn and silage raised on the ranch. This type of mixed enterprise became increasingly frequent all over the Plains. Of course, large spreads still existed everywhere, but as Mont Saunderson observed: "These ranches do not, as a rule, excel in their production per head or in any other unit measure of production efficiency." They usually produced steers for quick marketing. Even these outfits combined some dry-land farming with cattle husbandry.[23]

Consumer demand for younger cattle created a certain amount of hazard which became greater during drouth. Those who marketed baby beef could reduce their herds only by cutting their foundation herd. Many cattlemen concentrated on this uncertain type of enterprise. Their specialty carried a definite inflexibility with it, but the people wanted young beef, and that was that. Some of these ranchers obtained some flexibility by buying feeders when they had enough fodder on hand. Otherwise they carried only as many cattle as they could accommodate during the worst years. Their adjustment did not always prove satisfactory. In years of good weather they found feeder cattle high-priced, and so they often could not stock as many steers as they wanted.

Two unusual grazing areas existed on the Plains; the Flint Hills of Kansas, and the Sand Hills of Nebraska. Neither was large, although the Sand Hills came to fifteen million acres. Cattlemen in these places leased out grazing land. Plainsmen found the regions particularly useful in time of drouth. Resident cattlemen avoided the problems of cow-calf production, and generally managed to prosper even in time of drouth, or more correctly, especially during drouth.[24]

Most ranch and pasture farmers did not specialize so much, however. In spite of variations in their methods, they generally followed certain common procedures on most of the Plains. Everywhere, ranchers fed to supplement the range. On the southern Plains of Texas and New Mexico, however, they often fed cottonseed concentrates. Northerners depended mostly on grain, hay, and dry-land corn. Northerners also tended to shift a bit to breeding herds, although southerners still led in this business. In the North the land-holdings of some cattlemen reflected their origin as dry farmers. Small holdings of two to four sections with fifty to one hundred and fifty head were scattered about.

For the most part these family-sized ranches made fairly self-contained units. Throughout the Plains, ranch farmers predominated. In the fifties, however, they concentrated on good use of pasture grassland. All observers agreed that the old-time cattlemen and cowboys simply no longer existed. (Indeed, they had disappeared a generation before, but apparently the plainsmen had not noticed this.) [25]

Grassland contouring and reseeding were widely used by cattlemen, but Carl Kraenzel observed in *The Great Plains in Transition* that: "these are individual practices not yet supported by institutionalized efforts." [26] Or, put another way, the government had not yet fully undertaken the work.

Nonfarm technology also altered the cattle industry. Automotive machinery produced the greatest changes, but implements of the Second World War also became ever more significant during the fifties. Bulldozers did heavy jobs all over, and proved especially effective for grubbing mesquite and digging water holes. Jeeps entered civilian life without trouble. "The jeep, which climbs mountains like a goat and sneers at mud and snow, has gone a step farther toward changing the methods and the people. Along the highway outside Sulphur, Oklahoma, I watched a woman and a three-year-old child riding a jeep over cutbanks and ditches as they hazed a bunch of calves back into the barnyard. The little dogies were getting along faster than a horse could have moved them." [27] Even when horses had to be used they were carried to the field by a horse trailer. Sonnichsen observed in 1950:

A couple of men can do today what a whole crew did in Grandfather's heyday—and do it without perspiration. Hay loaders and stackers lighten the burdens of haying. Hot meals go out twenty miles to roundup crews who used to gather round the chuck wagon. There are stock tanks with kerosene burners to keep them from freezing and floats to keep them from running over. Two tractors dragging a cable can clear more brush off a pasture in a day than fifty axemen could in a month.[28]

As cattlemen used more feed, more grass, and more machinery, their land-holdings increased in size. On the northern Plains the average-sized ranch increased from 3,790
acres in 1950, to 3,990 acres in 1952. Between 1940 and 1950,
the acres in farms and ranches on the Plains increased
markedly. Colorado, Wyoming, Montana, and New Mexico
all showed acreage increases of over 20 per cent. Meanwhile, the number of farms and ranches steadily decreased
everywhere. The number of units decreased 30.8 per cent
in New Mexico, but only 8.3 per cent in South Dakota.
Fewer cattlemen, using more land, produced more beef than
ever before.

Wheat production went up then down. The amount grown
on the Plains rose during the Korean War, and then declined
rapidly. Total U.S. acreage harvested stood at 61,607,000
acres in 1950, rose to 71,130,000 acres in 1952, and fell to
47,285,000 acres in 1955. Much of this was dry-land wheat,
and, as in previous periods of wheat boom, when the boom
fell apart, the dry-landers shifted to producing cattle feeds.
Some became cattlemen once again, and others served the
cattle community. These changes did not affect sheepmen
much because the typical dry-land crops did not make good
sheep feed. Thus changes almost invariably involved a
change from wheat to cattle.[29]

The number of cattle on the Plains rose regularly between
1950 and 1955. This reflected the greater intensity with
which cattlemen pursued their business. Or put another
way: "In terms of feed requirements, the cattle industry
now places a greater burden on feed supplies than the combined sheep and cattle industry did ten to twenty years
ago." [30] Not only that, but the cattle of the 1950's were more
productive. "In 1954, 539 pounds of liveweight of cattle and
calves were produced for each cow on farms at the beginning
of the year. This was 148 pounds more than in 1924." [31]
Beef cattle on the Plains came to 23,832,000 head in 1950,
rose to 29,180,000 head in 1952, and stood at 29,259,000
head in 1955.[32]

In part, the great increase in productivity resulted from victories over diseases and weeds and the greater use of artificial hormones. In the great battle against foot-and-mouth disease, vaccination proved hearteningly successful. By 1950 vaccination had been shown to work, and from then on the war against the disease took this form. Here and there USDA agents attacked small but virulent outbreaks in Mexico by slaughtering, but generally the vaccination program predominated. By 1955 the disease had been eradicated in Mexico, and after eight years of quarantine the United States opened the border. In 1952 Congress set up a foot-and-mouth research laboratory on Plum Island, New York, and in 1954 the Department of Agriculture assumed operation of the facility.[33]

Brucellosis eradication and control received serious attention from Plains cattlemen during the fifties. Plains cattlemen apparently preferred the so-called Plan C which emphasized calfhood vaccination. The plan, developed by veterinarians and producers in 1952, gained momentum during the decade. The vaccine worked fairly well, as the dairymen could testify. In 1934, 11.5 per cent of all cattle had the disease, but in 1954, only 2.6 per cent of them had it. The greatest decrease had occurred in dairy herds. The success of the dairymen seems to have stimulated beefmen to attack the disease in earnest.

Meanwhile, anaplasmosis began to attract more attention. Anaplasmosis attacked blood cells, and resulted in at least a 10 per cent mortality rate of infected cattle. Furthermore, once infected, the animals became perpetual carriers of the disease. In 1951 the USDA began (in Montana) the first wide-scale testing for anaplasmosis in an effort to eliminate carriers. Stockmen had control measures readily at hand. Scientists had already developed a fairly effective vaccine, but cattlemen only slowly recognized the need for an intensive governmental program of research and prevention. In 1954 scientists estimated that anaplasmosis cost $10 million a year in mortality and unthriftiness of cattle. Nevertheless, cattlemen failed to demand eradication. In addition, the successful testing in Montana only slowly made its way to other places on the Plains. In 1955 a convention of the American National Livestock Association expressed interest in eradication, but they wanted the Department of Agriculture to develop a domestic vaccine rather than import South African vaccines of proven effectiveness. Meanwhile, the disease spread, and the scientists of the Department of Agriculture continued their work, more or less without success.[34]

On another front, antibiotics, long used for curing diseases, came to be used in feeds. In 1954 experimenters mixed aureomycin in cattle feed, and found that cattle produced twenty-seven pounds a day more than usual, with 16 per cent less feed than the control group. The savings more than paid for the aureomycin. The addition of antibiotics to cattle feed had not, however, become at all widespread by 1955.

Finally, veterinary scientists of the USDA at length solved the mystery of X-Disease, or hyperkeratosis. The disease had first been identified in the 1940's. Scientists found the disease to be caused by a lubricant additive. The disease was easier to prevent than cure. If manufacturers of pelleted feeds kept grease off the pellets, and if farmers kept cattle from licking greasy machinery, the disease could be, and soon was, virtually eliminated.

Meanwhile, in 1953, Wise Burroughs and C. C. Culbertson of Iowa State University discovered a new synthetic hormone which they called Stilbestrol. Stilbestrol caused cattle to gain 37 per cent faster than before, with 20 per cent less feed, at one-sixth the cost. This feed additive promised to alter beef producing completely. At first feeders found it more useful than did the plainsmen. In time, however, scientists devised ways for ranchers as well as feeders to use it. Other scientists discovered the hormone ECP. In initial tests, ECP assured conception in about 60 per cent of all apparently sterile cows. Few cattlemen seemed to use the hormone, even after 1952.[35]

Bugs and worms came under scientific attack. The screwworm, for example, seemed to be on the way out as the 1950's advanced. Screwworms fed at wounds, and deposited eggs in them. For some time cattlemen had put insecticide medications around wounds to kill flies and worms. During the fifties USDA scientists developed fairly effective new smears for wounds.

A more spectacular, and potentially more successful eradication technique was worked out by the USDA entomologists on the island of Curacao. On Curacao scientists sterilized male flies with gamma rays. Hordes of the male flies were then released on the island. Since the female bred only once, an infertile mating ended that generation. By saturating the island with infertile male flies, the scientists completely eradicated the insects on the island in less than a year. In the United States a similar attack would take more time, but a quarantine between clear and unclear areas could be established. Then the fly could be gradually eliminated from large regions. Ultimately the screwworm could be eradicated all over the United States. As of 1955, no one had begun the program in the United States, but the island experience of 1954 and 1955 had opened a new avenue of attack via atomic physics and entomology.[36]

Atomic physics did not, however, help much in the battle against ox warbles or grubs. In 1952 cattlemen could effectively only attack the heel flies before they laid their eggs. In the heel fly life cycle, the eggs entered the cattle, hatched, and then the grubs traveled through the host animal. The grubs then migrated to the back of the animal, and at length ate their way through the skin to the outside. Here they dropped to the ground, developed into mature flies, and started the cycle again. A systemic poison would have killed the grubs while they moved through the animal, but as of 1952 no systemic poisons had been perfected. In 1955, however, scientists of the Department of Agriculture announced success with the systemic poison, phenothiazine.[37]

Cattlemen also found chemistry a valuable ally in their unending fight against weeds and brush. The compounds

2,4-D and 2,4,5-T proved highly effective against most pasture brush. Mesquite, however, resisted attack fairly well. In 1952, mesquite infested about 112 million acres. Most of the infestation had taken place after domestic livestock had come onto the southern Plains. The shrub virtually ruined pasture land. Mechanical eradication by bulldozer proved effective but terribly expensive. As of 1955 no one could see any sure cure in prospect. Cactus also damaged pasture and resisted eradication. In some places well-to-do cattlemen used flame throwers to burn off the spines. Cattle could then eat the plants. This technique hardly served the needs of most cattlemen, and as of 1955, nothing else had been discovered.[38]

Cattle breeders made significant improvements too. On the southern Plains, the Santa Gertrudis breed began to spread out from its home on the King Ranch. In 1950 the first public sale of bulls took place. In April, 1951, the new breeders formed the Santa Gertrudis Breeders International with one hundred and sixty-nine charter members, and in 1954 they brought out their first herd book. By the late 1950's the breed had become very widely spread in the South.[39]

Meanwhile, cattle dwarfism afflicted Hereford breeders on a new scale. In 1952 Carl B. Roubicek of the University of Wyoming asserted that dwarfs made up 15 per cent of all calves born. Dwarfism, a genetically transmitted flaw, had apparently become alarmingly frequent. Cattlemen could protect themselves only by careful selection of breeding stock, and by careful control of the breeding. This called for a higher level of management than many cattlemen could undertake. Hereford breeders apparently preferred to ignore dwarfism rather than prevent it. In 1954, Montana Extension Service workers observed: "There was much less conversation concerning dwarfism in 1954 than in 1953—and quite a few more dwarf calves. The purebred men have pretty well succeeded in getting this topic smothered, unwise as this course seems to be." Sooner or later the problem had to be solved, but breeders chose to wait until their customers crashed the roof in. Other breeds made steady progress on the Plains.[40]

Charolais cattle, for example, had gained a small foothold in the United States, although their specific virtues seem a bit obscure. In 1954, six hundred and eleven head were registered with the International Charolais Cattle Raisers Association. The only other development in breeding centered on the re-exporting of three smuggled Charolais cattle. In 1956 they were sent back to Mexico from whence they had come the year before. The Charolais must have had some value since they excited the animosity of other Plains breeders.[41]

Animosities appeared other places. In 1950 cattlemen more or less united to urge the merger of the Forest Service and the Bureau of Land Management. Ostensibly cattlemen sought greater efficiency in government. No doubt they had more complex motives than they admitted. Anyhow, their proposed grazing bill failed to pass the House in 1954. On another front, however, they got what they wanted when the Grange-Thye Act passed on April 24, 1950. The act allowed ten-year permits on the forests. It also set up advisory boards for each forest when requested by a majority of the grazing permittees. Only time could tell if the law would still allow Foresters to protect the interests of nongrazing citizens. The Bureau of Land Management, by contrast, had little trouble with the Congress or the cattlemen. In 1951, and again in 1955, Congress raised grazing fees. The increases did not cover costs, however, and certainly the fees did not provide enough funds for real range management.[42]

By the 1950's, cattlemen seemed hardly even interested in the packers. Times had changed. About the only important news concerned the movement of packers out of Chicago. This was not very important to the cattlemen. They were interested in tariffs and trade agreements, however. On these matters, plainsmen sadly observed that the Eisenhower administration differed little from the Truman administration.

The free-trade harpies seemed strong regardless of who won the elections. A piddling 40 million pounds of commercial grade beef entered the United States from New Zealand in 1952, but even this dribble offended the delicate sensibilities of the cowboys.[43]

War, drouth, recession, science, and technology, all these and more, directly influenced the lives of the people of the Plains. For one thing, the lives of the people completely changed because of their easy automotive access to towns, cities, and one another. Automatic washing machines appeared in their homes. One cattleman expressed his distress when, returning from hauling water to his cattle, he stood and watched his wife's machine run through cycle after cycle, spilling out water and guzzling more. As of 1955, significantly, no one had yet mentioned television, but time even brought that. Television helped unify the nation, and probably this window on the world helped unify sections as well. Out in the West, however, before television was, sorghum had been. Sorghum served as the initial unifier of the Plains, although in a complex way.

In adjusting to life, plainsmen had long cherished certain cultural attitudes and customs which did not really meet their needs. In general, they held the idea that a landowner could do as he pleased with his land. This notion did not fit either the needs of the Plains, or of the nation. By the 1950's at the latest, most plainsmen seemed to recognize that they needed more, not less, governmental supervision of land use. Plainsmen found it difficult to adopt this view wholeheartedly, however, partly because of a lingering attachment to folklore, and partly because of their economic situation. The marketing routes ran east and west rather than north and south. Thus plainsmen of North and South tended to be divided in political objectives, and slow to cooperate on general governmental projects. Most often they found themselves unable to present a united view of Plains' problems to the several governmental agencies with which they dealt.

Northerners and southerners, however, had one common link in a common feed: sorghum. Sorghum and cattle provided the earliest connections between North and South. The federal government had long organized farmers along commodity lines through various price-support laws. This federally imposed unity, acting through sorghum and cattle, tended to draw North and South together. Price supports and federal regulations merged the regions as they had never been merged. Some decried this organization along commodity lines because they believed it fragmented the agricultural community, but federal policy helped unify the plainsmen. Their unity of outlook stemmed from their basic commodities and both proved more enduring than their differences.[44]

Plainsmen also achieved some cultural and social unity through their greater mobility. Trucks, cars, and even aircraft, made town residence possible for more and more cattlemen. They did not usually live in town, but increasingly they could, and in the fifties this promised a revision of life on the Plains. These changes also produced a greater unity of trade and of outlook.[45]

CHAPTER XV

The Age of Biochemistry
1956-1961

Dwight D. Eisenhower again won the presidential election in 1956. For the most part, Republican administrations dominated this period, although they did not always control Congress. Times were not bad, but neither were they good. Toward the end of 1958 an economic recession gripped the country. Recession continued until 1961. The generally unstable economic climate naturally affected cattlemen on the Plains. The recession brought with it a fairly hard core of 6 per cent unemployed, but the unemployed became economically important for cattlemen only after 1960. In 1956 cattle sold for an average of $16.34 a hundredweight. This price rose to $18.50 in 1957, and then shot up to $23.11 in 1958, and $23.91 in 1959. Cattle prices declined slightly in 1960 to an average of $21.98 a hundred.[1]

In part, advancing cattle prices and profits arose out of new price-support policies. In November, 1958, Midwest corngrowers voted "in favor of continued prosperity for Southwest cattlemen." The corngrowers voted against production restrictions, and thus also voted for a 10 per cent cut in price supports. As the editor of the Fort Worth *Cattleman* noted: "It means that corn and the other feed grains will be cheap for years to come. . . ." Simultaneously the profit margin rose steadily for cattlemen. Corn-Belt farmers did less well, but the Corn Belt had made its own choice.

A cost survey of 1959 suggested that the average cattlemen had rather high costs, if he counted a return on his own management and labor. Even so, producers seemed to do better

223

than the survey indicated. The labor costs of cattlemen appeared very small compared with other industries. All in all, during the late fifties and early sixties cattlemen enjoyed some prosperity, although many urbanites suffered from recession at the same time.[2]

Urban recession and high beef prices pushed beef and veal consumption steadily downward between 1956 and 1959. Each American ate an average of 94.9 pounds of beef and veal in 1956, but ate only 81.4 pounds in 1959. In 1960 low beef prices apparently caused average consumption to rise to 91.4 pounds. As cattlemen saw consumption fall they resolved, through their various associations, to push advertising campaigns. Most often they proposed a percentage check-off at the market place. With this money they proposed to establish a promotional fund. Cattlemen wanted the Department of Agriculture to collect the fund for them. Plains congressmen sponsored bills to provide for a compulsory check-off, and one Texas Congressman even bravely criticized the Farm Bureau because it opposed this bill. At the same time, cattlemen resolutely opposed governmental intervention in their affairs. The Texas association, for example, fought the passage of a humane slaughter bill.[3]

Meanwhile, cattlemen continued to ship ever more cattle to auction markets. In 1923, slaughterers had bought 90 per cent of their cattle at terminal markets. In 1956 they bought only 70 per cent at terminal markets, and by 1961, less than half the cattle moved through the terminal markets. As slaughtering and packing became widely scattered, federal officials had trouble dealing with the newer markets. They found it most difficult to insure honest weighing and honest meat inspection. Some buyers apparently actually tinkered with the scales. Supermarkets and food chains also greatly changed beef marketing. These newer enterprises packed their own beef, and threatened to become a new monopoly.

Although these problems of marketing interested cattlemen, they showed far more concern about foreign competition at their meetings. They considered the tariff to be a part of the general marketing machinery, and they sometimes requested both a study of the tariff, and the passage of a stronger Packers and Stockyards Act.[4]

Cattlemen sometimes also asked for an investigation of railroad charges and practices. At the same time, stockmen opposed any move that would increase the cost of truck transport. Instead, they wanted the cost of truck transport reduced. In 1958 at least one Texan noted that although truck rates were cheaper for distances of around two hundred miles, that above two hundred miles the railroads carried more cheaply. He and others wanted federal action to cut the cost of trucking. To this end, in both 1959 and 1960, cattlemen's associations vainly asked that the federal gasoline tax be reduced.

Meanwhile, cattlemen dimly perceived the growing importance of frozen foods. Sales of frozen foods multiplied twenty-five times between 1938 and 1957. Such growth had wide repercussions in the Plains cattle industry. Indeed, by the late fifties, the freezing industry had already made some impression on the cattlemen by way of the food-store chains.[5] Like weather and depression, however, the development of frozen foods seemed beyond the control of the producers.

Continual drouth characterized the years 1956 to 1960, apparently not reaching the emergency levels of previous years, but afflicting cattlemen from 1956 to 1958 on most of the Plains. Producers had long since come to expect federal aid in such emergencies. As usual, however, some of them thought they got less than they needed. In 1959 the drouth lifted and demands for help declined.[6]

Naturally enough, in the minds of many cattlemen, drouth relief and general agricultural programs were mixed together. The administration may have encouraged the confusion. As drouth began in 1956, the soil-bank program of Secretary Ezra T. Benson began to excite comment. On the whole, cattlemen approved the soil bank, provided that diverted acreages could not be used for grazing. When Democrats had attempted crop restrictions the cattlemen had screamed about regimentation, but they rather heartily approved a similar Republican measure. Said the editor of the Texas *Cattleman:* "The soil bank is a method of reducing surpluses and giving a lift to prices, and a conservation measure to safeguard our soil and water resources for future generations." Cattlemen also noted that a farmer could put into reserve any acreage on which the crop had been destroyed by nature. For ranch farmers with ruined feed crops this offered some additional drouth aid. By July soil-bank legislation had been clarified enough so that cattlemen no longer feared it. The law prevented diverted acreages from being used for grazing.

In 1957 the soil bank was altered to allow the federal government to rent pastures where grazing had been deferred. Cattlemen could also put their burned-out pastures in the soil bank. These provisions amounted to drouth relief for stockmen, although not explicitly. In 1957 and 1958, price supports on grain sorghums also helped Plains cattlemen. Few of them apparently opposed this sort of paternalism. The main opposition to Benson came from the Farm Bureau. His troubles stemmed from his efforts to return to a free market for agricultural produce. For years farmers and ranchers had been asking for a free market and no controls. In 1958 they almost got it, and they immediately discovered that they didn't like it after all.[7]

The soil bank excited the most comment, but cattlemen benefited from government aid in other ways. In 1956 the government increased beef purchases for its school lunches in an effort to reduce cattle numbers and raise beef prices. Texans wanted even more such buying, but processors apparently blocked the measure. Anyway, somebody blocked it, and cattlemen had to be content with moderate aid.[8]

In the meantime, conservation efforts continued to change cattle husbandry. For several decades federal officials had tried to interest cattlemen in conservation, and gradually the cattlemen had caught on. They discovered, most significantly, that conservation could be profitable, and probably was even necessary. They found that deferred grazing increased ground water which then provided watering pools where none had been before. The new pools and wells allowed greatly intensified operations because cattlemen could carry more head of stock per acre. Deferred grazing, in turn, was made possible because cattlemen grew greater quantities of feed crops. Sorghum and sorghum-legume rotations figured prominently in this change. Different legumes, used at different stages of soil building added nitrates to the soil, increased crop and grass production, and intensified beef production. Vetch, peas, and alfalfa all served their turn in the process. Stockmen had to use bacteria inoculated fertilizers for best results. They also used more commercial fertilizers. Few did all these things, but the more advanced cattlemen did most of them, and they obtained obvious results. Gradually they taught their neighbors. The cattlemen's press disseminated both the information and the success stories.[9]

Still, plainsmen did not generally follow conservation practices. In 1957, for example, reports from the ten Great Plains states showed that one hundred thousand acres had been damaged by wind erosion in that year. Furthermore, another eight and one-half million acres were ready to blow away. To meet this threat, in 1958 the USDA undertook a new long-range conservation program on the Plains. The department invited cattlemen in two hundred thirty-three counties in the Plains states to participate. The department provided technical assistance for farmers and ranchers who wanted to carry on long-term water and range conservation measures. By April, 1958, more than one thousand farmers and cattlemen had entered the program. The program involved more than seventy-four thousand acres. Congress appropriated $150 million for a ten-year program. Of this, $10 million had been made available for the first year. The cooperation of cattlemen was less than astounding, considering the benefits available, but something was being done.

Although general conservation proved less than startling, for the most part the administration had little trouble in handling the public domain and the Forests. The Eisenhower administrators announced in advance their determination to get along with the cattlemen. Harmony ruled everywhere. The administration held outright corruption to a minimum, and cattlemen seemed to approve the occasional efforts to liquidate parts of the federal holdings. The administration did little managing of the federal lands, and cattlemen approved that too.[10]

Meanwhile, cattlemen, states, and the federal government waged unending war against cattle diseases, and the losses they produced. In the late fifties, brucellosis remained as the most serious uncontrolled disease. The federal eradication plan called for state assistance in testing for the disease, along with slaughtering carriers and vaccinating calves. In 1956, Montanans proudly announced the success of their eradication program which they figured would be complete by December, 1957. The example showed what could be done, for many authorities had asserted that this victory was impossible. On January 1, 1957, the USDA announced a brucellosis quarantine of cattle, except for certain classes which included steers. The quarantine prevented shipments from counties or states where the disease was not controlled. Some states also required testing of breeding stock before the cattle could enter the state. This requirement, however, did not seem to advance brucellosis eradication since shippers merely delayed the testing until just before shipping, and otherwise did little to get rid of the disease.[11]

Of course, cattlemen much preferred vaccination to slaughter. So much so that local cattlemen's associations came to demand compulsory calf vaccination. In 1959 the American National extended these demands to mean 100 per cent vaccination of female calves. By then, however, local cattlemen's associations had begun to press for the end of the various testing and slaughter programs. Cattlemen wanted only the vaccination program. Had they been successful, eradication would have been set back considerably.[12]

Advances in the several branches of biochemistry dwarfed all other scientific and governmental activities. The advances came in bunches, and clearly dominated the history of the era:

1. Antibiotics proved useful not only to combat disease, but to increase gains when used as a feed supplement.

2. New systemic poisons controlled worms and insects.

3. Bacterial parasites successfully controlled insects.

4. Plant hormones killed weeds, brush, cactus, and other plants.

5. Animal hormones increased growth rates, and so did tranquilizers.

6. Combinations of antibiotics, hormones, and tranquilizers increased beef production with slight cost.

First of all, aureomycin as a feed additive proved effective against a complex of diseases ranging from foot-rot to liver abscesses. In 1958 the Food and Drug Administration approved the use of aureomycin as a feed additive. Scientists soon found that antibiotics generally increased cattle gains. The antibiotics reduced dangerous bacteria, and also stimulated the beneficial intestinal bacteria to produce more B-complex vitamins. Animals receiving antibiotics also used proteins more efficiently. Experimenters could not compute the exact statistical gains. Nevertheless, the addition of antibiotics to feed promised to be one of the major scientific advances of all time. The practice promised unbelievable intensity of meat production.[13]

Biochemists kept at work in other areas, and shortly worms and insect parasites gradually came under better control. In 1956, grubby cattle robbed cattlemen of an estimated $100 million. Then in 1957, the USDA (in association with Dow Chemical) announced a new systemic poison, Dow ET-57. This poison kept worms from growing in the animals. The heel fly was nearly done in. In 1958 more systemic poisons appeared. These not only killed grubs, but also lice, ticks, horn flies, and screwworms. Cattle certified to have been treated with Co-Ral or Trolene, brought cattlemen $1 a head extra when they sold to various Iowa packers. The heel fly was doomed. No one seemed sorry, for the benefits to cattlemen and to meat-eating Americans appeared unlimited.

Scientists also developed sprays to do much the same job. Cattlemen generally found these easier to apply. Systemic poison or spray, the Food and Drug Administration found that the new insecticides did not harm the meat for human consumption. In 1959 the administration cleared both for use by producers.[14]

Meanwhile, USDA workers successfully applied the sterilization method of screwworm eradication in Florida. Texans wanted the program attempted next in the Southwest. Such efforts, combined with the use of systemic insecticides, would certainly eliminate screwworms from all America.

Insects not only attacked stock, but also damaged feed crops. In 1959 this battle took a new turn when federal officials approved the use of bacterial warfare. The bacteria, sprayed on crops, entered the insects. There the spores germinated and broke down the tissues of the insects. The bugs died in a day or so. The bacteria selected their victims, and did not threaten either animal or human health. Bacterial insecticides killed too slowly to halt invasions of grasshoppers and such, but the new insecticides did promise long-term success.

Herbicides, such as 2,4-D, had long proved effective against weeds. By the 1950's some cattlemen used them rather extensively to restore pastures, but 2,4-D especially proved too expensive for effective use against pricklypear cactus. The Agricultural Stabilization and Conservation Committee, therefore, helped carry the cost of destroying the cactus by paying cattlemen from sixty cents to five dollars an acre for anti-cactus work. Cattlemen got nearly a 100 per cent kill by grubbing. They got only a 70 per cent when they used chemicals. Mesquite turned out to be more vulnerable to chemicals. Spraying with 2,4,5-T killed nearly all the brush. The mesquite seemed doomed on grasslands, provided cattlemen and their allies kept up the attack. They could not relax, however, for by 1957 mesquite infestation had reached gigantic proportions. In fifty years the infested area had almost doubled. In many areas cattlemen attacked mesquite with grubbing hoes. In any case, unless plainsmen acted promptly, the area of infestation threatened to grow rather than decrease. In the long run, chemicals and hormones offered the best chance of victory.[15]

In short, biochemistry introduced a brandnew era in the history of the Plains. The perplexing complexity of the age was outlined in a report published in the *National Live Stock Producer* of 1957:

In an 84-day trial with steers, Pfizer scientists found that Terramycin resulted in an 11% improvement in gain and a 9% increase in feed efficiency. Stilbestrol gave a 17% increase in rate of gain and a 13% improvement in feed efficiency. A combination of Terramycin and Stilbestrol resulted in a 23% boost in rate of gain and a 16% step-up in feed efficiency.

When a tranquilizer was added in all three cases, there was a *further 12% increase* in rate of gain and a *further 7% improvement* in feed efficiency.[16]

As of March, 1958, however, tranquilizers had not been approved by the Food and Drug Administration, although approval came by the end of the year. At the rate of discovery and use in the fifties, biochemical pills and shots seemed about to replace food altogether.

Scientists continued to try various combinations of antibiotics and hormones, and no matter what they did they invariably recorded impressive feeding gains. Pellet implants, feed additives, pills, and shots, all had their day in one way or another. Not all of these approaches could be used by cattlemen, but all of them did wonderful things. In 1958, Wise Burroughs of Iowa State University estimated that 70 per cent of the cattle fed in the winter of 1957 received hormones of one sort or another. Hormones obviously had tremendous repercussions.

Sweetness and light did not prevail universally. Feeders who used hormones didn't like to buy cattle that ranchers had already shot full of hormones. Few wanted to buy cow-shaped steers that looked like their mothers. Ranchers seemed unimpressed with the prejudice, however, and many went on using stilbestrol implants. In 1958, Congress told the Department of Health, Education, and Welfare not to approve any new stilbestrol feed formulas because the hormone reportedly caused cancer in laboratory animals. Oddly, the law did not cover feed formulas already approved. Neither did the law apply to implants. These apparently had no bad effects.[17]

Tranquilizers also increased in use, for they did far more than just help cattle gain weight. According to one authority, tranquilizers: "combat diseases before they start, reduce weight losses in shipment, acclimate cattle, combat shipping fever and . . . reduce the need for exercise or rough handling." [18] They made the animals more like machines, and more subject to some form of automation. The cattle business was changing beyond recognition.

Better breeding of higher-producing animals also led to greater meat production per animal. As before, drouth forced cattlemen to cull, and so helped them improve their herds. Just as importantly, cattlemen had become progressively more scientific and more selective in culling. Well, anyway, before they sold cows they checked to see which ones were with calf. In breeding, as in other things, cattlemen wanted federal help. Particularly they seemed to favor a program "to develop a meat type of beef animal that will produce a carcass more nearly meeting consumer demands with more high quality lean meat and less waste fat. . . ." [19] The urban demands had gradually impressed the cattlemen who quickly translated their impression into a demand for federal help.

At about the same time, artificial insemination of range

cattle developed more intensely. Artificial breeding worked only because plainsmen supervised their cattle more closely than before, and because they crowded more head on fewer acres. Artificial insemination could not replace bulls, but it could and did help improve the quality of bulls being kept on the Plains.

Cattlemen tended to avoid mentioning dwarfism in Hereford cattle. Dwarfism was genetically transmitted, caused great losses for cattlemen, and for years remained uncontrollable. The recessive nature of the genetic deformity made it difficult to predict. In 1957, however, John Lasley discovered a way to detect adult carriers of dwarfism even though the cattle appeared normal. The tester simply injected insulin into the animals, and then checked the rise in the white-blood-cell count. The white count rose more rapidly in dwarf-free animals than in dwarf-carriers. The road lay open to the elimination of dwarfism. Some time would be needed to eradicate it from the herds of America, but victory seemed sure. As a rule, producers tried to pretend the deformity did not exist; this attitude did not speed eradication, but cattlemen did have the test.[20]

The Santa Gertrudis breed, breaking into the open in the 1940's, apparently stimulated cattlemen everywhere to turn their hands to developing new breeds. In the fifties a virtual plague of new breeds broke out. Some of the new breeds might actually have been valuable. In 1956 the Beefmaster appeared. It had been developed by crossing Brahman, Hereford, and Shorthorn cattle. The Charbray, part Charolais and part Brahman also appeared in 1956, but it was just a cross and not a true breed. By the late fifties Brangus cattle had become well established, and the breeders had already formed an association. Another genetically distinct breed was the McCan breed, developed in Texas. McCan cattle were three-fourths Hereford and one-fourth Brahman. They first attracted important attention in 1958. No one knew how important these breeds might be. Anyhow, there were enough of them.[21]

Cattlemen devised few really new techniques during the late fifties and early sixties. Supplemental feeding, cattle guards on roads, trucks for moving cattle, and the raising of drouth-resistant grasses, all merely continued earlier practices. One cattleman at least followed the ancient practice of soiling. That is, he carried fresh-cut fodder to the cattle in their pens. This highly intensified operation pointed out how future cattlemen might carry on their business as people multiplied and land shrank. Certainly few cattlemen on the Plains followed the practice of soiling, but few of them doubted that land was getting scarcer. In the fifties the pressure came increasingly from urbanites, rather than from nesters and dry farmers. The editor of *The Cattleman* observed:

No county in Texas is completely free from the influence of the metropolitan trend in land values. Prices are higher, however, for land that is easily in reach of the larger cities. About the only way a farmer or rancher can compete with non-agricultural buyers is to pay the price for land that joins property he now owns, allowing for a larger operation with the same overhead.[22]

The metropolis, once considered only a market, had at length made an even stronger impress on the Plains cattle industry. Many a dry farmer might have smiled at this turn of events. As urbanites advanced, cattlemen responded as they had when the nesters first appeared. Plains cattlemen became more efficient, and simultaneously they increased the size of their ranches. Biochemistry now provided the efficiencies. The growing size of farms and ranches continued the trends of the distant past. The intensity of beef production made possible by biochemistry showed up clearly in the number of beef cattle kept in the Plains states. In 1954, the plainsmen had 30,447,000 head; by 1960 this had risen to 32,555,000 head.[23]

Advances in feeds and feeding accounted for most of the improvements. In turn, the key to feeding improvements had been scientific advances in nutrition, which in their way depended on biochemistry. A 1958 experiment proved conclusively how much the newer techniques had changed the industry. Scientists fed twin calves on different rations; one on 1908 rations, and one on 1958 rations. The 1958 animal gained 42 per cent faster on 30 per cent less feed at 33 per cent less cost.

Changes continued. In 1959 scientists reconfirmed their conviction that pasture should be supplemented with vitamin A, protein, and phosphorous additives.[24] In feed-crop production, Plains cattlemen relied ever more on irrigation. They found sprinkler irrigation to be the key to this development. Sprinklers allowed them to water land which had never before been suitable for irrigation. They found that sprinklers also made more economical use of the water. Further, the portable pipes made it easy and inexpensive to shift the system about. In Kansas, irrigated acreage rose from 530,000 acres in 1955 to 700,000 acres in 1956, and the story seemed about the same over the Plains. Acreage irrigated with federal assistance, mostly in western states, showed an over-all increase from 6,262,000 acres in 1955 to 6,757,000 acres in 1958. Charles Petit of Flat Top Ranch observed: "I consider the thousand acres of irrigated and subirrigated land to be equal in value to the sixteen thousand acres of grazing land on the ranch." The ratio of one to sixteen probably slightly understated the value of the irrigated land. Indeed, so far as producing native grass seeds went, irrigated land seemed a necessity. As one authority noted: "Experience shows that only by producing grass seed under cultivation—preferably under irrigation—can adequate and dependable supplies become available. . . ."[25] Thus technological advances in irrigation provided opportunities for even more intensified cattle raising on the Plains. In this way plainsmen responded to the ever greater needs of the growing city populations.

Vertical integration of cattle feeding, tried first in the thirties, made a hesitant revival in the fifties, and then grew in importance in the early sixties. Plains cattlemen, however, felt the effects only slightly. Still, plainsmen feared they would ultimately become captives of the corporations. Nothing in the history of corporations suggested they would treat the plainsmen well. The feeders, it turned out, also functioned as retailers and as packers. "Cattle fed by packers is definitely on the increase. In 1959, 152 packers fed 593,000 cattle 30 days or more; whereas in 1960, 160 packers fed 815,000—an increase of over 37 percent." [26] Chain stores accounted for much of this feeding. In 1961, cattlemen seriously discussed possible changes in the Packers and Stockyards Act in order to control the new business.

Cattlemen had ambivalent attitudes toward free enterprise. In nearly one breath the Texas cattlemen demanded free enterprise, and federal screwworm eradication. Under the heading of free enterprise, cattlemen especially wanted Mexican braceros kept off the list of those guaranteed a fair minimum wage. Further north, cattlemen wanted labor regulated as industry was regulated, except that they didn't want to be regulated themselves.[27]

Meeting at Colorado Springs, cattlemen opposed any effort to pass any sort of Wilderness Bill which would restrict their use of public land. They thus began the old fight all over, except that this time the urbanites, rather than the nesters, pressed upon the cattlemen. Probably the cattlemen would be no more able to halt this advance of civilization than they had any other. The more things changed, the more they remained the same.[28]

Rising beef prices, oddly combined with recession, resulted in low per-capita consumption of beef between 1956 and 1961. Drouth, drouth relief, price supports, and the soil bank, all helped cattlemen. So did the continued conservations programs of the federal government. Taking one thing with another, cattlemen produced more beef on each acre and with each animal than ever before. And they made fair profits at the same time. The key to their prosperity, such as it was, could be found in the astounding advances in biochemistry which were made during the fifties, and which cattlemen rapidly applied to their industry. Antibiotics, hormones, systemic poisons for worms and insects, and herbicides, all vastly increased productivity. Breeding advances also pushed the industry along, particularly the insulin test for dwarfism. Sprinkler irrigation, just making its way into the Plains cattle industry, also promised greater production as time went on. The contrast between the cattle of 1960 and of 1900 was so marked as to be nearly unbelievable. Whatever could be said for the rest of mankind, progress clearly characterized the history of the Great Plains.

CHAPTER XVI

Conclusions
1900-1961

The Great Plains began as a part of America, and since at least 1848, plainsmen have been Americans. In spite of their regional distinctiveness, plainsmen have always participated in the main stream of United States history. Plains cattlemen were, and are, American agriculturalists, and as such, they were neither better nor worse than any other Americans. They had special problems—but so does everyone—and they had special solutions to their problems—but in that they again were not unique.

All of this is not to say that the Plains are just like any other place. Obviously, the Plains are distinctive and their residents are different. The history of the plainsmen is primarily a history of accommodation to a rather harsh environment. Still, their lives have not always been a grim battle with nature, for the Plains have many charms. Few places on earth are possessed of such simple grandeur, and seldom did the Creator fashion a land with such awesome carelessness. An Oklahoman, moved to the East, complained of his new home: "Everywhere you look, you see something." The Plains have always been, and still are, a refuge for those who are oppressed by the crush of seething humanity. The Plains may yet become one of the few places where urbanites can find a moment's peace from the strains of city life. In any case, in overcoming their adversities, or enjoying their advantages, plainsmen have always acted within the framework of the age, and the nation, wherein they lived.

The economic life of Americans changed across the years,

and the plainsmen participated in that general change. In all areas of American life, the years between 1850 and 1900 were years of growing specialization. The sciences became specialized, periodicals for specialists proliferated, farmers became commercial specialists, and on the Plains, cattlemen specialized in ranching. If there was romance then, so was there romance in railroad building, steelmaking, and insurance underwriting.

In the early twentieth century, men made more intense use of natural resources, and they developed a professional sense in nearly every type of enterprise. Stockraising also became a profession, rather than just an adventurous way of life. Between 1900 and 1914 Americans took a general interest in reform, governmental control of business, and restriction on the exploitation of natural resources. Here, too, cattlemen on the Plains followed the national pattern.

The First World War brought the reforming binge to an end in America, and concurrently introduced an exceptional prosperity. Plains cattlemen shared in the good things of the era, and lost some of their reforming fervor at the same time. The business ethic of the twenties regarded government help as good, but government regulation as bad. Businessmen characteristically wanted special favors, but not controls—except for somebody else. Cattlemen felt the same as the rest of the Americans.

Clearly, depression and prosperity originated in causes far removed from anything that happened on the Plains. And yet nothing is so clear as the effects of the business cycles on the affairs of the cattlemen. Now and then, as in the later twenties, the cattlemen enjoyed a prosperity which other agriculturalists did not share, but generally the fortunes of Plains cattlemen fluctuated with the fortunes of other farmers in the United States. All of this may elaborate the obvious, but perhaps the obvious needs to be explained. The Great Depression and the New Deal showed beyond any doubt how closely the fortunes of cattlemen were tied to the fortunes of all Americans. The drouth and dust storms of the thirties were not peculiar to the Plains, but even had they been, it cannot be supposed that only plainsmen bore the burden of the disasters. These losses hurt all Americans.

Similarly, general governmental activities, such as the WPA, and the CCC, and the FERA, all bore immediately on the lives of the plainsmen. In short, the most general programs affected cattlemen, and they could not avoid the consequences, no matter what they did. On the other hand, the special programs for the Plains, such as the Taylor Grazing Act, had something to do with the prosperity and happiness of all Americans. During World War II, the Office of Price Administration influenced the lives of the plainsmen. A general war measure produced ramifications of all sorts. Only a special parochial conceit could cause anyone to insist that the OPA had no direct bearing on the history of the Great Plains. Cattlemen also shared in the general wartime prosperity.

Political theorists constantly assert that this is now "one world." Indeed it is, and has been for some time. Even the Plains are part of the world, and world history necessarily encompasses the Plains. Leaving aside international politics, developments in science and technology link the Plains with the main stream of western civilization. Science is cumulative and discovery is necessarily built upon discovery. Here the dependence of Plains cattlemen on the outside world was most marked, as the use of gamma rays on screwworms illustrated. Interestingly, the initial screwworm experiments were performed by Americans on the Dutch island of Curacao, located in the West Indies. The Santa Gertrudis is a native breed, but its stock was European and Asiatic. Sorghum came from Africa, wheatgrass from Russia. Examples could go on and on. In short, the history of the Plains cattlemen is not so remote from the history of mankind.

History is one thing, legends are another. Nothing is so striking in the records of the Plains cattle industry as the divergence between the history and the legend. Cattlemen have always seen themselves as fiercely independent, neither seeking nor receiving help from anyone, and certainly not getting help from the government. They represent themselves, without guile and without deceit, as the last-surviving defenders of ancient American liberties. Oddly, most Americans do not even take offense at these airs. Yet the slightest glance at the record reveals countless efforts by cattlemen to get governmental assistance of one sort or another. They continually sought help, and they often got it. This is true, and it is neither bad nor good, but just true. No tale is so widely repeated as the myth that cattlemen have never received price supports. Surely some hairsplitting must be involved in this yarn, for the simple evidence shows price assistance in the thirties, the forties, and the fifties. There was, of course, nothing wrong with getting help.

Then too, some things are either everybody's business or nobody's business. Virulent plagues of foot-and-mouth disease could not conceivably have been stamped out by private enterprise. Modern wars cannot be fought by just a few contractors. Some activities are appropriate for government, and for no one else. Cattlemen quite wisely discerned this early in their history, and yet they go on denying their insight.

Notes

CHAPTER I

1. Paul C. Henlein, *Cattle Kingdom in the Ohio Valley, 1783–1860* (Lexington: Univ. of Kentucky Press, 1959), pp. 59–60, 103–129; P. W. Bidwell and J. I. Falconer, *History of Agriculture in the Northern United States, 1620–1860* (New York: Peter Smith, 1941), pp. 21–25, 79, 107–109, 159–160, 177–180; F. J. Turner, *The Frontier in American History* (New York: Holt, Rinehart, and Winston, 1962), pp. 11, 16, 88–89.

2. Walter P. Webb, *The Great Plains* (Boston: Ginn, 1931), *passim.*

3. *Statistical Abstract of the United States, 1958* (Washington: U.S. Department of Commerce, 1958), p. 160; *Agricultural Statistics, 1957* (Washington: U.S. Department of Agriculture, 1958), p. 520; farm land as a percentage of total land area: 1850, 15.6 per cent; 1860, 21.4 per cent; 1870, 21.4 per cent; 1880, 28.2 per cent; 1890, 32.7 per cent; and 1900, 44.1 per cent. The land area of the Plains plus Idaho, Arizona, Utah, and Nevada: 1,495,204 square miles; land area of the United States, 2,974,726 square miles, *Statistical Abstract, 1958, loc. cit.*

4. Gilbert Fite and J. Reese, *An Economic History of the United States* (Boston: Houghton Mifflin, 1959), p. 406; Fred A. Shannon, *The Farmers' Last Frontier* (New York: Farrar and Rinehart, 1945), pp. 140–147.

5. Fite and Reese, *op. cit.,* p. 407.

6. *Statistical Abstract of the United States, 1901* (Washington: U.S. Statistics Bureau, 1901), pp. 14–15; *Statistical Abstract, 1958, loc. cit.,* p. 91; in 1880 people of foreign origin made up only 12.3 per cent of the Plains population, while they made up 15.3 per cent of the total for the United States. In 1890 the difference increased, with only 13.5 per cent of the Plains people being foreign born, but 17.3 per cent for the United States, and in 1900 only 11.1 per cent of the Plains population was foreign born, while for the United States the figure was 15.8 per cent.

7. Ray A. Billington, *Westward Expansion* (New York: Macmillan, 1949), pp. 671–687; Louis Pelzer, *The Cattlemen's Frontier* (Glendale, California: Arthur H. Clark, 1936).

8. Billington, *op. cit.,* p. 680.

9. *The Cattleman,* 8 (Fort Worth, March, 1922), 23.

10. Thomas D. Clark, *Frontier America* (New York: Scribner's, 1959), p. 629.

11. Billington, *op. cit.,* p. 677; Shannon, *op. cit.,* pp. 240–242.

12. Carl F. Kraenzel, *The Great Plains in Transition* (Norman: Univ. of Oklahoma Press, 1955), p. 115; Fite and Reese, *op. cit.,* p. 410.

13. James C. Malin, "The Adaptation of the Agricultural System to Sub-Humid Environment," *Agricultural History*, 10 (July, 1936), 123, 125.

14. C. W. Towne, *Her Majesty Montana* (Series of Radio Broadcasts, 1938–1939), pp. 82–83; Billington, *op. cit.*, pp. 685–686.

15. Towne, *op. cit.*

16. Kraenzel, *op. cit.*, p. 115; Shannon, *op. cit.*, pp. 40–41; Mary W. Hargreaves, *Dry Farming in the Northern Great Plains, 1900–1925* (Cambridge, Mass.: Harvard Univ. Press, 1957), pp. 62–63.

17. J. J. Wagoner, *History of the Cattle Industry in Southern Arizona, 1540–1940* (Tucson: Univ. of Arizona Press, 1952), p. 53; *Annual and Seasonal Precipitation in Montana* (Montana Agri. Exp. Sta. Bul. 447, 1947), p. 6; M. L. Wilson, R. H. Wilcox, G. S. Klemmedson, and V. V. Parr, *A Study of Ranch Organization and Methods of Range-Cattle Production in the Northern Great Plains Region* (USDA Tech. Bul. 45, 1928), p. 16; Hargreaves, *op. cit.*, p. 43; *The Cattleman*, 26 (Feb., 1940), 68.

18. Robert S. Fletcher, "The End of the Open Range in Eastern Montana," *Mississippi Valley Historical Review*, 16 (Sept., 1929), 208; Hargreaves, *op. cit.*, p. 46.

19. Bureau of the Census, *Historical Statistics of the United States, 1789–1945* (Washington: U.S. Department of Commerce, 1952); Hargreaves, *op. cit.*, p. 17.

20. G. Soule and V. P. Carosso, *American Economic History* (New York: Dryden Press, 1957), p. 336.

21. Richard O. Cummings, " 'And Roast Beef' (1841–80)," *The American and His Food* (Chicago: Univ. of Chicago Press, 2d ed., 1941), p. 80.

22. Cummings, *op. cit.*, pp. 75–90.

23. Oscar E. Anderson, Jr., *Refrigeration in America* (Princeton: Princeton Univ. Press for the Univ. of Cincinnati, 1953), pp. 58, 91–92, 122–123; John W. Oliver, *History of American Technology* (New York: Ronald Press, 1956), p. 386.

24. T. S. Harding, *Two Blades of Grass* (Norman: Univ. of Oklahoma Press, 1947), pp. 150–151; J. C. Lotze, D. W. Gates, and T. O. Roby, "Anaplasmosis of Cattle," *Animal Diseases* (USDA Yearbook, 1956), pp. 268–269; B. W. Bierer, *A Short History of Veterinary Medicine in America* (East Lansing: Michigan State Univ. Press, 1955), pp. 58–60.

25. Fletcher, *loc. cit.*, pp. 205–206; Hargreaves, *op. cit.*, pp. 21, 43–45; Malin, *loc. cit.*, p. 141.

26. Fletcher, *loc. cit.*, p. 205.

27. Charles W. Piper, *Forage Plants and Their Culture* (New York: Macmillan, 1947), pp. 348–349.

28. For a list of typical crops grown see: Malin, *loc. cit.*, p. 124; J. C. Stephens, J. H. Martin, and H. N. Vinall, *Identification, History, and Distribution of Common Sorghum Varieties* (USDA Tech. Bul. 506, 1936), pp. 2–17; J. T. Schlebecker, "Pliant Prairie—One Plant's Influence on One Prairie State," *Montana, the Magazine of Western History*, 8 (Winter, 1958), 30–41.

29. Nelson Klose, *The Introduction, Improvement, and Adaptation of Sorghum Varieties in Texas* (M.A. thesis, Austin: Univ. of Texas, 1937), p. 35; Malin, *loc. cit.*, pp. 122, 130–132, Quotation, p. 131.

30. Klose, *op. cit.*, p. 29.

31. Klose, *op. cit.*, p. 35; Hargreaves, *op. cit.*, p. 63; Schlebecker, "Pliant Prairie," pp. 30–41.

32. Schlebecker, "Pliant Prairie"; J. T. Schlebecker, "Grasshoppers in American Agricultural History," *Agricultural History*, 27 (July, 1953).

33. H. G. Reynolds and H. W. Springfield, *Reseeding Southwestern Range Lands with Crested Wheatgrass* (USDA Farmers' Bul. 2056, 1953), pp. 1–2; R. Peterson, "Crested Wheat Grass for Northern Plains," *American Cattle Producer*, 20 (Denver, Aug., 1938), 12; Harding, *op. cit.*, p. 105.

34. Joseph K. Howard, *Montana: High, Wide and Handsome* (New Haven: Yale Univ. Press, 1943), pp. 170–171; Fletcher, *loc. cit.*, p. 205; Hargreaves, *op. cit.*, pp. 47, 65; Shannon, *op. cit.*, p. 216.

35. Twelfth Census of the U.S.: *Agriculture*, 5 (Washington: GPO, 1902), 688; Hargreaves, *op. cit.*, pp. 62–63.

36. B. W. Allred, *Range Conservation Practices for the Great Plains* (USDA Misc. Pub. 410, 1940), p. 15.

37. "The Stanfield Grazing Bill," *The Cattleman*, 8 (June, 1926), 3–7.

38. Agricultural Marketing Service, *Livestock and Meat Statistics* (USDA Stat. Bul. 230, 1958), p. 283.

CHAPTER II

1. Agricultural Marketing Service, *Livestock and Meat Statistics* (USDA Stat. Bul. 230, 1958), p. 283.

2. Marion Clawson, *The Western Range Livestock Industry* (New York: McGraw-Hill, 1950), p. 174; Robert M. Barker, "The Economics of Cattle-Ranching in the Southwest," *American Monthly Review of Reviews*, 24 (Sept., 1901), 308; Lewis Corey, *Meat and Man* (New York: Viking, 1950), p. 97.

3. Clawson, *op. cit.*, p. 174.

4. J. F. Wrenn, "Marketing American Meat Products in Export Trade," *The Cattleman*, 12 (Fort Worth, June, 1925), 42; R. A. Clemen, *The American Livestock and Meat Industry* (New York: Ronald Press, 1923), pp. 282–284.

5. *Guide to the Records in the National Archives* (Washington: GPO, 1948), p. 60.

6. Oscar E. Anderson, Jr., *Refrigeration in America* (Princeton: Princeton Univ. Press for the Univ. of Cincinnati, 1953), p. 58.

7. *The Independent* (Miles City, Mont., May 12, 1904); Will C. Barnes, "Looking Backward," *The Producer*, 7 (Denver, April, 1926), 3–4.

8. E. N. Wentworth, "Changes in the Center of Beef Production," *The Cattleman*, 8 (Nov., 1921), 16.

9. *The Cattleman*, 8 (Mar., 1922), 23.

10. M. L. Wilson, R. H. Wilcox, G. S. Klemmedson, and V. V. Parr, *A Study of Ranch Organization and Methods of Range-Cattle Production in the Northern Great Plains Region* (USDA Tech. Bul. 45, 1928), p. 18; W.P.A., Historical Records Survey for Fergus County, mss. Montana State College collection (Bozeman, Mont., Dec. 19, 1939).

11. *The Independent* (Oct. 22, 1903), p. 4; on the problems of debt and

prices see *Montana Stockman and Farmer* (Helena, Oct. 1, 1905), p. 24; W.P.A., Historical Records Survey for Fergus County, *loc. cit.*

12. *The Independent* (Oct. 22, 1903), p. 4.

13. Wilson, Wilcox, Klemmedson, and Parr, *loc. cit.*, p. 16; J. J. Wagoner, *History of the Cattle Industry in Southern Arizona, 1540–1940* (Tucson: Univ. of Arizona Press, 1952), p. 55; *Annual and Seasonal Precipitation at Six Representative Locations in Montana* (Montana Agri. Exp. Sta. Bul. 447, 1947), pp. 6, 12, 18, 30; *Miles City Independent* (Oct. 8, 1903), p. 4; *Montana Stockman and Farmer* (May 15, 1905), p. 6.

14. Mary W. Hargreaves, *Dry Farming in the Northern Great Plains, 1900–1925* (Cambridge, Mass.: Harvard Univ. Press, 1957), *passim;* Joseph K. Howard, *Montana: High, Wide and Handsome* (New Haven: Yale Univ. Press, 1943), pp. 173–174; "South Dakota Farms," *New York Produce Review and American Creamery,* **12** (May 8, 1901), 10; *Montana Stockman and Farmer* (June 1, 1903), p. 1.

15. *Statistical Abstract of the United States, 1931* (Washington: U.S. Department of Commerce, 1931), p. 412.

16. O. O. Winther, *The Great Northwest* (New York: Knopf, 1952), pp. 275–281; William E. Hayes, *Iron Road to Empire* (Pub. by the Author, 1953), pp. 155–177.

17. Glenn K. Rule, *Crops Against the Wind on the Southern Great Plains* (USDA Farmers' Bul. 1833, 1939), pp. 4–42; G. K. Rule, *Toward Soil Security on the Northern Great Plains* (USDA Farmers' Bul. 1864, 1941), pp. 8–35.

18. Howard, *op. cit.*, pp. 173–174; *Montana Stockman and Farmer* (Nov. 1, 1902), p. 1; *ibid.* (Jan. 15, 1904), p. 17; *ibid.* (Oct. 1, 1904), p. 20; Hargreaves, *op. cit.*, p. 474; Howard, *op. cit.*, p. 278; *Montana Stockman and Farmer* (May 1, 1904), p. 5; *The Independent* (Mar. 16, 1905); Rule, *Southern Plains*, pp. 4–42; Rule, *Northern Plains*, pp. 8–35.

19. *Statistical Abstract of the United States, 1931*, pp. 8–9; Wilson, Wilcox, Klemmedson, and Parr, *loc. cit.*, p. 17; Hargreaves, *op. cit.*, p. 43; C. M. Harger, "Modern Methods in the Cattle Industry," *Outlook*, **72** (Sept. 6, 1902), pp. 39–47.

20. Harger, *loc. cit.*, pp. 41, 47; *Montana Stockman and Farmer* (May 15, 1902), p. 1; *ibid.* (May 1, 1904), p. 5; *ibid.* (May 15, 1904), p. 3; *ibid.* (Oct. 1, 1905), p. 24; *Twelfth Census of the United States: Agriculture,* **5** (Washington: GPO, 1902), clix; *Statistical Abstract of the U.S., 1931*, pp. 678–679.

21. R. S. Fletcher, "The End of the Open Range in Eastern Montana," *Mississippi Valley Historical Review,* **16** (Sept., 1929), 207, 210; W.P.A., Historical Records Survey for Fergus County, informant and subject, Joseph F. Vanek, mss. Montana State College collection (Bozeman, Mont., Dec. 19, 1939); B. W. Allred, *Range Conservation Practices for the Great Plains* (USDA Misc. Pub. 410, 1940), p. 15; Twelfth Census, *op. cit.*

22. Quote, Nelson Klose, *The Introduction, Improvement, and Adaptation of Sorghum Varieties in Texas* (M.A. thesis, Austin: Univ. of Texas, 1937), pp. 32–33; *The Independent* (Oct. 22, 1903), p. 4; W.P.A. Historical Records Survey for Fergus County, *loc. cit.; Montana Stockman and*

Farmer (Apr. 15, 1903), p. 10; *ibid.* (Oct. 15, 1903), p. 12; Klose, *op. cit.*, p. 34.

23. W. C. Barnes, "Brahman or Zebu Cattle," *The Producer*, 9 (Apr., 1928), 3–6; C. L. Douglas, "How the Hump-Backed Cattle Found Their Way to Texas," *The Cattleman*, 22 (Apr., 1936), 20–26.

24. H. B. Pingrey, *Cattle Ranching in Southeastern New Mexico* (New Mexico Agri. Exp. Sta. Bul. 336, 1948), p. 6; Maurice Haag (ed.), *The Range Lands of Wyoming* (Wyoming Exp. Sta. Bul. 289, 1949), p. 29; H. C. Hanson, "Administration of Western State Lands for Grazing," *The Producer*, 9 (June, 1927), 5.

25. Barker, *loc. cit.*, p. 308; Frank W. Blackmar, "Kansas After the Drought," *American Monthly Review of Reviews*, 24 (Sept., 1901), 317–318; *Montana Stockman and Farmer* (June 15, 1903).

26. Twelfth Census, *op. cit.*, p. 702.

27. Twelfth Census, *op. cit.*, pp. 422, 438, 456, 458, 462, 466, 470, 480, 494; *ibid.*, p. cliii.

28. R. S. Fletcher, *Organization of the Range Cattle Business in Montana* (Montana Agri. Exp. Sta. Bul. 265, 1932), p. 53.

29. R. T. Ely and G. S. Wehrwein, *Land Economics* (New York: Macmillan, 1940), p. 305; Samuel T. Dana, *Forest and Range Policy: Its Development in the United States* (New York: McGraw-Hill, 1956), pp. 115–116.

30. Memorial, Roaring Fork and Eagle River Stock Growers Association, Glenwood Springs, Colorado, Oct. 11, 1905, G-Cooperation, Region 2, Division of Range Management, National Archives, RG 95; Dana, *op. cit.*, pp. 142–144.

31. *Guide to the Records in the National Archives*, p. 60; C. L. Gooding, "Quarantining," *Animal Diseases* (USDA Yearbook, 1956), pp. 68–69.

32. C. D. Van Houweling, "Our Battle Against Animal Diseases," *Animal Diseases*, p. 3; A. Hunter Dupree, *Science in the Federal Government* (Cambridge, Mass.: Belknap Press, 1957), p. 166.

33. H. O. Brayer, "Colorado's Cattle Industry," *American Cattle Producer*, 27 (Sept., 1945), 10; Barnes, "Looking Backward," pp. 3–4; Charles A. Burmeister, "Six Decades of Rugged Individualism: The American National Cattlemen's Association, 1898–1955," *Agricultural History*, 30 (Oct., 1956), 145–146.

CHAPTER III

1. *Statistical Abstract of the United States, 1931* (Washington: U.S. Department of Commerce, 1931), pp. 3, 49.

2. Agricultural Marketing Service, *Livestock and Meat Statistics* (USDA Stat. Bul. 230, 1958), p. 283.

3. Agricultural Marketing Service, *loc. cit.*, p. 102.

4. Mont H. Saunderson, *Western Stock Ranching* (Minneapolis: Univ. of Minnesota Press, 1950), p. 26; Glenn K. Rule, *Toward Soil Security on the Northern Great Plains* (USDA Farmers' Bul. 1864, 1941), p. 56; M. G.

Burlingame and K. R. Toole, *A History of Montana*, I (New York: Lewis Historical Publishing Co., 1957), 327.

5. M. L. Wilson, R. H. Wilcox, G. S. Klemmedson, and V. V. Parr, *A Study of Ranch Organization and Methods of Range-Cattle Production in the Northern Great Plains Region* (USDA Tech. Bul. 45, 1928), p. 17.

6. *Statistical Abstract of the United States, 1910* (Washington: U.S. Department of Commerce and Labor, 1911), pp. 134–135.

7. Mary W. Hargreaves, *Dry Farming in the Northern Great Plains, 1900–1925* (Cambridge, Mass.: Harvard Univ. Press, 1957), pp. 182–184; G. K. Rule, *Crops Against the Wind on the Southern Great Plains* (USDA Farmers' Bul. 1833, 1939), pp. 4–5; Rule, *Northern Plains*, p. 56.

8. Saunderson, *op. cit.*, pp. 49–50, 26; Rule, *Northern Plains*, p. 56; Wilson, Wilcox, Klemmedson, and Parr, *loc. cit.*, pp. 16–17.

9. *The Producer*, 8 (Denver, Feb., 1927), p. 12.

10. J. J. Wagoner, *History of the Cattle Industry in Southern Arizona, 1540–1940* (Tucson: Univ. of Arizona Press, 1952), p. 77; Resolution, Western South Dakota Stockgrowers' Association, Apr. 14, 1908, Rapid City, G-Cooperation, Region 2, DRM, NA, RG 95.

11. *The Producer*, 8 (Feb., 1927), p. 12; Grazing Chapter—Supervisor's Annual Working Plan, by A. W. Cook, Nov. 1, 1913, G-Allowance, Regn. 2, DRM, NA, RG 95; Marion Clawson, *The Western Range Livestock Industry* (New York: McGraw-Hill, 1950), p. 262.

12. Grazing Report, Crazy Mountains Nat'l. Forest, 1907, by E. C. Russell, Supervisor, Nov. 12, 1907, G-Allowances, Region 1, DRM, NA, RG 95.

13. Kansas Nat'l. Forest, Grazing Rpt.—1908, by B. R. H. d'Allemand, Supervisor, Halsey, Neb., Dec. 13, 1908, G-Allowances, Region 2, DRM, NA, RG 95; Letter, Hans Olson, Medicine Bow Forest Reserve Cattle Protective Assn., Laramie, Wyo., to Gifford Pinchot, Forester, Wash., Jan. 12, 1908, *ibid.*

14. John H. Hatton, "National-Forest Grazing Regulations," *The Producer*, 4 (April, 1923), 5–9; Annual Grazing Rpt. on Kansas Nat'l. Forest, by B. R. H. d'Allemand, Supervisor, Halsey, Neb., Nov. 12, 1910, G-Allowances, Region 2, DRM, NA, RG 95; Wagoner, *op. cit.*, p. 79.

15. An animal unit was one steer or horse. Other animals were assigned values as parts of this unit, depending on the amount of feed they consumed. Two sheep, for example, made up one animal unit.

16. Wagoner, *op. cit.*, p. 76; *The Producer*, 8 (Feb., 1927), 12; Hatton, *loc. cit.*, pp. 5–9.

17. Hatton, *loc. cit.*, pp. 5–6.

18. B. W. Allred, *Range Conservation Practices for the Great Plains* (USDA Misc. Pub. 410, 1940), p. 15.

19. J. T. Schlebecker, "The World Metropolis and the History of American Agriculture," *Journal of Economic History*, 20 (June, 1960), 187–208.

20. Sanford A. Mosk, "Land Policy and Stock Raising in the Western United States," *Agricultural History*, 17 (Jan., 1943), 25; Kansas Nat'l. Forest, Grazing Rpt.—1908, by B. R. H. d'Allemand, Supervisor, Halsey, Neb., Dec. 13, 1908, G-Allowances, Region 2, DRM, NA, RG 95; *The Independent* (Miles City, Mont., Feb. 26, 1908), p. 2.

21. Kansas Nat'l. Forest, Grazing Rpt.—1908, *loc. cit.;* H. G. Reynolds and F. H. Tschirley, *Mesquite Control on Southwestern Rangeland* (USDA Leaflet 421, 1957), p. 2.

22. Charles V. Piper, *Forage Plants and Their Culture* (New York: Macmillan, 1947), pp. 248–249.

23. Kansas Nat'l. Forest, Grazing Rpt.—1908, *loc. cit.*

24. *Statistical Abstract of the United States, 1931,* p. 700; Nelson Klose, *The Introduction, Improvement and Adaptation of Sorghum Varieties in Texas* (M.A. thesis, Austin: Univ. of Texas, 1937), p. 94.

25. J. T. Schlebecker, "Pliant Prairie—One Plant's Influence on One Prairie State," *Montana, the Magazine of Western History,* 8 (Winter, 1958), 30–41.

26. W. C. Barnes, "Brahman or Zebu Cattle," *The Producer,* 9 (May, 1928), 3–6; C. L. Douglas, "How the Hump-Backed Brahma Cattle Found Their Way to Texas," *The Cattleman,* 22 (Fort Worth, Apr., 1936), 20–26.

27. Douglas, *loc. cit.,* pp. 20–26; Tom Lea, *The King Ranch* (Boston: Little, Brown, 1957), II, 648.

28. "Compulsory Use of Pure-Breds," *The Producer,* 3 (July, 1921), 6–8.

29. "Compulsory Use of Pure-Breds," *loc. cit.*

30. C. D. Van Houweling, "Our Battle against Animal Diseases," *Animal Diseases* (USDA Yearbook, 1956), pp. 3–4; *The Producer,* 5 (Feb., 1924), 37; T. Swann Harding, *Two Blades of Grass* (Norman: Univ. of Oklahoma Press, 1947), p. 151; Rpt., W. R. Mattoon, Forest Supervisor, Wichita Nat'l. Forest, Cache, Okla., to the Forester, Wash., D.C., Nov. 7, 1907, G-Allowances, Region 3, DRM, NA, RG 95; Rpt., Frank Rush, Acting Forest Supervisor, Wichita Nat'l. Forest, Cache, Okla., to the Forester, Wash., D.C., Dec. 1, 1908, *ibid.;* Rpt., Frank Rush, Game Warden in Charge, Wichita Nat'l. Forest, Cache, Okla., to Dist. Forester, Albuquerque, N.M., Dec. 10, 1910, *ibid.*

31. Aubrey B. Larsen and Howard W. Johnson, "Paratuberculosis (Johne's Disease)," *Animal Diseases,* p. 221; John C. Lotze, D. W. Gates, and T. O. Roby, "Anaplasmosis of Cattle," *Animal Diseases,* p. 269.

32. *Annual and Seasonal Precipitation at Six Representative Locations in Montana* (Montana Agri. Exp. Sta. Bul. 447, 1947), pp. 6, 12, 18, 30; Rpt., W. R. Mattoon, Forest Supervisor, Wichita Nat'l. Forest, Cache, Okla., to the Forester, Wash., D.C., Nov. 7, 1907, G-Allowances, Region 3, DRM, NA, RG 95; Annual Grazing Rpt., Absaroka Nat'l. Forest, V. G. Lantry, Supervisor, Livingston, Mont., Dec. 2, 1908, G-Allowances, Region 1, *ibid.;* Annual Grazing Rpt. Arapaho Nat'l. Forest, by C. J. Stahl, Supervisor, Sulphur Springs, Colo., Dec. 2, 1908, G-Allowances, Region 2, *ibid.;* Rpt., Frank Rush, Actg. Forest Supervisor, Wichita Nat'l. Forest, Cache, Okla., to Forester, Wash., D.C., Dec. 1, 1908, G-Allowances, Region 3, *ibid.;* Rpt., Frank Rush, Game Warden in Charge, Wichita Nat'l. Forest, Cache, Okla., to Dist. Forester, Albuquerque, N.M., Nov. 27, 1909, *ibid.;* Letter, P. D. Kelleter, Forest Supervisor, Deadwood, S.D., to the Dist. Forester, Dec. 1, 1909, G-Allowances, Region 2, *ibid.;* Annual Grazing Rpt., Kansas Nat'l. Forest, by B. R. H. d'Allemand, Supervisor, Halsey, Neb., Dec. 5, 1909, *ibid.*

33. Letter, W. E. Jackson, Forest Supervisor, Big Horn, Wyo., to Forester, Wash., D.C., Dec. 16, 1907, G-Allowances, Region 2, DRM, NA, RG 95; Letter, E. M. Hamilton, Actg. Supervisor, Deadwood, S.D., to the Forester, Wash., D.C., Dec. 12, 1907, *ibid.;* Grazing Rpt., Yellowstone, 1907, E. C. Russell, Supervisor, Livingston, Mont., Nov. 9, 1907, G-Allowances, Region 1, *ibid.;* Kansas Nat'l. Forest, Grazing Rpt., 1908, by B. R. H. d'Allemand, Halsey, Neb., Dec. 13, 1908, G-Allowances, Region 2, *ibid.;* Letter, W. E. Jackson, Forest Supervisor, Big Horn, Wyo., to Forester, Wash., D.C., Nov. 16, 1908, *ibid.;* Letter, E. M. Hamilton, Forest Supervisor, Deadwood, S.D., to the Dist. Forester, Denver, Dec. 7, 1908, *ibid.*

34. Quote, Annual Grazing Rpt., Kansas Nat'l. Forest, by B. R. H. d'Allemand, Supervisor, Halsey, Neb., Dec. 5, 1909, G-Allowances, Region 2, DRM, NA, RG 95; Annual Grazing Rpt., W. E. Jackson, Big Horn, Wyo., to Dist. Forester, Dec. 1, 1909, *ibid.;* Letter, P. D. Kelleter, Forest Supervisor, Deadwood, S.D., to the Dist. Forester, Denver, Dec. 1, 1909, *ibid.;* Annual Grazing Rpt., Arapaho Nat'l. Forest, by C. G. Poole, Supervisor, Sulphur Springs, Colo., Dec. 14, 1909, *ibid.*

35. Quote, Annual Grazing Rpt., Big Horn Nat'l. Forest, E. N. Kavanagh, Forest Supervisor, to Dist. Forester, Nov. 10, 1910, G-Allowances, Region 2, DRM, NA, RG 95; Annual Grazing Rpt., Black Hills Nat'l. Forest, William Wiehe, Actg. Forest Supervisor, to Dist. Forester, Denver, Nov. 15, 1910, *ibid.;* Arapaho Nat'l. Forest, Grazing Rpt. for 1910, Arthur W. Cook, Supervisor, Dec. 31, 1910, *ibid.*

36. C. W. Thornthwaite, "The Great Plains," in Carter Goodrich, *Migration and Economic Opportunity* (Philadelphia: Univ. of Pennsylvania Press, 1936), p. 223; *Annual and Seasonal Precipitation,* pp. 6, 12, 18, 24, 30; Annual Grazing Rpt., Bighorn Nat'l. Forest, E. N. Kavanagh, Forest Supervisor, to Dist. Forester, Nov. 10, 1910, G-Allowances, Region 2, DRM, NA, RG 95; Annual Grazing Rpt., Black Hills (n) Nat'l. Forest, William Wiehe, Actg. Forest Supervisor, to Dist. Forester, Denver, Nov. 15, 1910, *ibid.;* Annual Grazing Rpt., Bighorn Nat'l. Forest, E. N. Kavanagh, Forest Supervisor, to Dist. Forester, Nov. 19, 1910, *ibid.;* Absaroka Annual Rpt., Grazing, 1910, V. G. Lantry, Supervisor, Nov. 12, 1910, G-Allowances, Region 1, *ibid.;* Annual Grazing Rpt., Kansas Nat'l. Forest, B. R. H. d'Allemand, Supervisor, Halsey, Neb., Nov. 12, 1910, G-Allowances, Region 2, *ibid.*

37. *The Cattleman,* 8 (Mar., 1922), 23.

38. Wilson, Wilcox, Klemmedson, and Parr, *loc. cit.,* p. 16; Rudolf A. Clemen, *The American Livestock and Meat Industry* (New York: Ronald Press, 1923), p. 437; Rpt. W. R. Mattoon, Forest Supervisor, Wichita Nat'l. Forest, Cache, Okla., to Forester, Wash., D.C., Nov. 7, 1907, G-Allowances, Region 3, DRM, NA, RG 95; *The Independent* (Aug. 12, 1908); *The Cattleman,* 6 (Jan., 1920), 33.

39. *The Independent* (Sept. 1, 1909); *ibid.* (Oct. 20, 1909); *The Cattleman,* 6 (Jan., 1920), 33; Clemen, *op. cit.*

40. Clemen, *op. cit.,* pp. 286, 288, 291; J. E. Wrenn, "Marketing of American Meat Products in Export Trade," *The Cattleman,* 12 (June, 1925), 39–45.

41. E. N. Wentworth, "Changes in the Center of Beef Production," *The Cattleman*, 8 (Nov., 1921), 16.

42. Thirteenth Census of the U.S., *Agriculture, 1909 and 1910*, 5, "General Report and Analysis" (Washington: GPO, 1913), 67–75; *Statistical Abstract of the United States, 1915* (Washington: U.S. Department of Commerce, 1915), pp. 116–119.

CHAPTER IV

1. C. W. Thornthwaite, "The Great Plains," in Carter Goodrich, *Migration and Economic Opportunity* (Philadelphia: Univ. of Pennsylvania Press, 1936), p. 223; Grazing Rpt., William Wiehe, Deadwood, S.D., to Dist. Forester, Dec. 12, 1911, G-Allowances, Regn. 2, DRM, NA, RG 95; Rpt., Frank Rush, Wichita Nat'l. Forest, Cache, Okla., to Dist. Forester, Albuquerque, Nov. 1, 1911, G-Allowances, Regn. 3, *ibid.; Annual and Seasonal Precipitation at Six Representative Locations in Montana* (Montana Agri. Exp. Sta. Bul. 447, 1947), pp. 6, 13, 18, 24, 30.

2. Supervisor's Working Plan, 1912, A. W. Cook, Fraser, Colo., Dec. 1, 1912, G-Allowances, Regn. 2, *loc. cit.;* Graz. Rpt., Black Hills Nat'l. Forest, Paul Kelleter, Forest Supervisor, Deadwood, S.D., Nov. 18, 1912, *ibid.;* Supervisor's Working Plan, Pecos Nat'l. Forest, Oct. 22, 1914 [cf. 1912], G-Allowances, Regn. 3, *ibid.;* Supervisor's Working Plan, Pecos Nat'l. Forest, Oct. 30, 1912, *ibid.;* Supervisor's Working Plan, Nebraska Nat'l. Forest, H. E. French, Nov. 28, 1912, G-Allowances, Regn. 2, *ibid.; Annual and Seasonal Precipitation*, pp. 6, 13, 19, 24, 31.

3. Supervisor's Working Plan, Sundance Nat'l. Forest, Oct. 25, 1913, G-Allowances, Regn. 2, *loc. cit.;* Supervisor's Working Plan, A. W. Cook, Nov. 1, 1913, *ibid.;* J. M. Stephens, *et al., Report of the Northern Great Plains Field Station for the 10-Year Period, 1913–1922, Inclusive* (USDA Bul. 1301, 1925), pp. 4–5; Supervisor's Working Plan, Nebraska Nat'l. Forest, H. E. French, Nov. 1, 1913, G-Allowances, Regn. 2 *loc. cit.; Annual and Seasonal Precipitation*, pp. 6, 13, 19, 24, 31; Supervisor's Working Plan, Bighorn Nat'l. Forest, E. N. Kavanagh, Oct. 30, 1913, G-Allowances, Regn. 2, *loc. cit.;* Supervisor's Working Plan, Pecos Nat'l. Forest, Oct. 29, 1913, G-Allowances, Regn. 3, *ibid.*

4. Ike T. Pryor, "How Texas Came Back," *The Producer*, 1 (Denver, July, 1919), 14–15; Supervisor's Working Plan, Bighorn Nat'l. Forest, E. N. Kavanagh, Nov. 2, 1914, G-Allowances, Regn. 2, *loc. cit.*

5. Supervisor's Working Plan, Sundance Nat'l. Forest, P. Kelleter, Oct. 29, 1914, G-Allowances, Regn. 2, *loc. cit.;* Supervisor's Working Plan, Absaroka Nat'l. Forest, Dec. 1, 1914, G-Allowances, Regn. 1, *ibid.; Annual and Seasonal Precipitation*, pp. 6, 13, 19, 24, 31.

6. Supervisor's Working Plan, Nebraska Nat'l. Forest, Fred R. Johnson, Nov. 12, 1914, G-Allowances, Regn. 2, *loc. cit.;* John B. Sieglinger, *Grain-Sorghum Experiments at the Woodward Field Station in Oklahoma* (USDA Dept. Bul. 1175, 1923), p. 64; Supervisor's Working Plan, Pecos Nat'l.

Forest, Oct. 22, 1914, G-Allowances, Regn. 3, *loc. cit.;* Supervisor's Working Plan, A. A. Simpson, Nov. 11, 1914, G-Allowances, Regn. 2, *ibid.;* Supervisor's Working Plan, 1914, P. Kelleter, Black Hills Nat'l. Forest, Oct. 28, 1914, *ibid.;* I. T. Pryor, *loc. cit.,* pp. 14–15.

7. Grazing Rpt., William Wiehe, Deadwood, S.D., to Dist. Forester, Denver, Dec. 12, 1911, G-Allowances, Regn. 2, *loc. cit.;* Grazing Rpt., Bighorn Nat'l. Forest, E. N. Kavanagh, Sheridan, Wyo., Nov. 21, 1911, *ibid.*

8. Grazing Rpt., Arapaho Nat'l. Forest, F. L. Brock, Fraser, Colo., Dec. 2, 1911, G-Allowances, Regn. 2, *loc. cit.;* Kansas Nat'l. Forest Grazing Rpt., 1911, B. R. H. d'Allemand, Halsey, Neb., Nov. 14, 1911, *ibid.*

9. Quote, Supervisor's Working Plan, Sundance Nat'l. Forest, Dec. 1, 1912, G-Allowances, Regn. 2, DRM, NA, RG 95; other nearly identical reports: Supervisor's Working Plan, 1912, A. W. Cook, Fraser, Colo., Dec. 1, 1912, *ibid.;* Grazing Rpt., Black Hills Nat'l. Forest, P. Kelleter, Deadwood, S.D., Nov. 18, 1912, *ibid.;* Grazing Rpt., Bighorn Nat'l. Forest, Nov. 21, 1912, *ibid.;* Supervisor's Working Plan, Absaroka Nat'l. Forest, Dec. 12, 1912, G-Allowances, Regn. 1, *ibid.;* Supervisor's Working Plan, Pecos Nat'l. Forest, Oct. 30, 1912, G-Allowances, Regn. 3, *ibid.;* Supervisor's Working Plan, Nebraska Nat'l. Forest, H. E. French, Nov. 28, 1912, G-Allowances, Regn. 2, *ibid.*

10. Quote, *Miles City American* (Miles City, Mont., Oct. 30, 1913), p. 3; Supervisor's Working Plan, Bighorn Nat'l. Forest, E. N. Kavanagh, Oct. 30, 1913, G-Allowances, Regn. 2, *loc. cit.*

11. Supervisor's Working Plan, Nebraska Nat'l. Forest, H. E. French, Nov. 1, 1913, G-Allowances, Regn. 2, *loc. cit.;* Supervisor's Working Plan, Bighorn Nat'l. Forest, E. N. Kavanagh, Oct. 30, 1913, *ibid.;* Grazing Rpt., Absaroka Nat'l. Forest, Dec. 6, 1913, G-Allowances, Regn. 1, *loc. cit.;* Supervisor's Working Plan, 1913, P. T. Smith, Forest Examiner, Oct. 29, 1913, G-Allowances, Regn. 2, *ibid.*

12. "Cattle Scarcity More Pronounced," *Miles City American* (July 16, 1914), p. 2; Supervisor's Working Plan, P. Kelleter, Black Hills Nat'l. Forest, Oct. 28, 1914, G-Allowances, Regn. 2, *loc. cit.;* Supervisor's Working Plan, A. A. Simpson, Nov. 11, 1914 (Colo.), *ibid.;* Supervisor's Working Plan, Bighorn Nat'l. Forest, E. N. Kavanagh, Nov. 2, 1914, *ibid.;* Supervisor's Working Plan, Absaroka Nat'l. Forest, Dec. 1, 1914, G-Allowances, Regn. 1, *ibid.;* Supervisor's Working Plan, Nebraska Nat'l. Forest, Fred R. Johnson, Nov. 12, 1914, G-Allowances, Regn. 2, *ibid.*

13. Letter, L. F. Kneipp, Asst. Forester, Wash., to Dist. Forester, Denver, June 26, 1911, G-Cooperation, Regn. 2, *loc. cit.;* Letter, L. F. Kneipp, Asst. Forester, Wash., to Dist. Forester, Denver, Nov. 29, 1911, *ibid.;* Letter, A. F. Potter, Assoc. Forester, Wash., to Dist. Forester, Denver, Mar. 25, 1911, *ibid.;* Memo to Forest Supervisors, from Dist. Forester Riley, Jan. 5, 1915, G-Cooperation, *ibid.*

14. *Miles City American* (Sept. 11, 1913), p. 1; *ibid.* (Mar. 26, 1914), p. 1; Lewis Nordyke, *Great Roundup* (New York: William Morrow, 1955), p. 223.

15. C. D. Van Houweling, "Our Battle Against Animal Diseases," *Animal Diseases* (USDA Yearbook, 1956), p. 4; A. H. Dupree, *Science in the*

Federal Government (Cambridge, Mass.: Belknap Press, 1957), p. 166.

16. On blackleg: Letter, J. A. Blair, Forest Supervisor, Meeker, Colo., to Dist. Forester, Denver, Dec. 19, 1914, G-Cooperation, Regn. 2, *loc. cit.;* C. L. Gooding, "Quarantining," *Animal Diseases,* pp. 69–70; C. D. Stein, "Blackleg," *Animal Diseases,* p. 264.

17. *American Cattle Producer,* **20** (Apr., 1939), 13.

18. *Miles City American* (Nov. 12, 1914), p. 3.

19. "The Fight against Foot and Mouth Disease," *Miles City American* (Nov. 12, 1914), p. 2; *The Cattleman,* **6** (Fort Worth, Jan., 1920), 33.

20. Arthur W. Sampson, *Livestock Husbandry on Range and Pasture* (New York: John Wiley, 1928), p. 317; "40 Thousand Dollar Loss," *Miles City American* (Dec. 3, 1914), p. 1.

21. E. Louise Peffer, *The Closing of the Public Domain* (Stanford: Stanford Univ. Press, 1951), pp. 139–141.

22. Supervisor's Working Plan, Nebraska Nat'l. Forest, H. E. French, Nov. 28, 1912, G-Allowances, Regn. 2, *loc. cit.*

23. G. K. Rule, *Toward Soil Security on the Northern Great Plains* (USDA Farmers' Bul. 1864, 1941), p. 11; *Statistical Abstract of the United States, 1914* (Washington: U.S. Department of Commerce, 1915), p. 16.

24. Peffer, *op. cit.,* pp. 138, 151–153; Supervisor's Working Plan, A. W. Cook, Nov. 1, 1913, G-Allowances, Regn. 2, *loc. cit.;* "Stockmen Object to Elimination of National Forest," *Miles City American* (Nov. 20, 1913), p. 1.

25. Rule, *Northern Plains,* p. 11; Wilson, Wilcox, Klemmedson, and Parr, *loc. cit.,* p. 16; *Agricultural Statistics, 1957* (Washington: USDA, 1958), pp. 1–2.

26. Bureau of the Census, *Historical Statistics of the United States, 1789–1945* (Washington: U.S. Department of Commerce, 1949); Mary W. Hargreaves, *Dry Farming in the Northern Great Plains, 1900–1925* (Cambridge, Mass.: Harvard Univ. Press, 1957), pp. 168, 185, 189, 190; *Miles City American* (Oct. 30, 1913), p. 1.

27. *Statistical Abstract of the United States, 1921* (Washington: U.S. Department of Commerce, 1922), p. 153; *The Cattleman,* **8** (Mar., 1922), 23; *ibid.,* **6** (Jan., 1920), 33.

28. *Miles City American* (Sept. 11, 1913); Grazing Rpt., Bighorn Nat'l. Forest, Nov. 21, 1912, G-Allowances, Regn. 2, *loc. cit.;* Supervisor's Working Plan, Sundance Nat'l. Forest, Oct. 25, 1913, *ibid.;* Supervisor's Working Plan, Pecos Nat'l. Forest, Oct. 29, 1913, G-Allowances, Regn. 3, *ibid.*

29. Supervisor's Working Plan, Bighorn Nat'l. Forest, E. N. Kavanagh, Nov. 2, 1914, G-Allowances, Regn. 2, *loc. cit.;* "Record Price Paid for Cattle Off Range," *Miles City American* (Nov. 5, 1914).

30. Supervisor's Working Plan, Absaroka Nat'l. Forest, Dec. 12, 1912, G-Allowances, Regn. 1, *loc. cit.;* Supervisor's Working Plan, Bighorn Nat'l. Forest, E. N. Kavanagh, Oct. 30, 1913, G-Allowances, Regn. 2, *ibid.;* Quote, Supervisor's Working Plan, A. W. Cook, Nov. 1, 1913, *ibid.*

31. J. E. Wrenn, "Marketing of American Meat Products in Export Trade," *The Cattleman,* **12** (June, 1925), 42.

32. Agricultural Marketing Service, *Livestock and Meat Statistics,* (USDA Stat. Bul. 230, 1958), pp. 283, 102.

33. T. S. Harding, *Two Blades of Grass* (Norman: Univ. of Oklahoma Press, 1947), p. 128.

34. Supervisor's Working Plan, A. W. Cook, Nov. 1, 1913, G-Allowances, Regn. 2, *loc. cit.;* Supervisor's Working Plan, 1913, P. T. Smith, Oct. 29, 1913, *ibid.*

35. "Wealthy Montana Cattlemen Are Defendants," *Miles City American* (Mar. 26, 1914), p. 7; Charles A. Myers, "Co-operative Range Ownership," *The Producer,* 2 (Feb., 1921), 5–7.

36. Kansas Nat'l. Forest Grazing Rpt., 1911, B. R. H. d'Allemand, Halsey, Neb., Nov. 14, 1911, G-Allowances, Regn. 2, *loc. cit.,* Supervisor's Working Plan, A. W. Cook, Nov. 1, 1913, *ibid.;* Myers, *loc. cit.,* p. 6.

37. John H. Hatton, "National-Forest Grazing Regulations," *The Producer,* 4 (April, 1923), 7; Samuel T. Dana, *Forest and Range Policy: Its Development in the United States* (New York: McGraw-Hill, 1956), p. 146; Grazing Rpt., Bighorn Nat'l. Forest, E. N. Kavanagh, Sheridan, Wyo., Nov. 21, 1911, G-Allowances, Regn. 2, *loc. cit.*

38. Dana, *op. cit.,* pp. 183–184.

39. *The Producer,* 8 (Feb., 1927), 12; Supervisor's Working Plan, A. A. Simpson, Nov. 11, 1914, G-Allowances, Regn. 2, *loc. cit.;* Letter, H. S. Bushnell, Forest Supervisor, to Smith Riley, Dist. Forester, Denver, Jan. 23, 1913, *ibid.;* Letter, Acting Dist. Forester, to the Forester, Wash., Nov. 27, 1914, *ibid.*

40. Wilson, Wilcox, Klemmedson, and Parr, *loc. cit.,* p. 16; M. G. Burlingame and K. R. Toole, *A History of Montana* (New York: Lewis Historical Publishing Co., 1957), I, 327–328; Wrenn, *loc. cit.,* p. 43.

CHAPTER V

1. Gilbert C. Fite and J. Reese, *An Economic History of the United States* (Boston: Houghton Mifflin, 1959), pp. 505–508; A. B. Genung, "Agriculture in the World War Period," *An Historical Survey of American Agriculture* (USDA Yearbook Separate 1783, 1941), pp. 287–289; J. T. Schlebecker, "The World Metropolis and the History of American Agriculture," *Journal of Economic History,* 20 (June, 1960), 203–204; *The Cattleman,* 6 (Fort Worth, Jan., 1920), 33.

2. *The Cattleman,* 6 (Jan., 1920), 33; George S. Reeves, *A Man from South Dakota* (New York: E. P. Dutton, 1950), p. 13; Genung, *loc. cit.,* pp. 287–289.

3. George Soule and Vincent P. Carosso, *American Economic History* (New York: Dryden Press, 1957), pp. 504–505; C. W. Thornthwaite, "The Great Plains," in Carter Goodrich, *Migration and Economic Opportunity* (Philadelphia: Univ. of Pennsylvania Press, 1936), p. 215; G. K. Rule, *Crops against the Wind on the Southern Great Plains* (USDA Farmers' Bul. 1833, 1939), pp. 4–5; Letter, A. F. Potter, Acting Forester, Wash., to Senator John F. Shafroth, May 3, 1917, G-Supervision, DRM, NA, RG 95; M. L. Wilson, R. H. Wilcox, G. S. Klemmedson, and V. V. Parr, *A Study of*

Ranch Organization and Methods of Range-Cattle Production in the Northern Great Plains Region (USDA Tech. Bul. 45, 1928), p. 17; *The Cattleman*, 4 (Sept., 1917), 5, 47; Fite and Reese, *op. cit.*, pp. 516–517.

4. *The Cattleman*, 6 (Jan., 1920), 33; *ibid.*, 5 (June, 1918), 7; Rudolf A. Clemen, *The American Livestock and Meat Industry* (New York: Ronald Press, 1923), p. 294; *The Cattleman*, 5 (Aug., 1918), 5; Thornthwaite, *loc. cit.*, p. 215.

5. J. E. Wrenn, "Marketing of American Meat Products in Export Trade," *The Cattleman*, 12 (June, 1925), 43.

6. Agricultural Marketing Service, *Livestock and Meat Statistics* (USDA Stat. Bul. 230, 1958), p. 283.

7. *The Cattleman*, 8 (Mar., 1922), 23.

8. Supervisor's Working Plan, Nebraska Nat'l. Forest, by Jay Higgins, Nov. 10, 1916, G-Allowances, Regn. 2, *loc. cit.*; "Range Cattle Sold in East," *Miles City Independent* (Aug. 4, 1916), p. 5; *The Cattleman*, 6 (Jan., 1920), 33; Tom Lea, *The King Ranch* (Boston: Little, Brown, 1957), II, 593.

9. Marion Clawson, *The Western Range Livestock Industry* (New York: McGraw-Hill, 1950), pp. 281–282.

10. Clawson, *op. cit.*, pp. 281–282; "War Finance Corporation Opens Cattle Loans Agencies," *The Cattleman*, 5 (Sept., 1918), 13; *ibid.* (Oct., 1918), 14.

11. Supervisor's Working Plan, Nebraska Nat'l. Forest, Dec. 1, 1915, G-Allowance, Regn. 2, *loc. cit.*; Supervisor's Working Plan, Black Hills Nat'l. Forest, Nov. 29, 1915, *ibid.*; J. B. Sieglinger, *Grain-Sorghum Experiments at the Woodward Field Station in Oklahoma* (USDA Dept. Bul. 1175, 1923), p. 64; *Annual and Seasonal Precipitation at Six Representative Locations in Montana* (Montana Agri. Exp. Sta. Bul. 447, 1947), pp. 6, 13, 19, 24, 31; I. T. Pryor, "How Texas Came Back," *The Producer*, 1 (Denver, July, 1919), 14–15; Thornthwaite, *loc. cit.*, p. 223.

12. W. N. Waddell, "The Drouth and the Tick," *The Cattleman*, 3 (June, 1916), 20; *ibid.* (Sept., 1916), 27; *Annual and Seasonal Precipitation, loc. cit.*; J. T. Starvis, *Effects of Different Systems and Intensities of Grazing upon the Native Vegetation at the Northern Great Plains Field Station* (USDA Dept. Bul. 1170, 1923), p. 7; Supervisor's Working Plan, Bighorn Nat'l. Forest, Nov. 24, 1917, G-Allowances, Regn. 2, *loc. cit.*

13. Pryor, *loc. cit.*, pp. 14–15; *The Cattleman*, 3 (May, 1917), 37; Quote, *Hearings, Committee on Agriculture, House of Rep., 65th U.S. Cong., 2nd Sess., H.R. 9966, Feb. 19, 1918, Part 2* (Washington: GPO, 1918), p. 82; *The Cattleman*, 4 (Aug., 1917), 5, 19; *ibid.* (Sept., 1917), 5; *ibid.* (Nov., 1917), 25; Lea, *op. cit.*, p. 593.

14. Supervisor's Working Plan, Santa Fe Nat'l. Forest, Oct. 26, 1917, G-Allowances, Regn. 3, *loc. cit.*; *The Cattleman*, 3 (May, 1917), 43; Thornthwaite, *loc. cit.*, p. 223; *Annual and Seasonal Precipitation*, pp. 6, 13, 19, 24, 31; Supervisor's Working Plan, Bighorn Nat'l. Forest, 1917, Nov. 24, 1917, G-Allowances, Regn. 2, *loc. cit.*

15. *The Cattleman*, 4 (April, 1918), 23; Supervisor's Working Plan, Santa Fe Nat'l. Forest, Oct. 11, 1918, G-Allowances, Regn. 3, *loc. cit.*; Pryor, *loc.*

cit., p. 15; *The Producer*, 1 (June, 1919), 21; *Annual and Seasonal Precipitation*, *loc. cit.*; H. S. Schell, "Adjustment Problems in South Dakota," *Agricultural History*, 14 (April, 1940), 69–70.

16. Supervisor's Working Plan, Bighorn Nat'l. Forest, Nov. 10, 1915, G-Allowances, Regn. 2, *loc. cit.*; Supervisor's Working Plan, Nebraska Nat'l. Forest, Dec. 1, 1915, *ibid.*; Supervisor's Working Plan, Absaroka Nat'l. Forest, Nov. 19, 1915, G-Allowances, Regn. 1, *loc. cit.*; Supervisor's Working Plan, Santa Fe Nat'l. Forest, Nov. 19, 1915, G-Allowances, Regn. 3, *loc. cit.*

17. Supervisor's Working Plan, Black Hills Nat'l. Forest, Nov. 28, 1916, G-Allowances, Regn. 2, *loc cit.*; Supervisor's Working Plan, Bighorn Nat'l. Forest, Nov. 28, 1916, *ibid.*; Supervisor's Working Plan, Absaroka Nat'l. Forest, Oct. 31, 1916, G-Allowances, Regn. 1, *loc. cit.*; Supervisor's Working Plan, Santa Fe Nat'l. Forest, Oct. 24, 1916, G-Allowances, Regn. 3, *ibid.*; Supervisor's Working Plan, Nebraska Nat'l. Forest, Nov. 10, 1916, G-Allowances, Regn. 2, *ibid.*; *The Cattleman*, 3 (Dec., 1916), 24; Supervisor's Working Plan, Santa Fe Nat'l. Forest, Oct. 24, 1916, G-Allowances, Regn. 3, *loc. cit.*

18. Supervisor's Working Plan, Bighorn Nat'l. Forest, Nov. 24, 1917, G-Allowances, Regn. 2, DRM, NA, RG 95; Supervisor's Working Plan, Black Hills Nat'l. Forest, Nov. 20, 1917, *ibid.*; Supervisor's Working Plan, Absaroka Nat'l. Forest, Nov. 10, 1917, Regn. 1, *loc. cit.*; Supervisor's Working Plan, Nebraska Nat'l. Forest, Nov. 15, 1917, G-Allowances, Regn. 2, *loc. cit.*; *The Cattleman*, 4 (June, 1917), 21; *ibid.* (Nov., 1917), 25.

19. Wilson, Wilcox, Klemmedson, and Parr, *loc. cit.*, p. 17; *The Cattleman*, 5 (June, 1918), 19; Quote, Supervisor's Working Plan, Absaroka Nat'l. Forest, Nov. 23, 1918, G-Allowances, Regn. 1, *loc. cit.*; Grazing Rpt., Bighorn Nat'l. Forest, Oct. 30, 1918, G-Allowances, Regn. 2, *loc. cit.*; Supervisor's Working Plan, Black Hills Nat'l. Forest, Nov. 22, 1918, *ibid.*

20. Memorandum to the Forest Supervisors, from the District Forester, Jan. 5, 1915, G-Cooperation, *loc. cit.*

21. Letter, Will C. Barnes, Assistant Forester, Wash., to Dist. Forester Riley, Denver, Colo., April 27, 1915, G-Cooperation, *loc. cit.*

22. *The Producer*, 2 (Jan., 1921), 34; *ibid.*, 7 (Feb., 1926), 4; *The Cattleman*, 5 (Dec., 1918), 10.

23. Letter, E. W. Nelson, Chief Bio. Survey, to A. F. Potter, Acting Forester, June 6, 1917, G-Cooperation, *loc. cit.*

24. "Fresh Outbreak of Foot and Mouth," *Miles City Independent* (Feb. 12, 1915), p. 3; *ibid.* (Dec. 3, 1915), p. 6; A. H. Dupree, *Science in the Federal Government* (Cambridge, Mass.: Belknap Press, 1957), p. 166; *Guide to the Records in the National Archives* (Washington: GPO, 1948), p. 60; W. J. Hartman, *Annual Report*, Extension Service, Bozeman, Montana; W. C. Patterson and L. O. Mott, "Vesicular Stomatitis—V. S.," *Animal Diseases* (USDA Yearbook, 1956), p. 182.

25. Genung, *loc. cit.*, pp. 280–283; G. K. Rule, *Toward Soil Security on the Northern Great Plains* (USDA Farmers' Bul. 1864, 1941), p. 11.

26. Genung, *loc. cit.*; Bruce Nelson, *Land of the Dacotahs* (Minneapolis: Univ. of Minnesota Press, 1946), pp. 299–300; Supervisor's Working Plan,

Nov. 29, 1915, G-Allowances, Regn. 2, *loc. cit.;* Mary W. Hargreaves, *Dry Farming in the Northern Great Plains, 1900–1925* (Cambridge, Mass.: Harvard Univ. Press, 1957), p. 116.

27. *Statistical Abstract of the United States, 1921* (Washington: U.S. Dept. of Commerce, 1922), p. 181; Supervisor's Working Plan, Bighorn Nat'l. Forest, Nov. 24, 1917, G-Allowances, Regn. 2, *loc. cit.;* Hargreaves, *op. cit.,* p. 207.

28. *Statistical Abstract of the United States, 1921,* pp. 180–181; Nelson, *op. cit.,* p. 300; Joseph K. Howard, *Montana: High, Wide, and Handsome* (New Haven, Conn.: Yale Univ. Press, 1943), p. 279; Wilson, Wilcox, Klemmedson, and Parr, *loc. cit.,* p. 17.

29. *Miles City Independent* (Nov. 12, 1915), p. 4; Hargreaves, *op. cit.,* p. 207; Thornthwaite, *loc. cit.,* p. 215.

30. Supervisor's Working Plan, Santa Fe Nat'l. Forest, Nov. 19, 1915, G-Allowances, Regn. 3, *loc. cit.;* S. S. Metzger, "A Day on the Ranch," *Sunset,* 37 (July, 1916), 47.

31. Ronald Peterson, "Crested Wheat Grass for Northern Plains," *American Cattle Producer,* 20 (Aug., 1938), 12.

32. *The Cattleman,* 4 (Sept., 1917), 5, 47; *ibid.,* 5 (Sept., 1918), 5.

33. *The Cattleman,* 4 (Sept., 1917), 9; Frank Reeves, "West Texas Becoming 'Feed Minded,'" *ibid.,* 23 (Mar., 1937), 61; Fred Shannon, *The Farmer's Last Frontier* (New York: Farrar & Rinehart, 1945), p. 137.

34. Lea, *op. cit.,* pp. 648–649.

35. Supervisor's Working Plan, Black Hills Nat'l. Forest, Nov. 18, 1916, G-Allowances, Regn. 2, *loc. cit.;* Supervisor's Working Plan, Black Hills Nat'l. Forest, Nov. 22, 1918, *ibid.;* J. H. Hatton, "National Forest Grazing Regulations," *The Producer,* 4 (April, 1923), 5–9.

36. Supervisor's Working Plan, Black Hills Nat'l. Forest, Nov. 20, 1917, G-Allowances, Regn. 2, *loc. cit.;* Hatton, *loc. cit.;* Letter, Fred Morrell, Acting Dist. Forester, Denver, to Melvin S. Wheeler, Secretary, Egeria Park Stock Growers' Assn., April 27, 1918, G-Cooperation, Regn. 2, *loc. cit.;* U.S. Forest Service, G-Cooperation, Regn. 2, Division of Range Management, 1913–1922, File No. 7, *loc. cit.;* Letter, John Hatton, Acting Dist. Forester, Denver, to B. T. Hadley, Secretary, Main Elk Live Stock Assn., Colo., Feb, 20, 1918, G-Cooperation, Regn. 2, *loc. cit.*

37. *The Producer,* 8 (Feb., 1927), 12; Samuel T. Dana, *Forest and Range Policy: Its Development in the United States* (New York: McGraw-Hill, 1956), p. 229; Clawson, *op. cit.,* p. 262; Letter, Representative Edward T. Taylor, 4th Dist., Colo., to the Secretary of Agriculture, April 12, 1917, G-Supervision, *loc. cit.;* Letter, D. F. Houston, Secretary of Agriculture, to Hans Behrmann, Sec., Three Forks Stock Growers and Feeders Assn., Columbine, Colo., Jan. 10, 1917, G-Cooperation, DRM, NA, RG 95.

38. Dana, *op. cit.,* p. 198; Wilson, Wilcox, Klemmedson, and Parr, *loc. cit.,* p. 16.

39. Dana, *op. cit.,* pp. 198–199; Wilson, Wilcox, Klemmedson, and Parr, *loc. cit.,* p. 16; Sanford A. Mosk, "Land Policy and Stock Raising in the

Western United States," *Agricultural History*, 17 (Jan., 1943), 21–22; E. Louise Peffer, *The Closing of the Public Domain* (Stanford, Calif.: Stanford Univ. Press, 1951), pp. 160–163.

CHAPTER VI

1. James H. Shideler, *Farm Crisis, 1919–1923* (Berkeley: Univ. of California Press, 1957), pp. 46–75; Agricultural Marketing Service, *Livestock and Meat Statistics* (USDA Stat. Bul. 230, 1958), pp. 102, 283.

2. M. G. Burlingame and K. R. Toole, *A History of Montana* (New York: Lewis Historical Publishing Co., 1957), I, 328; I. T. Pryor, "How Texas Came Back," *The Producer*, 1 (Denver, July, 1919), 15; *The Cattleman*, 6 (Fort Worth, Jan., 1920), 33; Supervisor's Working Plan, Nebraska Nat'l. Forest, Nov. 7, 1919, G-Allowances, Regn. 2, DRM, NA, RG 95; Flossie Burson, *The Transition of Agriculture in the Great Plains from 1920 to 1929* (M.S. thesis, Ames: Iowa State University, 1934), p. 21.

3. Burson, *op. cit.*, p. 21; M. L. Wilson, R. H. Wilcox, G. S. Klemmedson, and V. V. Parr, *A Study of Ranch Organization and Methods of Range-Cattle Production in the Northern Great Plains Region* (USDA Tech. Bul. 45, 1928), p. 18; Marion Clawson, *The Western Range Livestock Industry* (New York: McGraw-Hill, 1950), p. 248; *The Cattleman*, 8 (Mar., 1922), 21; John A. Hopkins, *Economic History of the Production of Beef Cattle in Iowa* (Iowa City: Iowa Historical Society, 1928), p. 61.

4. Quote, Supervisor's Working Plan, Nebraska Nat'l. Forest, by Jay Higgins, Supervisor, Nov. 25, 1921, G-Management, Regn. 2, *loc. cit.*; *The Producer*, 3 (July, 1921), 41; Supervisor's Working Plan, Black Hills Nat'l. Forest, Dec. 2, 1921, G-Management, Regn. 2, *loc. cit.*

5. *The Producer*, 2 (Jan., 1921), 29; L. C. Brite, "Some Problems of the Livestock Industry," *The Cattleman*, 8 (June, 1921), 31.

6. *The Producer*, 4 (Nov., 1922), 24; *ibid.* (Dec., 1922), 13; *The Cattleman*, 10 (Nov., 1923), 33; *The Producer*, 4 (Nov., 1922), 20–21; J. E. Wrenn, "Marketing of American Meat Products in Export Trade," *The Cattleman*, 12 (June, 1925), 43–44.

7. The U.S. Dept. of Agriculture figures for all cattle slaughtered under federal inspection are used after 1921, but with caution and some modification since these figures do not adequately reflect the rather lower prices paid for Great Plains range cattle. Prices taken from: *The Cattleman*, 8 (Mar., 1922), 23; Wilson, Wilcox, Klemmedson, and Parr, *loc. cit.*, p. 17; *Livestock and Meat Statistics*, p. 204; *The Producer*, 4 (Sept., 1922), 27–28, 33.

8. *The Producer*, 4 (July, 1922), 23–25; *ibid.*, 6 (July, 1924), 26.

9. Henry T. Murray, *State Land Management in Montana* (M.S. thesis, Bozeman: Montana State College, 1942), p. 10; *The Producer*, 1 (Nov., 1919), 30; *ibid.* (Mar., 1920), 24; *ibid.*, 2 (Oct., 1920), 21.

10. *The Producer*, 2 (April, 1921), 17–18; *The Cattleman*, 8 (July, 1921), 7; *ibid.* (June, 1921), 5; *The Producer*, 3 (Nov., 1921), 13; *ibid.* (Feb., 1922), 20; Clawson, *op. cit.*, p. 282.

11. *The Producer*, 3 (Aug., 1921), 20.

12. *The Cattleman*, 8 (May, 1922), 32; Memo, Will C. Barnes, Asst. Forester, to W. B. Greeley, Chief Forester, Jan. 13, 1923, G-Cooperation, Washington Office, *loc. cit.*

13. *The Producer*, 4 (Dec., 1922), 16–17.

14. Oscar E. Anderson, Jr., *Refrigeration in America* (Princeton: Princeton Univ. Press for the Univ. of Cincinnati, 1953), p. 248; *The Producer*, 1 (June, 1919), 13; *The Cattleman*, 6 (Dec., 1919), 36.

15. Anderson, *op. cit.;* Lewis Nordyke, *Great Roundup* (New York: William Morrow, 1955), p. 226; *The Producer*, 2 (Oct., 1920), 22.

16. "The Uninvited Guest," *The Producer*, 2 (Feb., 1921), 23; *The Producer*, 2 (Mar., 1921), 21; "Summary of the Law": *ibid.*, 3 (Aug., 1921), 9–10.

17. *The Producer*, 3 (Nov., 1921), 19; *The Cattleman*, 8 (Nov., 1921), 5; *The Producer*, 3 (Jan., 1922), 13; *The Cattleman*, 8 (May, 1922), 21.

18. J. M. Stephens, *et al.*, *Report of the Northern Great Plains Field Station for the 10-Year Period, 1913–1922, Inclusive* (USDA Dept. Bul. 1301, 1925), pp. 4–5; *The Producer*, 1 (July, 1919), 23; Supervisor's Working Plan, Nebraska Nat'l. Forest, Nov. 7, 1919, G-Allowances, Regn. 2, *loc. cit.;* Grazing Rpt., Bighorn Nat'l. Forest, Nov. 21, 1921, G-Management, *ibid.;* *The Cattleman*, 6 (July, 1919), 13; Grazing Rpt., Santa Fe Nat'l. Forest, Oct. 7, 1919, G-Allowances, Regn. 3, *loc. cit.;* *The Producer*, 1 (Sept., 1919), 27, 41; Supervisor's Working Plan, Black Hills Nat'l. Forest, Nov. 17, 1919, G-Allowances, Regn. 2, *loc. cit.;* *The Producer*, 1 (Oct., 1919), 33.

19. J. T. Starvis, *Effects of Different Systems and Intensities of Grazing Upon the Native Vegetation at the Northern Great Plains Field Station* (USDA Department Bul. 1170, 1923), p. 7; "Northwest Is Hard Hit," *The Producer*, 1 (Jan., 1920), 32; Supervisor's Working Plan, Nebraska Nat'l. Forest, Nov. 23, 1920, G-Allowances, Regn. 2, *loc. cit.;* *The Cattleman*, 6 (April, 1920), 51; Grazing Rpt., Wichita Nat'l. Forest, Dec. 6, 1920, G-Management, Regn. 2, *loc. cit.;* *The Producer*, 2 (Aug., 1920), 22; *Annual and Seasonal Precipitation at Six Representative Locations in Montana* (Montana Agri. Exp. Sta. Bul. 447, 1947), pp. 7, 13, 19, 24, 31; *The Dawson County Review*, 23 (Glendive, Mont., Mar. 18, 1920), 1.

20. *The Producer*, 2 (April, 1921), 17; *The Cattleman*, 8 (Nov., 1921), 21; Supervisor's Working Plan, Nebraska Nat'l. Forest, Nov. 25, 1921, G-Management, Regn. 2, *loc. cit.;* Grazing Rpt., Bighorn Nat'l. Forest, Nov. 21, 1921, *ibid.;* Supervisor's Working Plan, Black Hills Nat'l. Forest, Dec. 2, 1921, *ibid.;* Starvis, *loc. cit.*, p. 7; *Annual and Seasonal Precipitation, loc. cit.*

21. *The Producer*, 4 (Feb., 1923), 26; *ibid.* (June, 1922), 25; Supervisor's Working Plan, Black Hills Nat'l. Forest, Nov. 28, 1922, G-Management, Regn. 2, *loc. cit.;* *The Producer*, 4 (Aug., 1922), 23; *ibid.*, 3 (Mar., 1922), 17, 23; *Annual and Seasonal Precipitation, loc. cit.*

22. Bruce Nelson, *Land of the Dacotahs* (Minneapolis: Univ. of Minn. Press, 1946), p. 301; *The Producer*, 3 (Sept., 1921), 15–16; *ibid.* (July, 1921), 14; *ibid.*, 4 (Nov., 1922), 15.

23. J. T. Schlebecker, "Grasshoppers in American Agricultural History,"

Agricultural History, **27** (July, 1953), 85–93; R. B. Millin, *Annual Report, Livestock,* Extension Service, Bozeman, Montana, 1921; *The Producer,* **3** (Aug., 1921), 21, 23; *ibid.,* **4** (Mar., 1922), 23; *ibid.* (July, 1922), 21; *ibid.* (Nov., 1922), 34.

24. *The Producer,* **1** (July, 1919), 42; *ibid.,* **4** (Dec., 1922), 36; *ibid.,* **2** (Nov., 1920), 44; *ibid.* (Feb., 1921), 41.

25. C. L. Cooding, "Quarantining," *Animal Diseases* (USDA Yearbook, 1956), pp. 68–69; *The Producer,* **2** (Feb., 1921), 29.

26. R. B. Millin, *Annual Report,* Livestock, Extension Service, Bozeman, Montana, 1922, p. 2; C. D. Stein, "Blackleg," *Animal Diseases,* p. 264.

27. Burlingame and Toole, *op. cit.,* p. 328; C. L. Sonnichsen, *Cowboys and Cattle Kings* (Norman: Univ. of Oklahoma Press, 1950), pp. 14–15; *The Producer,* **1** (Oct., 1919), 25; Supervisor's Working Plan, Absaroka Nat'l. Forest, Nov. 6, 1920, G-Allowances, Regn. 1, *loc. cit.;* Wilson, Wilcox, Klemmedson, and Parr, *loc. cit.,* p. 17; C. W. Thornthwaite, "The Great Plains," in Carter Goodrich, *Migration and Economic Opportunity* (Philadelphia: Univ. of Pennsylvania Press, 1936), p. 215; Quote, Interview, B. F. Gordon, Lewistown, Mont., W.P.A. Historical Records Survey, Fergus County, mss. Montana State College collection (Bozeman, Mont., 1936).

28. *The Producer,* **3** (Aug., 1921), 21; *ibid.,* **2** (Feb., 1921), 27; *ibid.,* **4** (Nov., 1922), 24; *ibid.* (Dec., 1922), 29.

29. Fourteenth Census of the U.S., *Agriculture,* **5,** "General Report and Analytical Tables" (Washington: GPO, 1922), pp. 555–559; *Statistical Abstract of the United States, 1931* (Washington: U.S. Department of Commerce, 1931), pp. 678–679.

30. Fourteenth Census, *op. cit.;* E. N. Wentworth, "Changes in the Center of Beef Production," *The Cattleman,* **8** (Nov., 1921), 16.

31. Mary W. Hargreaves, *Dry Farming in the Northern Great Plains, 1900–1925* (Cambridge, Mass.: Harvard Univ. Press, 1957), pp. 207–208, 19; *Abstract of the Fourteenth Census of the U.S., 1920* (Washington: U.S. Department of Commerce, 1923), pp. 821–822; *Statistical Abstract of the United States, 1921,* pp. 143–146; G. K. Rule, *Toward Soil Security on the Northern Great Plains* (USDA Farmers' Bul. 1864, 1941), p. 21; Nelson, *op. cit.,* p. 300; Grazing Rpt., Bighorn Nat'l. Forest, Nov. 5, 1920, G-Allowances, Regn. 2, *loc. cit.;* Wilson, Wilcox, Klemmedson, and Parr, *loc. cit.,* p. 17; J. E. Hult, "Dry Land Farmers Are Hard Up—But So Is Everybody," *Ekalaka Eagle* (Ekalaka, Mont., Nov. 25, 1921), p. 5; *Ekalaka Eagle* (Apr. 8, 1921), p. 1.

32. Nelson, *op. cit.,* p. 300; Wilson, Wilcox, Klemmedson, and Parr, *loc. cit.,* p. 17; *Kansas Stockman,* **5** (Topeka, Aug. 15, 1921), 4.

33. Harry A. Steele, *Farm Mortgage Foreclosures in South Dakota, 1921–32* (South Dakota Agri. Exp. Sta. Circ. 17, 1934), p. 9; Rule, *Northern Plains,* p. 21.

34. Supervisor's Working Plan, Nebraska Nat'l. Forest, Nov. 7, 1919, G-Allowances, Regn. 2, *loc. cit.;* Supervisor's Working Plan, Absaroka Nat'l. Forest, Dec. 18, 1919, G-Allowances, Regn. 1, *loc. cit.;* Grazing Rpt. Bighorn Nat'l. Forest, Nov. 5, 1919, G-Allowances, Regn. 2, *loc. cit.;* Supervisor's

Working Plan, Black Hills Nat'l. Forest, Nov. 17, 1919, *ibid.;* Grazing Rpt., Bighorn Nat'l. Forest, Nov. 5, 1920, *ibid.; The Producer*, 2 (Sept., 1920), 28; *ibid.*, 3 (June, 1921), 22; *ibid.* (Nov., 1921), 22; Grazing Rpt., Wichita Nat'l. Forest, Dec. 10, 1921, G-Management, Regn. 2, *loc. cit.;* Grazing Rpt., Bighorn Nat'l. Forest, Nov. 21, 1921, *ibid.;* Supervisor's Working Plan, Black Hills Nat'l. Forest, Dec. 2, 1921, *ibid.;* Supervisor's Working Plan, Nebraska Nat'l. Forest, Nov. 25, 1921, *ibid.; The Producer*, 4 (Dec., 1922), 33–34; Grazing Rpt., Wichita Nat'l. Forest, Dec. 1, 1922, G-Management, Regn. 2, *loc. cit.;* Clawson, *op. cit.*, p. 61.

35. *Abstract of the Fourteenth Census*, pp. 831, 850; B. W. Allred, *Range Conservation Practices for the Great Plains* (USDA Misc. Pub. 410, 1940), p. 15.

36. J. J. Wagoner, *History of the Cattle Industry in Southern Arizona, 1540–1940* (Tucson: Univ. of Arizona Press, 1952), p. 57; Harry R. O'Brien, "It Was Livestock or Starve," *Country Gentleman*, 110 (Dec., 1940), 13; W. M. Peterson, "Stock-Feeding and Soil-Building," *The Producer*, 1 (June, 1919), 18–19; Quote, Hargreaves, *op. cit.*, p. 472.

37. Burson, *op. cit.*, p. 12; Rule, *Northern Plains*, p. 56; Burlingame and Toole, *op. cit.*, I, 330–331; O'Brien, *loc. cit.*, p. 13.

38. *Ekalaka Eagle* (Apr., 1921), p. 2.

39. Grazing Rpt., Bighorn Nat'l. Forest, Nov. 21, 1921, G-Management, Regn. 2, *loc. cit.;* Hargreaves, *op. cit.*, p. 212; R. B. Millin, *Annual Report*, Livestock, Extension Service, Bozeman, Montana, 1922, p. 5; *Ekalaka Eagle* (Sept. 8, 1922), p. 2; Peterson, *loc. cit.*, p. 20.

40. Charles V. Piper, *Forage Plants and Their Culture* (New York: Macmillan, 1947), pp. 131–133; Peterson, *loc. cit.*, p. 19; T. S. Harding, *Two Blades of Grass* (Norman: Univ. of Oklahoma Press, 1947), p. 105; Sam Freed, "The Beet-Sugar Industry in Its Relation to Live Stock," *The Producer*, 2 (Dec., 1920), 5.

41. Harding, *op. cit.*, p. 129.

42. Letter, Fred Morrell, Acting Dist. Forester, to J. C. Thexton, Secretary, Elk Park Livestock Assn., May 16, 1919, G-Cooperation, Regn. 2, *loc cit;* John E. Pickett, "White Faces," *Country Gentleman*, 84 (Jan. 18, 1919), 5.

43. J. W. Mantz, "The Charollaise Beef Look," *American Cattle Producer*, 37 (Denver, Jan., 1956), 32.

44. "Brahma Cattle Increasing—A Little of Their Early History in Texas," *The Cattleman*, 6 (July, 1919), 23; Tom Lea, *The King Ranch* (Boston: Little, Brown, 1957), II, 650–651.

45. John H. Hatton, "National Forest Grazing Regulations," *The Producer*, 4 (April, 1923), 7–8; *The Producer*, 8 (Feb., 1927), 12; Clawson, *op. cit.*, p. 262; Samuel T. Dana, *Forest and Range Policy: Its Development in the United States* (New York: McGraw-Hill, 1956), p. 229; *The Producer*, 3 (July, 1921), 17; *ibid.*, 1 (Mar., 1920), 15.

46. *The Producer*, 1 (June, 1919), 35; *ibid.* (June, 1919), 9; *ibid.*, 2 (Sept., 1920), 29.

47. *The Producer*, 2 (Dec., 1920), 21.

CHAPTER VII

1. *Statistical Abstract of the United States, 1931* (Washington: U.S. Department of Commerce, 1931), pp. 7–8.

2. Agricultural Marketing Service, *Livestock and Meat Statistics* (USDA Stat. Bul. 230, 1958), p. 102.

3. *Kansas Stockman,* 7 (Topeka, Apr. 1, 1923), 3; Supervisor's Working Plan, Black Hills Nat'l. Forest, Nov. 30, 1923, G-Management, Region 2, DRM, NA, RG 95; Supervisor's Working Plan, Nebraska Nat'l. Forest, Dec. 8, 1923, *ibid.; The Producer,* 5 (Denver, Jan., 1924), 12; *Annual and Seasonal Precipitation at Six Representative Locations in Montana* (Montana Agri. Exp. Sta. Bul. 447, 1947), pp. 7, 13, 19, 24, 31; Supervisor's Working Plan, Wichita Nat'l. Forest, Dec. 31, 1923, G-Management, Regn. 2, *loc. cit.; The Producer,* 5 (June, 1923), 35; *The Cattleman,* 10 (Fort Worth, June, 1923), 45; *The Producer,* 5 (Sept., 1923), 34.

4. *The Producer,* 6 (Nov., 1924), 30; *Annual and Seasonal Precipitation, loc. cit.*

5. *The Producer,* 6 (Apr., 1925), 30; *ibid.* (May, 1925), 10; *The Cattleman,* 12 (June, 1925), 29; *The Producer,* 7 (July, 1925), 15; *The Cattleman,* 12 (Aug., 1925), 37; *The Producer,* 7 (Nov., 1925), 18; *Annual and Seasonal Precipitation, loc. cit.; The Producer,* 6 (Apr., 1925), 30; *ibid.,* 7 (July, 1925), 15.

6. *The Producer,* 5 (Feb., 1924), 37.

7. Arthur W. Sampson, *Livestock Husbandry on Range and Pasture* (New York: Wiley, 1928), p. 317; *The Producer,* 6 (July, 1924), 7; "30 Years Ago," *American Hereford Journal,* 45 (Sept. 15, 1954), 122, 219; *The Producer,* 6 (Oct., 1924), 12; *ibid.* (Aug., 1924), 31; T. S. Harding, *Two Blades of Grass* (Norman: Univ. of Oklahoma Press, 1947), p. 161.

8. *Kansas Stockman,* 9 (Sept. 15, 1925), 4; *The Producer,* 7 (Sept., 1925), 10; *Kansas Stockman,* 9 (Nov. 1, 1925), 6.

9. *The Producer,* 7 (June, 1925), 18; W. C. Patterson and L. O. Mott, "Vesicular Stomatitis—V. S.," *Animal Diseases* (USDA Yearbook, 1956), pp. 182–183; Charles V. Piper, *Forage Plants and Their Culture* (New York: Macmillan, 1947), p. 72.

10. A. Dale Saunders, *Trends in Size, Land Tenure, Income, Organization, and Management of Selected Cattle Ranches in Southeastern Montana, 1924–48* (M.S. thesis, Bozeman: Montana State College, 1949), p. 7; *The Producer,* 6 (Nov., 1924), 24; *Livestock and Meat Statistics,* p. 283; *Kansas Stockman,* 7 (Apr. 15, 1923), 9; Supervisor's Working Plan, Black Hills Nat'l. Forest, Nov. 30, 1923, G-Management, Regn. 2, *loc. cit.;* Supervisor's Working Plan, Dec. 8, 1923, *ibid.;* Supervisor's Working Plan, Wichita Nat'l. Forest, Dec. 31, 1923, *ibid.*

11. Supervisor's Working Plan, Wichita Nat'l. Forest, Dec. 31, 1923, G-Management, Regn. 2, *loc. cit.*

12. M. L. Wilson, R. H. Wilcox, G. S. Klemmedson, and V. V. Parr, *A Study of Ranch Organization and Methods of Range-Cattle Production in the Northern Great Plains Region* (USDA Tech. Bul. 45, 1928), p. 43.

13. Wilson, Wilcox, Klemmedson, and Parr, *loc. cit.*, p. 18; Herbert O. Brayer, "Colorado's Cattle Industry," *American Cattle Producer*, 27 (Denver, Sept. 1945), 22.

14. *Livestock and Meat Statistics*, p. 204.

15. Saunders, *op. cit.*, pp. 46, 47.

16. *The Cattleman*, 10 (April, 1924), 19; Marion Clawson, *The Western Range Livestock Industry* (New York: McGraw-Hill, 1950), p. 282; *The Producer*, 5 (Sept., 1923), 20; Harry A. Steele, *Farm Mortgage Foreclosures in South Dakota, 1921–1932* (South Dakota Agr. Exp. Sta. Circ. 17, 1934), p. 9.

17. Bruce Nelson, *Land of the Dacotahs* (Minneapolis: Univ. of Minnesota, 1946), pp. 303–304.

18. Nelson, *op. cit.*, pp. 303–304; "Intermediate Credit Banks," *The Producer*, 6 (Dec., 1924), 11; Saunders, *op. cit.*, pp. 7, 47; Wilson, Wilcox, Klemmedson, and Parr, *loc. cit.*, p. 18; Steele, *loc. cit.*, p. 9.

19. *The Producer*, 6 (June, 1924), 17.

20. *The Producer*, 4 (May, 1923), 19; *ibid.* (Mar., 1923), 12–13; *ibid.* (May, 1926), 13; *ibid.* (Mar., 1925), 19.

21. *The Producer*, 4 (Jan., 1923), 20; *ibid.* (April, 1923), 16.

22. *Kansas Stockman*, 7 (Feb. 15, 1923), 13; *The Producer*, 4 (Feb., 1923), 43; *The Cattleman*, 10 (June, 1923), 57; *The Producer*, 5 (Sept., 1923), 34; *The Cattleman*, 10 (Nov., 1923), 47; Supervisor's Working Plan, Bighorn Nat'l. Forest, Nov. 24, 1923, G-Management, Regn. 2, *loc. cit.*; *The Producer*, 6 (Nov., 1924), 30; V. V. Parr, G. W. Collier, and G. S. Klemmedson, *Ranch Organization and Methods of Livestock Production in the Southwest* (USDA Tech. Bul. 68, 1928), pp. 33–35; *The Producer*, 7 (Dec., 1925), 30.

23. Saunders, *op. cit.*, pp. 31–32; Parr, Collier, and Klemmedson, *loc. cit.*, pp. 33–35.

24. L. J. Norton, "Some Recent Changes in Meat and Feed Crop Production," *Journal of Farm Economics*, 9 (July, 1927), 311–317; Saunders, *op. cit.*, pp. 38–39.

25. C. A. Bonnen and B. H. Thibodeaux, *A Description of Agriculture and Type-of-Farming Areas in Texas* (Texas Agri. Exp. Sta. Bul. 544, 1937), p. 20; C. W. Thornthwaite, "The Great Plains," in Carter Goodrich, *Migration and Economic Opportunity* (Philadelphia: Univ. of Pennsylvania Press, 1936), pp. 215–216.

26. G. K. Rule, *Crops against the Wind on the Southern Great Plains* (USDA Farmers' Bul. 1833, 1939), pp. 4–5; Quote, *The Producer*, 5 (Jan., 1924), 9.

27. "Passing of the South Plains Ranches," *The Cattleman*, 10 (Mar., 1924), 59–61; *The Cattleman*, 10 (Jan., 1924), 31; Flossie Burson, *The Transition of Agriculture in the Great Plains from 1920 to 1929* (M.S. thesis, Ames: Iowa State University, 1934), p. 23.

28. John C. Burns, "Value of Beef Cattle in Diversified Farms," *The Cattleman*, 12 (June, 1925), 35; Wilson, Wilcox, Klemmedson, and Parr, *loc. cit.*, p. 18.

29. Mary W. Hargreaves, *Dry Farming in the Northern Great Plains*,

1900–1925 (Cambridge, Mass.: Harvard Univ. Press, 1957), p. 200.

30. Nelson, *op. cit.*, p. 302; Burson, *op. cit.*, p. 29.

31. Burns, *loc. cit.*, p. 35; William Peterson, *et al.*, *Cattle Ranching in Utah* (Utah Agr. Exp. Sta. Bul. 203, 1927), p. 37; *The Producer*, 7 (July, 1925), 15; *The Cattleman*, 12 (Dec., 1925), 39; Parr, Collier, and Klemmedson, *loc. cit.*, pp. 22–23.

32. "A *pasture* is a field or area covered with grass or other plants (commonly herbaceous) and used for grazing animals. The product of pastures is called *pasturage. Permanent pastures* are those covered with perennial or self-seeding annual plants and are kept for grazing indefinitely. In many cases, such pastures are seldom or never plowed. *Rotation* (or *short lay*) *pastures* are those used for a few years' lay, usually only two or three, and then plowed up to plant crops. Temporary pastures are those used for grazing during a short period, not more than one crop season." Charles V. Piper, *Forage Plants and Their Culture* (New York: Macmillan, 1947), p. 102; See also, for part of the development, Hargreaves, *op. cit.*, pp. 213–214.

33. Quote, letter from F. A. Welty to the editor, *The Producer*, 6 (Dec., 1924), 17; Saunders, *op. cit.*, p. 30; Wilson, Wilcox, Klemmedson, and Parr, *loc. cit.*, p. 24.

34. *The Producer*, 6 (Sept., 1924), 29; Wilson, Wilcox, Klemmedson, and Parr, *loc. cit.*, pp. 34–37.

35. Wilson, Wilcox, Klemmedson, and Parr, *loc. cit.*, pp. 21–22, 29.

36. Parr, Collier, and Klemmedson, *loc. cit.*, p. 59; *The Producer*, 7 (June, 1925), 31; Peterson, *loc. cit.*, pp. 21, 28.

37. *American Cattle Producer*, 37 (Sept., 1955), 8; Wilson, Wilcox, Klemmedson, and Parr, *loc. cit.*, p. 31; Peterson, *loc. cit.*, p. 45; Saunders, *op. cit.*, pp. 7, 47.

38. Parr, Collier, and Klemmedson, *loc. cit.*, p. 28.

39. Wilson, Wilcox, Klemmedson, and Parr, *loc. cit.*, p. 38; Saunders, *op. cit.*, p. 50; Peterson, *loc. cit.*, p. 46.

40. Wilson, Wilcox, Klemmedson, and Parr, *loc. cit.*, p. 28; Piper, *op. cit.*, pp. 355, 358, 361, 371–372, 380, 389.

41. Parr, Collier, and Klemmedson, *loc. cit.*, p. 44; Piper, *op. cit.*, pp. 47–48, 318–319, 321–322.

42. Arthur W. Sampson, *Native American Forage Plants* (New York: Wiley, 1924), pp. 112–113, 128, 191; Piper, *op. cit.*, pp. 37, 247, 248.

43. Piper, *op. cit.*, pp. 23–24, 28, 35, 37–38, 43.

44. Piper, *op. cit.*, pp. 39–40, 41; *Ekalaka Eagle* (Ekalaka, Mont., Mar. 16, 1923), p. 2.

45. Matt J. Culley, *An Economic Study of the Cattle Business on a South-Western Semidesert Range* (USDA Circ. 448, 1937), p. 1; Parr, Collier, and Klemmedson, *loc. cit.*, p. 29; Maudeen Marks, "The Brahmans Go Places," *American Cattle Producer*, 31 (Dec., 1949), 43; *American Cattle Producer*, 36 (Feb., 1955), 36; Tom Lea, *The King Ranch* (Boston: Little, Brown, 1957) II, 650.

46. Fourteenth Census of the U.S., *Agriculture*, 5, "General Report and Analytical Tables" (Washington: GPO, 1922), pp. 555–559; Sixteenth Cen-

sus of the U.S., 1940, *Agriculture*, **1**, Part 2 (Washington: GPO, 1942), 213, 321, 371, 457, 565, 707, and Part 6, pp. 5, 175, 223, 323.

47. Supervisor's Working Plan, Black Hills Nat'l. Forest, Nov. 30, 1923, G-Management, Regn. 2, DRM, NA, RG 95.

48. *Statistical Abstract of the United States, 1931*, pp. 640–641; Fifteenth Census of the U.S., 1930, *Agriculture*, **2**, "The Western States" (Washington: GPO, 1932), 25.

49. Wilson, Wilcox, Klemmedson, and Parr, *loc. cit.*, p. 32; *The Producer*, **6** (Oct., 1924), 9; *The News*, **2** (Chicago, June, 1924), 10.

50. Quote, *National Live Stock Producer*, **3** (Chicago, April, 1925), 4; *National Live Stock Producer*, **4** (July, 1926); *The Producer*, **7** (Jan., 1926), 5.

51. Saunders, *op. cit.*, p. 7; Wilson, Wilcox, Klemmedson, and Parr, *loc. cit.*, p. 22; Herbert C. Hanson, "Administration of Western State Lands for Grazing," *The Producer*, **9** (June, 1927), 3–6; "American National Livestock Ass'n. Resolutions, 1923," enclosure, letter, American National Livestock Association to W. B. Greeley, Forester, Feb. 24, 1923, G-Cooperation, Washington Office, *loc. cit.*; *The Producer*, **6** (Dec., 1924), 15; *ibid.* (Oct., 1925), 13.

52. *The Producer*, **4** (Mar., 1923), 13; *ibid.*, **5** (June, 1923), 12; *ibid.*, **6** (Mar., 1925), 13; Samuel T. Dana, *Forest and Range Policy: Its Development in the United States* (New York: McGraw-Hill, 1956), pp. 229–230; Marion Clawson, *op. cit.*, pp. 99, 262.

CHAPTER VIII

1. J. J. Wagoner, *History of the Cattle Industry in Southern Arizona, 1540–1940* (Tucson: Univ. of Arizona Press, 1952), p. 59; Agricultural Marketing Service, *Livestock and Meat Statistics* (USDA Stat. Bul. 230, 1958), p. 283.

2. *Livestock and Meat Statistics*, p. 204.

3. H. M. Conway, *Animal Livestock Market Review, 1926* (Washington: USDA, 1927), p. 6; *Kansas Stockman*, **10** (Topeka, Sept. 1, 1926), 11; John H. Hatton, "Livestock Vicissitudes and Rainbows," *American Cattle Producer*, **22** (Denver, Sept., 1940), 7; *The Producer*, **10** (Oct., 1928), 19.

4. *The Producer*, **9** (Jan., 1928), 21; *Kansas Stockman*, **12** (Jan. 1, 1928), 5.

5. Marion Clawson, *The Western Range Livestock Industry* (New York: McGraw-Hill, 1950), p. 248; Conway, *op. cit.*, pp. 1, 6; Hatton, *loc. cit.*, p. 7; *Kansas Stockman*, **10** (July 15, 1926), 2.

6. Harry A. Steele, *Farm Mortgage Foreclosures in South Dakota, 1921–32* (South Dakota Agri. Exp. Sta. Circ. 17, 1934), p. 10; Annual Rpt., Black Hills Nat'l. Forest, Jan. 8, 1929, G-Management, Region 2, DRM, NA, RG 95; Quote, Annual Rpt., Wichita Nat'l. Forest, Feb. 6, 1929), *ibid.*

7. Quote, *The Producer*, **10** (Jan., 1929), 12; "The Farm Situation," *The Producer*, **11** (Aug., 1929), 19.

8. *The Producer,* 9 (July, 1927), 12; *ibid.* (Sept., 1927), 23; *ibid.* (Dec., 1927), 7.

9. *The Producer,* 8 (Jan., 1927), 19.

10. L. H. Rochford, *Influence of California Demand on Colorado Beef-Cattle Prices* (Colorado Agri. Ext. Serv. Bul. 316-A, 1932), p. 10; Clawson, *op. cit.,* p. 248; L. A. Moorhouse, "Analysis of Ranch Operations—Factors That Make for Success in the Cattle Business," *The Cattleman,* 14 (Fort Worth, Mar., 1928), 83; M. B. Johnson, "Cattle Ranch Operations in Northern Great Plains Region," *The Producer,* 12 (Nov., 1930), 6.

11. Grazing Rpt., Wichita Nat'l. Forest, Feb. 1, 1928, G-Management, Regn. 2, *loc. cit.;* Quote, *National Live Stock Producer,* 5 (Chicago, Sept., 1926), 4.

12. Bruce Nelson, *Land of the Dacotahs* (Minneapolis: Univ. of Minnesota Press, 1946), p. 303.

13. *The Producer,* 8 (June, 1926), 18; Memo for Dist. Forester, from Supervisor, Black Hills Nat'l. Forests, Dec. 9, 1926, G-Management, Regn. 2, *loc. cit.; The Producer,* 8 (Jan., 1927), 31; *Annual and Seasonal Precipitation at Six Representative Locations in Montana* (Montana Agri. Exp. Sta. Bul. 447, 1947), pp. 7, 12, 19, 24, 31; C. W. Thornthwaite, "The Great Plains," in Carter Goodrich, *Migration and Economic Opportunity* (Philadelphia: Univ. of Pennsylvania Press, 1936), p. 223; *The Producer,* 9 (July, 1927), 7; *ibid.,* 8 (Feb., 1927), 17.

14. Annual Rpt., Black Hills Nat'l. Forest, Jan. 8, 1929, G-Management, Regn. 2, *loc. cit.; The Producer,* 10 (Aug., 1928), *Annual and Seasonal Precipitation, loc. cit.; The Producer,* 10 (June, 1928), 15.

15. Memo for Dist. Forester, from Supervisor, Black Hills Nat'l. Forest, Dec. 9, 1926, G-Management, Regn. 2, *loc. cit.;* Annual Rpt., Wichita Nat'l. Forest, Dec. 28, 1926, *ibid.; The Producer,* 8 (July, 1926), 29; *The Cattleman,* 12 (May, 1926), 9.

16. *Kansas Stockman,* 11 (Apr. 15, 1927), 4; Memo for Dist. Forester, from Supervisor, Nebraska Nat'l. Forest, Jan. 14, 1928, G-Management, Regn. 2, *loc. cit.; Kansas Stockman,* 12 (Dec. 1, 1927), 15.

17. Annual Rpt., Wichita Nat'l. Forest, Feb. 6, 1929, G-Management, Regn. 2, *loc. cit.; The Producer,* 19 (Dec., 1928), 30; Annual Rpt., Black Hills Nat'l. Forest, Jan. 8, 1929, G-Management, Regn. 2, *loc. cit.*

18. *The Producer,* 8 (June, 1926), 18; *ibid.,* 9 (Dec., 1927), 17; Memo for Dist. Forester from Supervisor, Black Hills Nat'l. Forest, Jan. 10, 1928, G-Management, Regn. 2, *loc. cit.*

19. Arthur W. Sampson, *Livestock Husbandry on Range and Pasture* (New York: Wiley, 1928), p. 298.

20. *Kansas Stockman,* 11 (Sept. 1, 1927), 3; Sampson, *op. cit.,* pp. 299–300.

21. Sampson, *op. cit.,* pp. 302–303.

22. *Ibid.,* pp. 305–307.

23. *Ibid.,* pp. 307–309.

24. *Ibid.,* pp. 314–317.

25. *Ibid.,* pp. 317–318; Annual Grazing Rpt., Wichita Nat'l. Forest, Feb. 1, 1928, G-Management, Regn. 2, *loc. cit.;* John C. Lotze, D. W. Gates,

and T. O. Roby, "Anaplasmosis of Cattle," *Animal Diseases* (USDA Yearbook, 1956), p. 269.

26. *The Cattleman,* 14 (Nov., 1927), 11–12; "Livestock Treaty Approved," *The Cattleman,* 14 (May, 1928), 10–11.

27. *The Producer,* 7 (Feb., 1926), 4; *ibid.,* 8 (Apr., 1927), 15–16; Sampson, *op. cit.,* p. 347; W.P.A. Historical Records Survey, Interviewer, William Buchanan, Jr., Informant and Subject, Joseph F. Vanek, mss. Montana State College Collection (Bozeman, Dec. 19, 1939); J. T. Schlebecker, "Grasshoppers in American Agricultural History," *Agricultural History,* 27 (July, 1953), 85–93.

28. M. L. Wilson, R. H. Wilcox, G. S. Klemmedson, and V. V. Parr, *A Study of Ranch Organization and Methods of Range-Cattle Production in the Northern Great Plains Region* (USDA Tech. Bul. 45, 1928), p. 19.

29. Maurice Haag (ed.), *The Range Lands of Wyoming* (Wyoming Exp. Sta. Bul. 289, 1949), p. 27; Johnson, *loc. cit.,* p. 6; Sampson, *op. cit.,* p. 278.

30. Flossie Burson, *The Transition of Agriculture in the Great Plains from 1920 to 1929* (M.S. thesis, Ames: Iowa State University, 1934), pp. 23–24.

31. Johnson, *loc. cit.,* p. 6; Sampson, *op. cit.,* p. 274.

32. *Kansas Stockman,* 11 (Jan. 15, 1927), 6; George S. Reeves, *A Man From South Dakota* (New York: E. P. Dutton, 1950), pp. 69–70.

33. Glen Staten, R. S. Troud, and John Carter, *Alfalfa Production Investigation in New Mexico* (New Mexico Agri. Exp. Sta. Bul. 323, 1945), pp. 14–15; Sampson, *op. cit.,* p. 277.

34. Sampson, *op. cit.,* pp. 276–277.

35. *Kansas Stockman,* 13 (Nov. 15, 1928), 17; Sampson, *op. cit.,* pp. 274–277.

36. *Kansas Stockman,* 11 (Feb. 1, 1927), 29; *The Producer,* 9 (June, 1927), 8.

37. Sampson, *op. cit.,* pp. 245–246, 274, 278.

38. Sampson, *op. cit.,* pp. 243–244; Quote, Charles M. Russell, *Trails Plowed Under* (New York: Doubleday, 1927), pp. 159–160.

39. A. D. Read, "I Like Ranching in the Rockies," *Breeders' Gazette,* 89 (Mar., 1926), 264; Johnson, *loc. cit.,* pp. 5–6.

40. *Kansas Stockman,* 10 (July 15, 1926), 2; *ibid.* (Aug. 15, 1926), 14; *The Cattleman,* 14 (June, 1927), 9.

41. Johnson, *loc. cit.,* pp. 7–8.

42. M. G. Burlingame and K. R. Toole, *A History of Montana* (New York: Lewis Historical Publishing Co., 1957), I, 329–330.

43. *The Producer,* 12 (Feb., 1931), 8; Joseph K. Howard, *Montana: High, Wide and Handsome* (New Haven: Yale Press, 1943), pp. 298–299; Burlingame and Toole, *op. cit.*

44. Herbert C. Hanson, "Administration of Western State Lands for Grazing," *The Producer,* 8 (May, 1927), 3–5; and continued in *ibid.,* 9 (June, 1927), 3–6.

45. Letter, P. V. Woodhead, Forest Supervisor, to Dist. Forester, Denver, Oct. 26, 1926, G-Management, Regn. 2, *loc. cit.; The Producer,* 7 (Feb., 1926), 19; *ibid.,* 8 (Dec., 1926), 9, 12; *ibid.* (Feb., 1927), 10.

46. *The Producer*, 9 (Mar., 1928), 17.

47. *The Producer*, 7 (Mar., 1926), 19; "The Stanfield Grazing Bill," *The Producer*, 8 (June, 1926), 3–7; *The Producer*, 8 (June, 1926), 18; E. Louise Peffer, *The Closing of the Public Domain* (Stanford: Stanford Univ. Press, 1951), pp. 190–201.

48. Letter, Wallace J. Pearce, Forest Supervisor, Lander, Wyo., to Dist. Forester, Denver, Apr. 21, 1926, G-Management, *loc. cit.;* Quote, *The Producer*, 7 (Apr., 1926), 12.

49. *The Producer*, 7 (Apr., 1926), 12; *The Cattleman*, 14 (Apr., 1928), 13.

50. *The Producer*, 7 (Feb., 1926), 13; *National Live Stock Producer*, 5 (Chicago, Apr., 1927), 4; *The Producer*, 9 (Sept., 1927), 11; *The Producer*, 9 (Dec., 1927), 12.

51. *The Producer*, 9 (Apr., 1928), 12.

52. *Kansas Stockman*, 11 (Mar. 1, 1927), 7; *The Producer*, 9 (June, 1927), 13.

53. *National Live Stock Producer*, 7 (Sept., 1928), 9; *Kansas Stockman*, 12 (Apr., 1928), 5.

CHAPTER IX

1. Agricultural Marketing Service, *Livestock and Meat Statistics* (USDA Stat. Bul. 230, 1958), pp. 204, 283; *The Producer*, 10 (Denver, Mar., 1929), 13

2. George Soule and V. P. Carosso, *American Economic History* (New York: Dryden Press, 1957), pp. 528–529.

3. E. N. Wentworth, "Outlook for Beef Consumption," *Montana Stockgrower*, 3 (Helena, Dec. 1, 1931), 9.

4. *Livestock and Meat Statistics*, p. 102; *Montana Stockgrower*, 2 (Jan. 1, 1930); D. E. Richards, *Annual Report*, Livestock, Extension Service, Bozeman, Montana, 1929; John H. Hatton, "Livestock Vicissitudes and Rainbows," *American Cattle Producer*, 22 (Sept., 1940), 7; *The Producer*, 12 (July, 1930), 26; *ibid.* (June, 1930), 26.

5. James K. Poole, "Cattle Business Out of the Woods," *The Producer*, 12 (Sept., 1930), 11; Hatton, *loc. cit.;* Soule and Carosso, *op. cit.*, p. 431.

6. Hatton, *loc. cit.;* Dale A. Saunders, *Trends in Size, Land Tenure, Income, Organization, and Management of Selected Cattle Ranches in Southeastern Montana, 1924–48* (M.S. thesis, Bozeman: Montana State College, 1949), p. 74; Marion Clawson, *The Western Range Livestock Industry* (New York: McGraw-Hill, 1950), p. 248; C. M. Hampson, *Some Factors of Success in Cattle Ranch Management, Western South Dakota* (South Dakota Agri. Exp. Sta. Circ. 13, 1933), pp. 2, 6, 8; M. B. Johnson and R. D. Jennings, *Cattle Ranching and Range Utilization in Western North Dakota* (USDA Bur. Agri. Econ. Spec. Rpt., Mimeo., 1937), p. 4.

7. *The Producer*, 13 (Sept., 1931), 16; Hampson, *loc. cit.*, p. 7; Quote, George S. Reeves, *A Man from South Dakota* (New York: E. P. Dutton, 1950), p. 137.

8. Events on the Plains were not uniform, but a steady increase in acre-

age foreclosed in western South Dakota is instructive. The worst year was 1931 when 658 farms, with 190,496 acres were lost by the farmers. *See* Harry A. Steele, *Farm Mortgage Foreclosures in South Dakota, 1921–32* (South Dakota Agri. Exp. Sta. Circ. 17, 1934), p. 10.

9. Herbert O. Brayer, "Colorado's Cattle Industry," *American Cattle Producer*, 27 (Sept., 1945), 22; Quote, "Jimmie Poole Says," *Montana Stockgrower*, 2 (July 1, 1930), 7.

10. *The Producer*, 13 (Mar., 1932), 3; Quote, "Jimmie Poole Says," *loc. cit.*

11. L. H. Rochford, *Influence of California on Colorado Beef-Cattle Prices* (Colorado Agri. Coll. Ext. Serv. Bul. 316-A, 1932), pp. 3, 4, 8, 27.

12. *The Producer*, 11 (June, 1929), 16; *ibid.* (Aug., 1929), 20; *Kansas Stockman*, 15 (Topeka, Nov. 1, 1930), 6.

13. *The Producer*, 12 (Feb., 1931), 13.

14. *Ibid.*, 11 (Oct., 1929), 16.

15. *Ibid.*, 12 (Aug., 1930), 20–21; *National Live Stock Producer*, 11 (Chicago, Dec., 1932), 14.

16. *The Producer*, 11 (Mar., 1930), 17.

17. *Ibid.* (Aug., 1929), 23, 28.

18. *Ibid.*, 12 (Aug., 1930), 36; *Kansas Stockman*, 14 (Sept. 15, 1930), 4; *ibid.*, 15 (Nov. 15, 1930), 4; *The Producer*, 12 (Dec., 1930), 20.

19. *Kansas Stockman*, 15 (Apr. 15, 1931), 5; C. W. Thornthwaite, "The Great Plains," in Carter Goodrich, *Migration and Economic Opportunity* (Philadelphia: Univ. of Pennsylvania Press, 1936), p. 223; *Kansas Stockman*, 15 (May 1, 1931), 13.

20. Reeves, *op. cit.*, pp. 123–124.

21. *The Producer*, 13 (Aug., 1931), 32.

22. *Ibid.* (Feb., 1931), 32; *Annual and Seasonal Precipitation at Six Representative Locations in Montana* (Montana Agri. Exp. Sta. Bul. 447, 1947), pp. 7, 13, 19, 24, 31; *The Producer*, 14 (Oct., 1932), 28; Thornthwaite, *loc. cit.*

23. *The Producer*, 10 (May, 1929), 10; *Kansas Stockman*, 12 (Feb. 1, 1929), 13; T. Swann Harding, *Two Blades of Grass* (Norman: Univ. of Oklahoma Press, 1947), pp. 160–161.

24. C. A. Manthei, A. K. Kuttler, and E. R. Goode, Jr., "Brucellosis," *Animal Diseases* (USDA Yearbook, 1956), p. 206; *American Cattle Producer*, 36 (Feb., 1955), 20; *The Producer*, 13 (Oct., 1931), 9; *ibid.*, 14 (Oct., 1932), 6.

25. M. R. Benedict, *Farm Policies of the United States, 1790–1950* (New York: Twentieth Century Fund, 1953), pp. 239–241; *The Producer*, 11 (July, 1929), 15.

26. Reeves, *op. cit.*, pp. 125–141; *Kansas Stockman*, 15 (Apr. 15, 1931), 4; *National Live Stock Producer*, 11 (Oct., 1932), 3.

27. *Kansas Stockman*, 13 (Mar. 1, 1929), 52; *The Producer*, 10 (Apr., 1929), 16; *Montana Stockgrower*, 2 (Jan. 1, 1930); C. L. Gooding, "Quarantining," *Animal Diseases*, p. 70.

28. "Wyoming Stockmen to Receive Federal Money," *The Producer*, 13 (Apr., 1932), 31; Clawson, *op. cit.*, pp. 282–283.

29. Reeves, *op. cit.*, p. 137; Hatton, *loc. cit.*

30. Letter, F. E. Mollin, Sec., American National Live Stock Ass'n., to C. E. Ratchford, Assistant Forester, Dec. 27, 1929, G-Cooperation, Washington Office, DRM, NA, RG 95; *The Producer*, 11 (Dec., 1929), 18.

31. *The Producer*, 12 (Aug., 1930), 21; *ibid.*, 13 (Aug., 1931), 18; *ibid.*, 14 (Oct., 1932), 12.

32. I. M. C. Anderson, *Annual Report, Livestock, Extension Service,* Bozeman, Montana, 1932, pp. 12–13; *The Producer*, 11 (Aug., 1929), 19; *ibid.*, 12 (Apr., 1931), 14; Quote, *The Producer*, 12 (Mar., 1931), 10–11.

33. *Montana Stockgrower*, 3 (June, 1931), 5.

34. *The Producer*, 11 (Oct., 1929), 16–17; *ibid.* (Dec., 1929), 12; *Kansas Stockman*, 14 (June 15, 1930), 5; *Montana Stockgrower*, quoted in *The Producer*, 12 (Dec., 1930), 11.

35. *Kansas Stockman*, 17 (Mar. 1, 1933), 45.

36. *The Producer*, 13 (Apr., 1932), 11; *ibid.*, 14 (Dec., 1932), 23; J. T. Schlebecker and A. W. Hopkins, *A History of Dairy Journalism in the United States, 1810–1950* (Madison: Univ. of Wisconsin Press, 1957).

37. Jay L. Lush, "Conference on Stock Cattle Problem," *Kansas Stockman*, 13 (June 15, 1929), 5; *ibid.*, 14 (Nov. 15, 1929), 6; Clawson, *op. cit.*, p. 183.

38. *Statistical Abstract of the United States, 1926* (Washington: U.S. Department of Commerce, 1927), pp. 640–641; *Statistical Abstract of the United States, 1931* (Washington: U.S. Department of Commerce, 1931), p. 714.

39. Glenn K. Rule, *Crops against the Wind on the Southern Great Plains* (USDA Farmers' Bul. 1833, 1939), pp. 56–58; *The Producer*, 11 (Feb., 1930), 24; G. K. Rule, *Toward Soil Security on the Northern Great Plains* (USDA Farmers' Bul. 1864, 1941), p. 56; Reeves, *op. cit.*, p. 124; and indirectly informative, G. A. Sallee and G. A. Pond, *An Economic Study of Livestock Possibilities in the Red River Valley of Minnesota* (Univ. of Minnesota Agri. Exp. Sta. Bul. 283, 1931), p. 3; *Kansas Stockman*, 15 (Nov. 15, 1930), 2.

40. *Statistical Abstract of the United States, 1931*, pp. 640–641; Fifteenth Census of the U.S., 1930: *Agriculture*, 2, "The Western States" (Washington: GPO, 1932), pp. 23–25.

41. P. W. Cockerill, B. Hunter, and H. B. Pingrey, *Type of Farming and Ranching Areas in New Mexico* (New Mexico Agri. Exp. Sta. Bul. 267, 1939), p. 30; James R. Gray and Chester B. Baker, *Cattle Ranching in the Northern Great Plains* (Montana Agri. Exp. Sta. Circ. 204, 1953), p. 7.

42. Clawson, *op. cit.*, p. 220.

43. Gray and Baker, *loc. cit.*, p. 4; Fifteenth Census of the U.S., 1930: *Agriculture*, 2, "The Southern States" (Washington: GPO, 1932), pp. 60–61; *See* also Ch. VII.

44. Saunders, *op. cit.*, p. 30; Johnson and Jennings, *loc. cit.*, pp. 7, 9; Hampson, *loc. cit.*, pp. 2, 3; T. G. Stewart, *Pasture and Feed Crops for Plains Area of Colorado* (Colorado Agri. Coll. Ext. Serv. Bul. 315-A, 1932), pp. 10–12; Thornthwaite, *loc. cit.*, p. 229; Clawson, *op. cit.*, p. 179; Cockerill, Hunter, and Pingrey, *loc. cit.*, p. 37.

45. "Dude Ranching and Diversification of Ranch Investments," *Montana Stockgrower*, 2 (June 1, 1930), 7.

46. B. W. Allred, *Range Conservation Practices for the Great Plains* (USDA Misc. Pub. 410, 1940), p. 15; *The Producer*, 11 (June, 1929), 30; *ibid.*, 10 (Feb., 1929), 30; *ibid.* (Jan., 1930), 48; Letter, C. E. Ratchford, Asst. Forester, Wash., to the Forester, Wash., Sept. 20, 1930, G-Cooperation, Washington Office, *loc. cit.; The Producer*, 12 (Apr., 1931), 32; *ibid.*, 13 (Feb., 1932), 32; *ibid.*, 14 (Oct., 1932), 28.

47. *National Live Stock Producer*, 7 (Aug., 1929), 20; *The Producer*, 11 (Nov., 1929), 36; *ibid.*, 10 (Feb., 1929), 31; *ibid.*, 12 (Dec., 1930), 20.

48. B. Hunter, P. W. Cockerill, and H. B. Pingrey, *Type of Farming and Ranching Areas in New Mexico* (New Mexico Agri. Exp. Sta. Bul. 261, 1939), pp. 45–47; *Montana Stockgrower*, 1 (Dec. 1, 1929); Frank Reeves, "West Texas Becoming 'Feed Minded,'" *The Cattleman*, 23 (Mar., 1937), 61; *Montana Stockgrower*, 2 (July 1, 1930), 8; *ibid.* (May 1, 1930); George Reeves, *op. cit.*, p. 119.

49. H. B. Osland, *Silage and Trench Silos in Colorado* (Colorado Agri. Coll. Ext. Serv. Bul. 315-A, 1931), p. 3; Hampson, *loc. cit.*, p. 5; D. E. Richards, *Annual Report*, Livestock, Extension Service, Bozeman, Montana, 1932; Johnson and Jennings, *loc. cit.*, p. 9; Stewart, *loc. cit.*, pp. 3–4.

50. *American Cattle Producer*, 19 (Apr., 1938), 26–27.

51. Gooding, *loc. cit.*, p. 70; *The Cattleman*, 26 (Mar., 1940), 84; Robert J. Kleberg, Jr., "The 'Santa Gertrudis' Breed of Beef Cattle," *The Producer*, 13 (June, 1931), 3–7; Tom Lea, *The King Ranch* (Boston: Little, Brown, 1957), II, 650.

52. W. H. Black and V. V. Parr, *Dehorning, Castrating, and Marking Beef Cattle* (USDA Farmers' Bul. 1600, 1929), p. 11; W. H. Black and V. V. Parr, *Feed-Lot and Ranch Equipment for Beef Cattle* (USDA Farmers' Bul. 1584, 1929), pp. 1, 3, 13, 15, 16; Hampson, *loc. cit.*, p. 5.

53. D. E. Richards, *Annual Report*, Livestock, Extension Service, Bozeman, Montana, 1930, pp. 4–6; I. M. C. Anderson, *Annual Report*, Livestock, Extension Service, Bozeman, Montana, 1932, p. 20.

CHAPTER X

1. George Soule and V. P. Carosso, *American Economic History* (New York: Dryden Press, 1957), p. 431.

2. Gilbert Fite and J. E. Reese, *An Economic History of the United States* (Boston: Houghton Mifflin, 1959), p. 604; Soule and Carosso, *op. cit.*, p. 373.

3. Agricultural Marketing Service, *Livestock and Meat Statistics* (USDA Stat. Bul. 230, 1958), pp. 283, 204; *Montana Stockgrower*, 5 (Helena, Sept. 1, 1933), 4; John H. Hatton, "Livestock Vicissitudes and Rainbows," *American Cattle Producer*, 22 (Denver, Sept., 1940), 7; *National Live Stock Producer*, 12 (Chicago, Nov., 1933), 14.

4. C. W. Thornthwaite, "The Great Plains," in Carter Goodrich, *Migration and Economic Opportunity* (Philadelphia: Univ. of Pennsylvania Press, 1936), p. 223; *Kansas Stockman*, 17 (Topeka, June 1, 1933), 4; *The Pro-*

ducer, **15** (July, 1933), 23; *ibid.* (Nov., 1933), 32; *Kansas Stockman,* **17** (Sept. 1, 1933), 2.

5. R. D. Lusk, "Life and Death of 470 Acres, Kernstrum Farm in Beadle County, South Dakota," *Saturday Evening Post,* **211** (Aug. 13, 1938), 5–6.

6. I. M. C. Anderson, *Annual Report,* Livestock, Extension Service, Bozeman, Montana, 1933, pp. 5–0; *The Producer,* **15** (July, 1933), 18.

7. Samuel T. Dana, *Forest and Range Policy: Its Development in the United States* (New York: McGraw-Hill, 1956), p. 248.

8. Marion Clawson, *The Western Range Livestock Industry* (New York: McGraw-Hill, 1950), p. 283; *The Producer,* **15** (July, 1933), 18.

9. D. A. Fitz-Gerald, *Livestock under the A.A.A.* (Washington: Brookings Institution, 1935), pp. 175–177; Murray R. Benedict and Oscar C. Stine, *The Agricultural Commodity Programs* (New York: Twentieth Century Fund, 1956), pp. 201–202.

10. Quote, F. E. Mollin, "Agricultural Adjustment Program as Cattle-Producers View It," *The Producer,* **15** (Nov., 1933), 6–7.

11. Fitz-Gerald, *op. cit.,* p. 179; *Kansas Stockman,* **18** (Nov. 1, 1933), 6; *The Producer,* **15** (Oct., 1933), 9.

12. *The Producer,* **15** (Nov., 1933), 19.

13. *Ibid.,* **14** (Apr., 1933), 14; *ibid.,* **15** (June, 1933), 16; Letter, R. R. Hill, Inspector of Grazing, to the Forester, Aug. 16, 1933, G-Cooperation, Washington Office, DRM, NA, RG 95.

14. Letter, Henry A. Wallace, Secretary of Agriculture, to F. E. Mollin, American National Livestock Ass'n., June 1, 1933, G-Cooperation, Washington Office, *loc. cit.;* Letter, C. E. Ratchford, Assistant Forester, to F. E. Mollin, Sec., American Livestock Ass'n., May 31, 1933, *ibid.*

15. Letter, R. R. Hill, Inspector of Grazing, to the Forester, Aug. 16, 1933, G-Cooperation, Washington Office, *loc. cit.;* *The Producer,* **15** (Aug., 1933), 16–17; *ibid.* (Sept., 1933), 16–17; *ibid.* (Oct., 1933), 9.

16. *Guide to the Records in the National Archives* (Washington: GPO, 1948), p. 367.

17. *Livestock and Meat Statistics,* pp. 283–284.

18. *Livestock and Meat Statistics,* p. 204.

19. *Montana Stockgrower,* **6** (Mar. 15, 1934), 1; Arthur H. Roth, Jr., *A Study of the Comparative Advantages of Raising Beef Cattle in the Corn Belt and on Montana Ranges* (M.S. thesis, Bozeman: Montana State College, 1936), p. 85; Allen R. Clark, *Cattle Movements and Livestock Auction Markets in Montana* (M.S. thesis, Bozeman: Montana State College, 1947), p. 29.

20. Thornthwaite, *loc. cit.,* p. 223; Hatton, *loc. cit.,* pp. 7, 28; George S. Reeves, *A Man from South Dakota* (New York: Dutton, 1950), pp. 151–152; "Montana," *American Cattle Producer,* **16** (June, 1934), 32; *The Producer,* **16** (Aug., 1934), 17.

21. Reeves, *op. cit.,* p. 153.

22. G. K. Rule, *Toward Soil Security on the Northern Great Plains* (USDA Farmers' Bul. 1864, 1941), p. 55; *American Cattle Producer,* **16** (Jan., 1935), 32; *Kansas Stockman,* **18** (June 15, 1934), 4.

23. Quote, *American Cattle Producer*, **16** (June, 1934), 32; Thornthwaite, *loc. cit.*, pp. 237–238.

24. G. K. Rule, *Crops against the Wind on the Southern Great Plains* (USDA Farmers' Bul. 1833, 1939), pp. 56–58; Robert Brittain, *Let There Be Bread* (New York: Simon and Schuster, 1952), pp. 143, 148; Jess L. Fults, *Blue Grama Grass for Erosion Control and Range Reseeding in the Great Plains and a Method of Obtaining Seed in Large Lots* (USDA Circ. 402, 1936), pp. 2, 7.

25. *The Producer*, **15** (Apr., 1934), 7; Fitz-Gerald, *op. cit.*, p. 193.

26. *American Cattle Producer*, **16** (June, 1934), 9; *Kansas Stockman*, **18** (June 15, 1934), 4; *American Cattle Producer*, **16** (July, 1934), 20; "Government Buying of Drought Live Stock," *American Cattle Producer*, **16** (Aug., 1934), 13; *ibid.*, **18** (Sept., 1936), 15; *Kansas Stockman*, **18** (Oct. 15, 1934), 7; Reeves, *op. cit.*, p. 154.

27. Reeves, *op. cit.*, p. 154.

28. *Ibid.*, p. 156.

29. *Ibid.*, p. 156.

30. *Montana Stockgrower*, **6** (Dec. 20, 1934), 2.

31. Benedict and Stine, *op. cit.*, pp. 202–203.

32. C. L. Sonnichsen, *Cowboys and Cattle Kings* (Norman: Univ. of Oklahoma Press, 1950), p. 134.

33. *American Cattle Producer*, **16** (Dec., 1934), 14–15; I. M. C. Anderson, *Annual Report*, Livestock, Extension Service, Bozeman, Montana, 1934, p. 8; Paul B. Sears, *Deserts on the March* (Norman: Univ. of Oklahoma Press, 1935), 70–71.

34. "Public Land Legislation," *Montana Stockgrower*, **6** (Jan. 15, 1934), 9; *The Producer*, **15** (Jan., 1934), 12; *ibid.* (Feb., 1934), 32–33; J. J. Wagoner, *History of the Cattle Industry in Southern Arizona, 1540–1940* (Tucson: Univ. of Arizona Press, 1952), pp. 69–70.

35. Some of this land was made available later for homesteading, and all of it was opened later for mineral prospecting.

36. Dana, *op. cit.*, pp. 43, 259–260; *American Cattle Producer*, **16** (July, 1934), 14–15.

37. *American Cattle Producer*, **16** (July, 1934), 15.

38. *Ibid.* (Sept., 1934), 12; "Conference on the Taylor Grazing Act," *Montana Stockgrower*, **6** (Aug. 20, 1934), 1; *American Cattle Producer*, **16** (Oct., 1934), 18; *National Live Stock Producer*, **13** (Aug., 1935), 5; Clawson, *op. cit.*, p. 263.

39. Saunders, *op. cit.*, p. 32; Clawson, *op. cit.*, p. 263; *American Cattle Producer*, **16** (Jan., 1935), 13.

40. *American Cattle Producer*, **16** (Jan., 1935), 13; "Reindeer Competition," *The Producer*, **14** (Mar., 1933), 18.

41. *American Cattle Producer*, **36** (Feb., 1955), 20; *Montana Stockgrower*, **6** (Apr. 15, 1934), 6; Benedict and Stine, *op. cit.*, p. 202.

42. *Livestock and Meat Statistics*, pp. 204, 283; Hatton, *loc. cit.*, p. 28.

43. *Kansas Stockman*, **19** (Apr. 1, 1935), 5; *American Cattle Producer*, **17** (June, 1935), 32; *ibid.* (Nov., 1935), 17; *ibid.*, **16** (Mar., 1935), 39–40; *ibid.*, **17** (Sept., 1935), 27; A. G. Nelson and G. Korzan, *Profits and Losses*

in Ranching, Western South Dakota, 1931–1940 (South Dakota Agri. Exp. Sta. Bul. 352, 1941), p. 8.

44. *American Cattle Producer,* 16 (Feb., 1935), 48; Thornthwaite, *loc. cit.,* pp. 237–238; Quote, *Kansas Stockman,* 19 (Apr. 15, 1935), 4.

45. *American Cattle Producer,* 17 (June, 1935), 3.

46. *National Live Stock Producer,* 15 (Oct., 1936), 15.

47. *American Cattle Producer,* 16 (Feb., 1935), 33; *National Live Stock Producer,* 13 (Jan., 1935), 7.

48. *American Cattle Producer,* 16 (Apr., 1935), 15.

49. *Ibid.,* 21 (Sept., 1939); Sears, *op. cit.,* pp. 130–131.

50. Stanley W. Brown and Virgil E. Baugh, "Preliminary Inventory of Records of the Farmers Home Administration," mss. (Washington: National Archives Records Service, 1959), pp. 1–6; *Guide to the Records in the National Archives, op. cit.,* pp. 367–368.

51. *American Cattle Producer,* 17 (Oct., 1935), 16; I. M. C. Anderson, *Annual Report,* Livestock, Extension Service, Bozeman, Montana, 1935, pp. 7–8.

52. *American Cattle Producer,* 16 (May, 1935), 14; "Argentine Pact," *American Cattle Producer,* 18 (May, 1937), 15.

53. *American Cattle Producer,* 17 (June, 1935), 16; *ibid.,* 21 (Sept., 1939), 7; *ibid.,* 22 (June, 1940).

54. Letter, C. E. Ratchford, Assistant Forester, Wash., to G. W. Thomas, Norge, Okla., Jan. 2, 1935, G-Management, Regn. 2, *loc. cit.;* Letter, F. E. Mollin, American National Live Stock Ass'n., to E. A. Sherman, Acting Forester, Mar. 21, 1935, G-Cooperation, Washington Office, *loc. cit.;* Letter, E. A. Sherman, Acting Chief, Forest Service, to Russell Thorp, Sec., Wyo. Stock Growers Ass'n., G-Cooperation, Regn. 2, *loc. cit.*

55. I. M. Howard, "Anchoring Ranches and Ranchers," *American Cattle Producer,* 18 (Jan., 1937), 4–5; *Statistical Abstract of the United States, 1941* (Washington: U.S. Department of Commerce, 1941).

56. *Statistical Abstract of the United States, 1936* (Washington: U.S. Department of Commerce, 1936).

57. Rule, *Southern Plains,* pp. 26, 52, 56–59; Rule, *Northern Plains,* p. 21.

58. Harold Halcrow, *The Problem of the Unsuccessful Dry Farm in the Northern Great Plains* (M.S. thesis, Bozeman: Montana State College, 1938), pp. 13–14, 20, 29, 96–97, 21.

59. Sears, *op. cit.,* pp. 73–74; James R. Gray and Chester B. Baker, *Cattle Ranching in the Northern Great Plains* (Montana Agri. Exp. Sta. Circ. 204, 1953), p. 7.

60. Sixteenth Census of the U.S., 1940: *Agriculture,* I, Parts 2, 5, 6 (Washington: GPO, 1942); *Statistical Abstract of the United States, 1936.*

61. *Statistical Abstract of the United States, 1936.*

62. B. W. Allred, *Range Conservation Practices for the Great Plains* (USDA Misc. Pub. 410, 1940), p. 15.

63. Harry G. Anderson and Alva H. Benton, *Cattle Marketed in North Dakota, 1929–30–31 and Some Factors Underlying Their Production* (North Dakota Exp. Sta. Bul. 275, 1933), p. 4; I. M. C. Anderson, *Annual Report,* Livestock, Extension Service, Bozeman, Montana, 1933, p. 17; Nelson Klose,

The Introduction Improvement, and Adaptation of Sorghum Varieties in Texas (M.A. thesis, Austin: Univ. of Texas, 1937), p. 24; *National Live Stock Producer*, 13 (May, 1935), 5.

64. Nelson and Korzan, *loc. cit.*, p. 10.

65. Frank Reeves, "West Texas Becoming 'Feed Minded,'" *The Cattleman*, 23 (Mar., 1937), 61; *Kansas Stockman*, 19 (Sept. 1, 1935), 3; *American Cattle Producer*, 16 (Apr., 1935), 31.

66. *The Producer*, 14 (Mar., 1933), 5; Oscar E. Anderson, Jr., *Refrigeration in America* (Princeton: Princeton Univ. Press for the Univ. of Cincinnati, 1953), p. 248; Roth, *op. cit.*, pp. 76–77.

67. *Statistical Abstract of the United States, 1935* (Washington: U.S. Department of Commerce, 1935).

CHAPTER XI

1. George Soule and V. P. Carosso, *American Economic History* (New York: Dryden Press, 1957), p. 431.

2. Agricultural Marketing Service, *Livestock and Meat Statistics* (USDA Sta. Bul. 230, 1958), pp. 204, 283.

3. Aaron G. Nelson and Gerald Korzan, *Profits and Losses in Ranching, Western South Dakota, 1931–1940* (South Dakota Agri. Exp. Sta. Bul. 352, 1941), p. 8; I. M. C. Anderson, *Annual Report*, Livestock, Extension Service, Bozeman, Montana, 1936, pp. 29–30; *American Cattle Producer*, 22 (Denver, June, 1940), 5; I. M. C. Anderson and Howard Lewis, *Annual Report*, Livestock, Extension Service, Bozeman, Montana, 1937, p. 6; *Kansas Stockman*, 21 (Topeka, Mar. 1, 1937), 57; *American Cattle Producer*, 21 (Apr., 1940), 38; *ibid.*, 20 (Jan., 1939), 15.

4. *Kansas Stockman*, 22 (Dec. 1, 1937), 4; *American Cattle Producer*, 19 (Nov., 1937), 18; *National Live Stock Producer*, 16 (Chicago, Jan., 1938), 5.

5. Day Monroe, *et al.*, *Family Income and Expenditures, Pacific Region and Plains and Mountain Region, Part 1, Family Income* (USDA Misc. Pub. 356, 1939), pp. 94–96.

6. Leon C. Michaelson, *Some Size, Income and Organization Characteristics of the Ranches of 46 Montana Counties* (M.S. thesis, Bozeman: Montana State College, 1938), pp. 88–89; H. B. Pingrey, *Cattle Ranching in Southeastern New Mexico* (New Mexico Agri. Exp. Sta. Bul. 336, 1948), p. 18; *American Cattle Producer*, 20 (Aug., 1938), 19; Monroe, *loc. cit.*, pp. 86–87, 120–122.

7. George S. Reeves, *A Man From South Dakota* (New York: E. P. Dutton, 1950), p. 162.

8. G. K. Rule, *Toward Soil Security on the Northern Great Plains* (USDA Farmers' Bul. 1864, 1941), p. 55; Reeves, *op. cit.*, p. 171; *American Cattle Producer*, 18 (July, 1936), 16; "Conserve All Feed and Water," *Kansas Stockman*, 20 (Sept. 1, 1936), 3; *ibid.* (July 15, 1936), 2; *ibid.*, 21 (Nov. 1, 1936), 27; *Annual and Seasonal Precipitation at Six Representative Locations in Montana* (Montana Agri. Exp. Sta. Bul. 447, 1947), pp. 7, 13, 19, 25, 31; *Kansas Stockman*, 21 (Dec. 1, 1936), 5; Quote, *American Cattle Producer*, 18 (Feb., 1937), 28; *ibid.*, 19 (June, 1937), 11.

9. I. M. C. Anderson and Howard Lewis, *Annual Report*, Livestock, Extension Service, Bozeman, Montana, 1937, p. 5; *American Cattle Producer*, 19 (June, 1937), 2; *ibid.* (Dec., 1937), 48; *Annual and Seasonal Precipitation, loc. cit.; American Cattle Producer*, 19 (Apr., 1938), 2; *ibid.* (Mar., 1938), 35; *Kansas Stockman*, 23 (Nov. 1, 1938), 9; F. E. Mollin, *If and When It Rains—The Stockman's View of the Range Question* (Denver: American National Live Stock Association, 1938).

10. *American Cattle Producer*, 21 (June, 1939), 32.

11. Nelson and Korzan, *loc. cit.*, p. 8; *American Cattle Producer*, 21 (June, 1939), 32; *Kansas Stockman*, 23 (Sept. 15, 1939), 14, 24; *American Cattle Producer*, 21 (Sept., 1939), 27; *The Cattleman*, 26 (Fort Worth, Oct., 1939), 16; *American Cattle Producer*, 21 (Nov., 1939), 32.

12. *American Cattle Producer*, 18 (Nov., 1936), 32; I. M. C. Anderson, *Annual Report*, Livestock, Extension Service, Bozeman, Montana, 1936, p. 6; *Kansas Stockman*, 20 (July 15, 1936), 4; J. T. Schlebecker, "Grasshoppers in American Agricultural History," *Agricultural History*, 27 (July, 1953), 85–93.

13. *Kansas Stockman*, 21 (June 15, 1937), 4; *American Cattle Producer*, 19 (Dec., 1937), 48; Reeves, *op. cit.*, pp. 192–197; Schlebecker, "Grasshoppers," *loc. cit.; Kansas Stockman*, 23 (Aug. 1, 1938), 10; G. K. Rule, *Toward Soil Security on the Northern Great Plains* (USDA Farmers' Bul. 1864, 1941), p. 58; J. T. Schlebecker, "Pliant Prairie: One Plant's Influence on One Prairie State," *Montana, the Magazine of Western History*, 8 (Winter, 1958), 30–41.

14. *Kansas Stockman*, 23 (May 15, 1939), 3; *American Cattle Producer*, 21 (June, 1939), 32; Reeves, *op. cit.*, p. 206.

15. Mollin, *op. cit.*, pp. *iii*, 6, 7, 60; *American Cattle Producer*, 18 (June, 1936), 13; *National Live Stock Producer*, 14 (Apr., 1936), 17; Dana, *op. cit.*, p. 262; *American Cattle Producer*, 18 (Oct., 1936), 17–18.

16. *Kansas Stockman*, 20 (May 15, 1936), 4; *ibid.*, 22 (Nov. 1, 1937), 6; Francesca M. Blackmer, "The West, Water, and the Grazing Laws," *Survey Graphic*, 26 (July, 1937), 387.

17. *American Cattle Producer*, 22 (Sept., 1940), 30; *ibid.*, 23 (July, 1941), 19; Dana, *op. cit.*, p. 262; *American Cattle Producer*, 20 (Aug., 1938), 21; *ibid.* (Dec., 1938), 11–12.

18. *American Cattle Producer*, 21 (Sept., 1939), 14; Dana, *op. cit.*

19. *American Cattle Producer*, 17 (Mar., 1936), 14; "Term Permits on Forests Still Available," *American Cattle Producer*, 19 (Oct., 1937), 15; Telegram, J. A. Hill, Laramie, Wyo., to Allen S. Peck, Regional Forester, Denver (n.d., 1936?), G-Cooperation, Region 2, DRM, NA, RG 95; Telegram, L. H. Douglas, Assistant Regional Forester, Denver, to Dean J. A. Hill, University of Wyoming, Oct. 21, 1936, *ibid.;* Letter, Ray Ward for Acting Director, Plains Shelterbelt Project, Lincoln, to Chief, Forest Service, Washington, Dec. 9, 1936, *ibid.;* Letter, Allen S. Peck, to Chief, Forest Service, June 6, 1936, *ibid.; American Cattle Producer*, 17 (Feb., 1936), 17; Memo for the Acting Director, by Assistant to the Director, F. Lee Kirby, Sept. 30, 1936, Lincoln, Neb., G-Cooperation, Regn. 2, *loc. cit.;* Letter, Wyo. Stock Growers Ass'n., to DRM, June 28, 1937, *ibid.*

20. F. R. Carpenter, "Problems of Grazing on Public Lands," *American Cattle Producer,* 21 (Dec., 1939), 16–17.

21. *American Cattle Producer,* 17 (Jan., 1936), 20; *National Live Stock Producer,* 14 (Feb., 1936), 12; for examples, *see* "Range Building Practices and Rates of Payment Approved for North Dakota for 1936," *Memorandum of Instruction for Range Examiners,* G-Cooperation, Regn. 2, *loc. cit.;* "Range Building Practices and Rates of Payment Approved for Kansas for 1936," *ibid.;* "A.A.A. Range Program," *American Cattle Producer,* 18 (Nov., 1936), 19; J. J. Wagoner, *History of the Cattle Industry in Southern Arizona, 1540–1940* (Tucson: Univ. of Arizona Press, 1952), p. 61.

22. "A.A.A. Range Program," p. 18.

23. Memo for the Acting Director, by Assistant to Director, F. Lee Kirby, Sept. 30, 1936, Lincoln, Neb., G-Cooperation, Regn. 2, *loc. cit.;* Letter, Allen S. Peck, Regional Forester, Denver, to Chief, Forest Service, Wash., Jan. 18, 1937, *ibid.;* News Release from Forest Service, USDA, Denver, *ibid.;* "Soil and Range Practices for West," *American Cattle Producer,* 18 (Feb., 1937), 17.

24. *American Cattle Producer,* 19 (Apr., 1938), 16; *ibid.,* 20 (Sept., 1938), 12; *ibid.* (Jan., 1939), 21; H. B. Pingrey, *Combination Ranching in Southeastern New Mexico* (New Mexico Agri. Exp. Sta. Bul. 332, 1946), p. 39.

25. *Guide to the Records in the National Archives* (Washington: GPO, 1948), pp. 367–368; Stanley W. Brown and Virgil E. Baugh, Preliminary Inventory of Records of the Farmers Home Administration, mss. (Washington: National Archives and Records Service, 1959), pp. 4–5; Howard G. Lewis, *Annual Report,* Livestock, Extension Service, Bozeman, Montana, 1938, p. 2.

26. Letter, Paul H. Roberts, Acting Director, Plains Shelterbelt Project, Lincoln, to Mr. Clapp, Wash., Sept. 14, 1936, G-Cooperation, Regn. 2, *loc. cit.;* Reeves, *op. cit.,* pp. 172, 180–182, 189; *American Cattle Producer,* 21 (Sept., 1939), 7; Dana, *op. cit.,* pp. 248–249.

27. Rule, *Northern Plains,* pp. 60–61, 57, 64; Rule, *Southern Plains,* pp. 53–54, 56–58; *American Cattle Producer,* 21 (Sept., 1939), 28.

28. *American Cattle Producer,* 18 (July, 1936), 16; *ibid.* (Aug., 1936), 12; Murray R. Benedict and Oscar C. Stine, *The Agricultural Commodity Programs* (New York: Twentieth Century Fund, 1956), p. 203.

29. Rule, *Southern Plains,* pp. 26, 39–40, 52, 56, 58, 54; Thornthwaite, *loc. cit.,* p. 243; *Kansas Stockman,* 23 (July 15, 1939), 12; I. M. C. Anderson, *Annual Report,* Livestock, Extension Service, Bozeman, Montana, 1936, pp. 14–15; M. H. Saunderson and D. W. Chittenden, *Cattle Ranching in Montana* (Montana Agri. Exp. Sta. Bul. 341, 1937), pp. 7, 16; Pingrey, *Combination Ranching in New Mexico, loc. cit.*

30. Nelson and Korzan, *loc. cit.,* p. 10; O. W. Nolen, "Feeding Pens of William Heuermann Are Practically Empty," *The Cattleman,* 30 (Jan., 1944), 31; B. Hunter, P. W. Cockerill, and H. B. Pingrey, *Type of Farming and Ranching Areas in New Mexico* (New Mexico Agri. Exp. Sta. Bul. 261, 1939), pp. 46–47; *American Cattle Producer,* 20 (Feb., 1939), 18; Pingrey, *Cattle Ranching in Southeastern New Mexico, loc. cit.,* p. 21.

31. *National Live Stock Producer,* **17** (Feb., 1939), 9; Quote, Rule, *Southern Plains,* p. 30; also *see* Nelson Klose, *The Introduction, Improvement and Adaptation of Sorghum Varieties in Texas* (M.A. thesis, Austin: Univ. of Texas, 1937), pp. 97–98, 102, 43; *Kansas Stockman,* **22** (Apr. 15, 1938), 4; *ibid.* (Mar. 15, 1938), 3; *ibid.,* **23** (Sept. 15, 1939), 10.

32. I. M. Howard, "More Moisture, More Grass," *American Cattle Producer,* **19** (June, 1937), 3; *Kansas Stockman,* **23** (Aug. 1, 1938), 11; Rule, *Southern Plains,* pp. 26, 47.

33. *Kansas Stockman,* **21** (Sept. 1, 1937), 3; *ibid.* (Aug. 15, 1937), 5; *ibid.* (Apr. 15, 1938), 5; *ibid.* (Aug. 15, 1937), 4; C. A. Mathei, A. K. Kuttler, and E. R. Goode, Jr., "Brucellosis," *Animal Diseases* (USDA Yearbook, 1956), pp. 81, 204; *American Cattle Producer,* **20** (Apr., 1939), 13.

34. *Kansas Stockman,* **22** (Apr. 15, 1938), 4; *ibid.,* **24** (Mar. 15, 1940); *American Cattle Producer,* **21** (June, 1939), 20; Marion Clawson, *The Western Range Livestock Industry* (New York: McGraw-Hill, 1950), p. 160; James R. Gray and Chester B. Baker, *Cattle Ranching in the Northern Great Plains* (Montana Agri. Exp. Sta. Circ. 204, 1953), p. 4; Nelson and Korzan, *loc. cit.,* p. 10; L. B. Mann, *Cooperative Marketing of Range Livestock* (Farm Credit Admin. Bul. 7, 1930), p. 20; Howard G. Lewis, *Annual Report,* Livestock, Extension Service, Bozeman, Montana, 1938, p. 1.

35. Monroe, *loc. cit.,* pp. 91, 93; Leon C. Michaelson, *Some Size, Income and Organization Characteristics of the Ranches of 46 Montana Counties* (M.S. thesis, Bozeman: Montana State College, 1938), pp. 8, 88a, 88b; Gray and Baker, *loc. cit.,* p. 7; Saunderson and Chittenden, *loc. cit.,* p. 24; *Kansas Stockman,* **20** (Oct. 1, 1936), 7.

36. Harold Halcrow, *The Problem of the Unsuccessful Dry Farm in the Northern Great Plains* (M.S. thesis, Bozeman: Montana State College, 1938), p. 97; Monroe, *loc. cit.,* pp. 87, 89–90, 98.

37. Reeves, *op. cit.,* pp. 182–183; Rule, *Southern Plains,* pp. 6, 18, 52–53; *Statistical Abstract of the United States, 1941* (Washington: U.S. Department of Commerce, 1942).

38. *Statistical Abstract of the United States, 1941.*

39. *National Live Stock Producer,* **16** (Apr., 1938), 10; Herrell De-Graff, *Beef Production and Distribution* (Norman: Univ. of Oklahoma Press, 1960), pp. 161–164.

40. *American Cattle Producer,* **18** (Feb., 1937), 27; *ibid.,* **20** (Sept., 1938), 24; *The Cattleman,* **26** (Nov., 1939), 7; *Kansas Stockman,* **22** (Jan. 15, 1938), 4; *American Cattle Producer,* **20** (July, 1938), 31; *National Live Stock Producer,* **17** (Sept., 1939), 4.

41. *Kansas Stockman,* **20** (Apr. 1, 1936), 5; "Argentine Pact," *American Cattle Producer,* **18** (May, 1937), 15; *ibid.,* **20** (Aug., 1938), 20; *Kansas Stockman,* **23** (June 15, 1939), 4; *American Cattle Producer,* **21** (June, 1939), 5–6.

CHAPTER XII

1. In 1941, farmers made up 23.2 per cent of the population; in 1945 they made up only 18.1 per cent of the total. George Soule and V. P.

Carosso, *American Economic History* (New York: Dryden Press, 1957), pp. 431, 462–468; Seymour Harris (ed.), *American Economic History* (New York: McGraw-Hill, 1961), p. 227; *Statistical Abstract of the United States, 1958* (Washington: U.S. Department of Commerce, 1958), p. 611.

2. Herrell DeGraff, *Beef Production and Distribution* (Norman: Univ. of Oklahoma Press, 1960), pp. 122–123; *Livestock and Meat Statistics* (USDA Stat. Bul. 230, 1958), pp. 102, 283; Harvey C. Mansfield, and Associates, *A Short History of the OPA* (Washington: Historical Reports on War Administration, Office of Price Administration, 1947), pp. 51, 193–194; *National Live Stock Producer,* 20 (Chicago, Sept., 1942), 3; Quote, *American Cattle Producer,* 24 (Denver, Aug., 1942), 17.

3. *National Live Stock Producer,* 24 (June, 1943), 4; *Kansas Stockman,* 30 (Topeka, Jan., 1945), 6; Mansfield, *op. cit.,* pp. 39, 43; *National Live Stock Producer,* 20 (Mar., 1942), 8.

4. *American Cattle Producer,* 24 (June, 1942), 17; Mansfield, *op. cit.,* pp. 42, 51–53; *Kansas Stockman,* 26 (July, 1942), 4; *ibid.* (Oct., 1942), 25; *American Cattle Producer,* 26 (July, 1944), 7.

5. Mansfield, *op. cit.,* pp. 53, 55–56; *The Cattleman,* 30 (Fort Worth, March, 1944), 13; *Kansas Stockman,* 28 (Feb., 1944), 14; J. R. Edwards, "The Cattle Feed Situation," *The Cattleman,* 30 (Feb., 1944), 80.

6. *Livestock and Meat Statistics,* p. 204.

7. *National Live Stock Producer,* 22 (Nov., 1943), 4; *The Cattleman,* 32 (June, 1945), 7; Gilbert Fite and J. E. Reese, *An Economic History of the United States* (Boston: Houghton Mifflin, 1959), pp. 632–633; Quote, Mansfield, *op. cit.,* p. 150; *National Live Stock Producer,* 21 (Dec., 1942), 6; *ibid.,* 20 (Sept., 1942), 3; *American Cattle Producer,* 24 (Nov., 1942), 19; *Kansas Stockman,* 27 (Dec., 1942), 5.

8. Mansfield, *op. cit.,* pp. 150, 167, 168, 172; *American Cattle Producer,* 24 (Apr., 1943), 20; *The Cattleman,* 30 (June, 1943), 6.

9. Mansfield, *op. cit.,* pp. 170, 173, 175; *The Cattleman,* 30 (Aug., 1943), 12.

10. *American Cattle Producer,* 26 (June, 1944), 7; Mansfield, *op. cit.,* pp. 189, 190, 193–194.

11. *American Cattle Producer,* 27 (Oct., 1945), 7.

12. *Kansas Stockman,* 30 (Mar., 1945), 13; *ibid.* (Dec., 1945), 6.

13. Quote, Marion Clawson, *The Western Range Livestock Industry* (New York: McGraw-Hill, 1950), p. 174; *National Live Stock Producer,* 18 (Sept., 1940), 4; *ibid.,* 23 (June, 1945), 1; H. E. Selby and D. T. Griffith, "Western Range Livestock Production," *American Cattle Producer,* 28 (Aug., 1946), 13.

14. *Kansas Stockman,* 27 (Mar., 1943), 8; T. Swann Harding, *Two Blades of Grass* (Norman: Univ. of Oklahoma Press, 1947), pp. 162–163.

15. G. K. Rule, *Toward Soil Security on the Northern Great Plains* (USDA Farmers' Bul. 1864, 1941), pp. 22, 63; *The Cattleman,* 28 (Dec., 1941), 73; Harry R. O'Brien, "It Was Livestock or Starve," *Country Gentleman,* 110 (Dec., 1940), 13; John D. McCully, "1940 Range-Improvement Program," *The Cattleman,* 26 (Nov., 1939), 15; *Kansas Stockman,* 25 (Mar. 15, 1941), 7.

16. *American Cattle Producer*, 22 (June, 1940), 19; Samuel T. Dana, *Forest and Range Policy: Its Development in the United States* (New York: McGraw-Hill, 1956), p. 248.

17. *American Cattle Producer*, 23 (Mar., 1942), 24; L. R. Short and E. J. Woolfolk, *Reseeding to Increase the Yield of Montana Range Lands* (USDA Farmers' Bul. 1924, 1943, revised, 1952), p. 1; Nicholas Helburn, *Land Use Adjustments in Blaine, Phillips, and Valley Counties, Montana, 1934 to 1940* (M.S. thesis, Bozeman: Montana State College, 1941), p. 101.

18. Helen H. Smith, "How to Live 70 Miles from Town," *Saturday Evening Post*, 217 (Sept. 23, 1944), 26 ff.; *National Live Stock Producer*, 19 (Feb., 1941), 10; Helburn, *op. cit.*, p. 100.

19. *American Cattle Producer*, 22 (Oct., 1940), 21; Clawson, *op. cit.*, p. 263; *American Cattle Producer*, 26 (June, 1944), 19; *ibid.* (April, 1945), 34; *ibid.*, 23 (Jan., 1942), 32.

20. Stanley W. Brown and Virgil E. Baugh, "Preliminary Inventory of Records of the Farmers Home Administration," mss. (Washington: National Archives and Records Service, 1959), pp. 6–7; Helburn, *op. cit.*, p. 102; O'Brien, *loc. cit.*, p. 27.

21. Brown and Baugh, *op. cit.*, pp. 3, 6; Helburn, *op. cit.*, p. 100; *American Cattle Producer*, 25 (June, 1943), 19.

22. *American Cattle Producer*, 26 (Sept., 1944), 20; *Kansas Stockman*, 30 (Nov., 1944), 6–7; *The Cattleman*, 32 (July, 1945), 36; *Kansas Stockman*, 30 (July, 1945), 6–8; Quote, *ibid.* (Aug., 1945), 7.

23. *The Cattleman*, 26 (Apr., 1940), 25; *American Cattle Producer*, 21 (May, 1940), 20; *ibid.*, 36 (June, 1954), 7.

24. *Statistical Abstract of the United States, 1941* (Washington: U.S. Department of Commerce, 1942), p. 613; *Statistical Abstract of the United States, 1958* (Washington: U.S. Department of Commerce, 1958), p. 680.

25. *American Cattle Producer*, 22 (Sept., 1940), 32; *ibid.*, 21 (Apr., 1940), 35; *Annual and Seasonal Precipitation at Six Representative Locations in Montana* (Montana Agri. Exp. Sta. Bul. 447, 1947), pp. 7, 13, 19, 25, 31.

26. *American Cattle Producer*, 23 (Jan., 1942), 40; *Kansas Stockman*, 26 (Sept., 1942), 6; *American Cattle Producer*, 24 (July, 1942), 4; *ibid.* (Dec., 1942), 27; *ibid.*, 25 (July, 1943), 21; *The Cattleman*, 30 (Jan., 1944), 16; *American Cattle Producer*, 24 (Feb., 1943), 4; *ibid.* (Apr., 1943), 33; *The Cattleman*, 30 (Oct., 1943), 71; *Annual and Seasonal Precipitation, loc. cit.*; Smith, *loc. cit.*, p. 37; *American Cattle Producer*, 26 (July, 1944), 4; *Kansas Stockman*, 28 (Sept., 1944), 9.

27. Scientists of the biological survey discovered that 78 per cent of a prairie dog's food came from crop and forage plants. *Kansas Stockman*, 24 (June 1, 1940), 15; E. P. Orcutt, *Annual Report*, Livestock, Extension Service, Bozeman, Montana, 1941, p. 3; *Kansas Stockman*, 24 (Apr. 15, 1940), 6; F. A. Ralson, *Annual Report*, Livestock, Extension Service, Bozeman, Montana, 1945, p. 24.

28. *National Live Stock Producer*, 20 (Mar., 1942), 3; W. A. Aitken,

"Shipping Fever," *Animal Diseases* (USDA Yearbook, 1956), p. 259; C. A. Manthei, A. K. Kuttler, and E. R. Goode, Jr., "Brucellosis," *Animal Diseases,* p. 204; *National Live Stock Producer,* 19 (June, 1941), 7.

29. *Kansas Stockman,* 30 (Apr., 1945), 6; A. O. Foster, "Chemotherapeutic Agents for Internal Parasites," *Animal Diseases,* p. 81; Gaines W. Eddy and R. C. Bushland, "Screwworms That Attack Livestock," *Animal Diseases,* p. 174; *American Cattle Producer,* 24 (Mar., 1943), 10; *Kansas Stockman,* 28 (Jan., 1944), 9.

30. Henry T. Murray, *State Land Management in Montana* (M.S. thesis, Bozeman: Montana State College, 1942), pp. 86–87; Helburn, *op. cit.,* p. 101; *The Cattleman,* 30 (Feb., 1944), 14; Brown and Baugh, *op. cit.,* p. 6.

31. Glen Staten, R. S. Stroud and John Carter, *Alfalfa Production Investigations in New Mexico* (New Mexico Agri. Exp. Sta. Bul. 323, 1945), p. 3; E. P. Orcutt, *Annual Report,* Livestock, Extension Service, Bozeman, Montana, 1941, p. 33.

32. *Kansas Stockman,* 26 (Apr. 1, 1942), 11; *ibid.* (Apr. 15, 1942), 4; M. M. Kelso, "The Place of Grassland Farming," *Grass* (USDA Yearbook, 1948), pp. 479–482; *Kansas Stockman,* 27 (Jan., 1943), 4; *ibid.,* 30 (Dec., 1944), 6.

33. J. H. Martin and J. C. Stephens, *The Culture and Use of Sorghums for Forage* (USDA Farmers' Bul. 1844, 1940), pp. 2–4; O'Brien, *loc. cit.,* p. 26; *Kansas Stockman,* 25 (Mar. 15, 1941), 4; O. W. Nolen, "Feeding Pens of William Heuermann Are Practically Empty," *The Cattleman,* 30 (Jan., 1944), 31; *Kansas Stockman,* 30 (Dec., 1944), 11; *The Cattleman,* 30 (Feb., 1944), 12; *Kansas Stockman,* 30 (Feb., 1945), 9.

34. Aaron G. Nelson, *Planning Minimum Sized Ranches and Farms for the Hyde County Area in South Dakota* (South Dakota Agri. Exp. Sta. Bul. 346, 1940), p. 2; Helburn, *op. cit.,* p. 100; B. W. Allred, *Range Conservation Practices for the Great Plains* (USDA Misc. Pub. 410, 1940), pp. 14–15; O'Brien, *op. cit.,* pp. 13, 26.

35. *Kansas Stockman,* 30 (Nov., 1944), 11; Tom Lea, *The King Ranch* (Boston: Little, Brown, 1957), II, 651; *The Cattleman,* 28 (June, 1941), 20; E. P. Orcutt, *Annual Report,* Livestock, Extension Service, Bozeman, Montana, 1941, p. 11; "Life Visits an Oklahoma Ranch," *Life,* 17 (July 10, 1944), 99.

36. Sixteenth Census of the U.S., 1940: *Agriculture,* I, Parts 2, 5, 6 (Washington: GPO, 1942); U.S. Bureau of the Census, *U.S. Census of Agriculture, 1950,* II (Washington: GPO, 1952), 30; A. Dale Saunders, *Trends in Size, Land Tenure, Income, Organization, and Management of Selected Cattle Ranches in Southeastern Montana, 1924–48* (M.S. thesis, Bozeman: Montana State College, 1949), p. 30; James R. Gray and Chester B. Baker, *Cattle Ranching in the Northern Great Plains* (Montana Agri. Exp. Sta. Circ. 204, 1953), p. 7.

37. *American Cattle Producer,* 23 (Sept., 1941), 19; *Kansas Stockman,* 28 (June, 1944), 9.

CHAPTER XIII

1. Howard Smith, *American Economic History* (New York: Ronald Press, 1955), pp. 657–659, 664–666; *National Live Stock Producer,* 25 (Chicago, Oct., 1946), 6; *Kansas Stockman,* 31 (Topeka, Nov., 1946), 8; Quote, Lewis Nordyke, *Great Roundup* (New York: William Morrow, 1955), p. 263.

2. Agricultural Marketing Service, *Livestock and Meat Statistics* (USDA Stat. Bul. 230, 1958), p. 204; *American Cattle Producer,* 30 (Denver, May, 1949), 9; Murray R. Benedict and Oscar C. Stine, *The Agricultural Commodity Programs* (New York: Twentieth Century Fund, 1956), p. 216; A. Dale Saunders, *Trends in Size, Land Tenure, Income, Organization, and Management of Selected Cattle Ranches in Southeastern Montana, 1924–48* (M.S. thesis, Bozeman: Montana State College, 1949), p. 13; Marion Clawson, *The Western Range Livestock Industry* (New York: McGraw-Hill, 1950), p. 160.

3. *Livestock and Meat Statistics,* pp. 102, 283; *American Cattle Producer,* 31 (Sept., 1949), 33; *Kansas Stockman,* 31 (July, 1947), 11; *American Cattle Producer,* 30 (Sept., 1948), 9; *Kansas Stockman,* 30 (Aug., 1946), 9; *ibid.,* 32 (Feb., 1948), 8; *Statistical Abstract of the United States* (Washington: U.S. Department of Commerce, 1947, 1948, 1949, 1950); Saunders, *op. cit.,* pp. 74–75; Mont H. Saunderson, "Ranch Prices—Whither Bound?" *American Cattle Producer,* 31 (Sept., 1949), 13.

4. Saunders, *op. cit.,* p. 7; Stanley W. Brown and Virgil E. Baugh, "Preliminary Inventory of Records of the Farmers Home Administration," mss. (Washington: National Archives and Records Service, 1959), pp. 7–8; F. A. Ralston and H. L. Dusenberry, *Annual Report,* Livestock, Extension Service, Bozeman, Montana, 1947, pp. 40–41; Clawson, *op. cit.,* pp. 199–200, 214, 215.

5. *Kansas Stockman,* 30 (July, 1946), 6; Quote, *The Cattleman,* 36 (Fort Worth, June, 1949), 5; *National Live Stock Producer,* 27 (May, 1949), 12; *The Cattleman,* 36 (June, 1949), 7; *American Cattle Producer,* 31 (July, 1949), 21; *ibid.* (Sept., 1949), 9.

6. Allen S. Clark, *Cattle Movements and Livestock Auction Markets in Montana* (M.S. thesis, Bozeman: Montana State College, 1947), pp. 4, 44–47, 69–70; *National Live Stock Producer,* 25 (Sept., 1947), 14; *American Cattle Producer,* 29 (June, 1947), 22; C. L. Gooding, "Quarantining," *Animal Diseases* (USDA Yearbook, 1956), p. 70.

7. Clark, *op. cit.,* pp. 18, 20; Clawson, *op. cit.,* p. 78; Saunders, *op. cit.,* pp. 41–43.

8. P. W. Cockerill, *Freight Rates on New Mexico Livestock and Feed* (New Mexico Agri. Exp. Sta. Bul. 346, 1948), pp. 9, 12–13; Clawson, *op. cit.,* pp. 79, 81–82.

9. Clawson, *op. cit.,* p. 223.

10. Saunderson, *loc. cit.,* p. 13; *American Cattle Producer,* 29 (Feb., 1948), 9; J. R. Gray and C. B. Baker, *Cattle Ranching in the Northern Great Plains* (Montana Agri. Exp. Sta. Circ. 204, 1953), p. 7; Clawson, *op. cit.,* p. 199.

11. Clawson, *op. cit.*, pp. 212–215.

12. H. E. Selby and D. T. Griffith, "Western Range Livestock Production," *American Cattle Producer*, 28 (Aug., 1946), 12; Clawson, *op. cit.*, p. 180; Lewis Corey, *Meat and Man* (New York: Viking, 1950), p. 102.

13. *Kansas Stockman*, 33 (Dec., 1948), 6; *Statistical Abstract of the United States* (Washington: U.S. Department of Commerce, 1945, 1946, 1947, 1948, 1950); Clawson, *op cit.*, p. 160; Gray and Baker, *loc. cit.*, p. 4; F. A. Ralston and E. P. Orcutt, *Annual Report*, Livestock, Extension Service, Bozeman, Montana, 1946 to 1949; *American Cattle Producer*, 27 (Apr., 1946), 4; *Kansas Stockman*, 30 (Aug., 1946), 6; *ibid.*, 31 (July, 1947), 12; *American Cattle Producer*, 29 (Aug., 1947), 34; *Kansas Stockman*, 32 (May, 1948), 5; *American Cattle Producer*, 30 (Aug., 1948), 4; *Kansas Stockman*, 33 (Nov., 1948), 31.

14. *Kansas Stockman*, 33 (Dec., 1948), 7.

15. "Storms Batter West," *American Cattle Producer*, 30 (Feb., 1949), 20; *ibid.* (Mar., 1949), 7; *The Cattleman*, 36 (July, 1949), 20; *National Live Stock Producer*, 27 (Apr., 1949), 10; *Annual Report*, Livestock, Extension Service, Bozeman, Montana, pp. 38, 43, and for the quote, p. 57; *The Kansas Stockman*, 33 (May, 1949), 7, 8, 29.

16. B. W. Allred and J. C. Dykes (eds.), *Flat Top Ranch* (Norman: Univ. of Oklahoma Press, 1957), p. 104; "Answering the Sportsman," *American Cattle Producer*, 30 (Nov., 1948), 10.

17. Clawson, *op. cit.*, p. 145; R. S. Campbell and Edward C. Crafts, *How to Keep and Increase Black Grama on Southwestern Ranges* (USDA Leaflet 180, 1948), p. 8; Annual Extension Service Report, Montana, 1949, *loc. cit.*, pp. 7, 41; *National Live Stock Producer*, 27 (Nov., 1948), 8.

18. Selby and Griffith, *loc. cit.*, p. 12; Annual Extension Service Report, Montana, 1946, *loc. cit.*, p. 34; *Kansas Stockman*, 31 (July, 1947), 21; Campbell and Crafts, *loc. cit.*, pp. 2, 3, 5–7.

19. Clawson, *op. cit.*, pp. 29, 144; Saunders, *op. cit.*, p. 30.

20. William Dusenberry, "Foot and Mouth Disease in Mexico, 1946–1951," *Agricultural History*, 29 (Apr., 1955), 82–90.

21. "Livestock Treaty Approved," *The Cattleman*, 14 (May, 1928), 10–11; *American Cattle Producer*, 28 (June, 1946), 7, 32; *ibid.* (Feb., 1947), 8; *ibid.*, 29 (June, 1947), 9; "Bad News from Mexico," *ibid.* (Jan., 1948), 9; *Kansas Stockman*, 32 (Jan., 1948), 7; *American Cattle Producer*, 31 (June, 1949), 21; *ibid.*, 36 (Feb., 1955), 29; M. S. Shahan and J. Traum, "Foot-and-Mouth Disease," *Animal Diseases* (USDA Yearbook, 1956), p. 194.

22. *American Cattle Producer*, 28 (June, 1946), 11; Annual Extension Service Report, Montana, 1946, *loc. cit.*, p. 13; *American Cattle Producer*, 28 (Apr., 1947), 4; *Kansas Stockman*, 30 (May, 1946), 27; Annual Extension Service Report, Montana, 1947, *loc. cit.*; *Kansas Stockman*, 31 (June, 1947), 45; *ibid.* (Sept., 1947), 9; Annual Extension Service Report, Montana, 1948, *loc. cit.*, p. 37; *Kansas Stockman*, 33 (Mar., 1949), 15; *ibid.* (Apr., 1949), 6.

23. *The Cattleman*, 36 (Aug., 1949), 70; W. C. Patterson and L. O. Mott, "Vesicular Stomatitis—V. S.," *Animal Diseases*, p. 183; A. O. Foster, "Chemotherapeutic Agents for Internal Parasites," *Animal Diseases*, p. 81.

24. *American Cattle Producer*, 30 (Aug., 1948), 4; *The Cattleman*, 36 (July, 1949), 42; *American Cattle Producer*, 31 (Oct., 1949), 6; *ibid.* (Sept., 1949), 38; *ibid.* (Aug., 1949), 28; *Kansas Stockman*, 31 (Sept., 1947), 7.

25. *Annual Report*, Livestock, Extension Service, Montana, 1949, *loc. cit.*, p. 35; E. H. Mims, "Buzzards—Another Foe to Conquer," *The Cattleman*, 34 (Oct., 1947), 25.

26. *National Live Stock Producer*, 27 (June, 1949), 7; *The Cattleman*, 34 (Mar., 1948), 27–28.

27. *American Cattle Producer*, 27 (Feb., 1946), 7; Samuel T. Dana, *Forest and Range Policy: Its Development in the United States* (New York: McGraw-Hill, 1956), 288; *National Live Stock Producer*, 27 (Nov., 1948), 12; *American Cattle Producer*, 31 (June, 1949), 7; Lynn H. Douglas, "Why Public Land Controversies Arise in the West," *ibid.*, 30 (July, 1948), 17.

28. Clawson, *op. cit.*, pp. 100, 110, 263–264; Dana, *op. cit.*, p. 287; *American Cattle Producer*, 30 (July, 1948), 11.

29. Clawson, *op. cit.*, pp. 118–119.

30. Saunders, *op. cit.*, p. 29; Clawson, *op. cit.*, pp. 27–29, 212–215.

31. D. A. Savage and D. F. Costello, "The Southern Great Plains," *Grass* (USDA Yearbook, 1948), p. 505; Annual Extension Service Report, Montana, 1949, *loc. cit.*, pp. 38–41; Saunders, *op. cit.*, p. 7; Allred and Dykes, *op. cit.*, p. 92; Clawson, *op. cit.*, pp. 57–58; Maurice Hagg (ed.), *The Range Lands of Wyoming* (Wyoming Exp. Sta. Bul. 289, 1949), p. 25.

32. Clawson, *op. cit.*, pp. 196–197; Allred and Dykes, *op. cit.*, p. 109; Saunders, *op. cit.*, p. 7; *American Cattle Producer*, 31 (Jan., 1950), 5.

33. *American Cattle Producer*, 28 (May, 1947), 7.

CHAPTER XIV

1. George Soule and V. P. Carosso, *American Economic History* (New York: Dryden Press, 1957), pp. 562–563; August C. Bolino, *The Development of the American Economy* (Columbus: Charles E. Merrill, 1961), pp. 273–274; *Statistical Abstract of the United States, 1958* (Washington: U.S. Department of Commerce, 1958).

2. *American Cattle Producer*, 32 (Denver, July, 1950), 5; *National Live Stock Producer*, 30 (Chicago, May, 1952), 7; *American Cattle Producer*, 37 (June, 1955), 5.

3. Agricultural Marketing Service, *Livestock and Meat Statistics* (USDA Stat. Bul. 230, 1958), pp. 283, 204; Murray Benedict and Oscar Stine, *The Agricultural Commodity Programs* (New York: Twentieth Century Fund, 1956), p. 216.

4. *American Cattle Producer*, 32 (Sept., 1950), 5; *ibid.* (Feb., 1951), 5; *Kansas Stockman*, 36 (Apr., 1951), 8; *American Cattle Producer*, 32 (Apr., 1951), 9; *ibid.*, 32 (May, 1951), 5; "Protest," *ibid.*, p. 7.

5. *American Cattle Producer*, 32 (May, 1951), 5; *ibid.*, 33 (July, 1951), 5; *ibid.* (Aug., 1951), 5; *Kansas Stockman*, 37 (Jan., 1952), 3, 46; *Ameri-*

can Cattle Producer, 33 (May, 1952), 5; *ibid.,* 34 (Sept., 1952), 5; *ibid.,* 35 (June, 1953), 8.

6. C. L. Sonnichsen, *Cowboys and Cattle Kings* (Norman: Univ. of Oklahoma Press, 1950), pp. 91–92; *American Cattle Producer,* 34 (Aug., 1952), 7; Mont H. Saunderson, *Western Stock Ranching* (Minneapolis: Univ. of Minnesota Press, 1950), p. 30.

7. *American Cattle Producer,* 32 (Feb., 1951), 13; S. H. Hart, "Treasury Acquiesces in Capital Gains—With Reservations," *American Hereford Journal,* 42 (May 1, 1951), 18; *American Cattle Producer,* 33 (Nov., 1951), 7; *ibid.,* 36 (Nov., 1954), 15–16.

8. *American Cattle Producer,* 31 (Apr., 1950), 7; quote, *Kansas Stockman,* 34 (Apr., 1950), 5; *ibid.,* 38 (May, 1953), 3, 37; *American Cattle Producer,* 35 (July, 1953), 5; *Kansas Stockman,* 38 (July, 1953), 5; *American Cattle Producer,* 35 (Nov., 1953), 9.

9. *Kansas Stockman,* 39 (Nov., 1953), 7, 47.

10. B. W. Allred and J. C. Dykes (eds.), *Flat Top Ranch* (Norman: Univ. of Oklahoma Press, 1957), pp. 131–132; *American Cattle Producer,* 35 (July, 1953), 5; *ibid.* (Oct., 1953), 5; *ibid.,* 36 (Nov., 1954), 31; *Kansas Stockman,* 39 (Sept., 1954), 7; Stanley W. Brown and Virgil E. Baugh, "Preliminary Inventory of Records of the Farmers Home Administration," mss. (Washington: National Archives and Records Service, 1959), p. 8.

11. *Kansas Stockman,* 35 (July, 1950), 5; *American Cattle Producer,* 32 (Aug., 1950), 4; *Kansas Stockman,* 35 (Nov., 1950), 19; Allred and Dykes, *op. cit.,* p. 67; *Kansas Stockman,* 36 (Mar., 1951), 10; *ibid.* (June, 1951), 3; *American Cattle Producer,* 33 (Sept., 1951), 38.

12. Allred and Dykes, *op. cit.,* pp. 67, 132; *Kansas Stockman,* 37 (Jan., 1952), 5; *ibid.* (Aug., 1952), 7; *American Cattle Producer,* (Jan., 1953), 5; *ibid.* (Mar., 1953), 16; *National Live Stock Producer,* 31 (Apr., 1953), 10; *Kansas Stockman,* 38 (July, 1953), 7; *American Cattle Producer,* 35 (July, 1953), 5; *Kansas Stockman,* 38 (Sept., 1953), 9; *American Cattle Producer,* 35 (Oct., 1953), 5; *ibid.,* 35 (Dec., 1953), 26.

13. Allred and Dykes, *op. cit.,* pp. 67, 106; *Kansas Stockman,* 39 (Feb., 1954), 7; *ibid.* (May, 1954), 5; *ibid.,* 39 (Aug., 1954), 7; *ibid.* (Sept., 1954), 9; *American Cattle Producer,* 36 (Sept. 1954), 5; *ibid.* (Nov., 1954), 5; "Damaged Land," *ibid.* (May, 1955), 20; *Kansas Stockman,* 40 (Mar., 1955), 91; *ibid.* (June, 1955), 9; *American Cattle Producer,* 37 (Sept., 1955), 5; *ibid.* (June, 1955), 31.

14. Allred and Dykes, *op. cit.,* pp. 104–105; E. P. Orcutt and F. A. Ralston, *Annual Report,* Livestock, Extension Service, Bozeman, Montana, 1950, p. 29; *American Cattle Producer,* 37 (June, 1955), 12.

15. E. P. Orcutt and N. A. Jacobsen, *Annual Report,* Livestock, Extension Service, Bozeman, Montana, 1952, pp. 19–20.

16. E. P. Orcutt and N. A. Jacobsen, *Annual Report,* Livestock, Extension Service, Bozeman, Montana, 1954, pp. 10–11, 37; Allred and Dykes, *op. cit.,* pp. 70–71, 106; B. W. Allred and W. M. Nixon, *Grass for Conservation in the Southern Great Plains* (USDA Farmers' Bul. 2093, 1955), p. 12.

17. Allred and Dykes, *op. cit.*, pp. 33–34; Allred and Nixon, *loc. cit.*, pp. 3, 6, 18–19; H. G. Reynolds and H. W. Springfield, *Reseeding Southwestern Range Lands with Crested Wheatgrass* (USDA Farmers' Bul. 2056, 1953), p. 2.

18. Charles W. Towne and E. N. Wentworth, *Cattle and Men* (Norman: Univ. of Oklahoma Press, 1955), pp. 327–328; Sonnichsen, *op. cit.*, p. 167; *Northern Great Plains Agricultural Council Sessions* (Lincoln: The Council, Mimeo, 1951), p. 36.

19. Reynolds and Springfield, *loc. cit.*, p. 3; *American Cattle Producer*, **36** (Aug., 1954), 14.

20. *American Cattle Producer*, **37** (Sept., 1955), 18; Allred and Nixon, *loc. cit.*, p. 12; Allred and Dykes, *op. cit.*, p. 34.

21. *Kansas Stockman*, **40** (Dec., 1954), 14; *American Cattle Producer*, **35** (Aug., 1953), 25; Orcutt and Jacobsen, Annual Extension Service Report, Montana, 1954, *loc. cit.*, pp. 36–37; *Kansas Stockman*, **40** (June, 1955), 11.

22. Orcutt and Jacobsen, Annual Extension Service Report, Montana, *loc. cit.*, 1952, p. 47; Allred and Nixon, *loc. cit.*, p. 28; *Kansas Stockman*, **38** (Mar., 1953), 100; *American Cattle Producer*, **37** (July, 1955), 9; Towne and Wentworth, *op. cit.*, pp. 329–330.

23. E. P. Orcutt and N. A. Jacobsen, *Annual Report*, Livestock, Extension Service, Bozeman, Montana, 1951, pp. 7, 11; *National Live Stock Producer*, **33** (Nov., 1954), 3; Sonnichsen, *op. cit.*, pp. 14, 16; Saunderson, *op. cit.*, pp. 8, 27, 28, 29, Quote, 27.

24. Carl F. Kraenzel, *The Great Plains in Transition* (Norman: Univ. of Oklahoma Press, 1955), pp. 339–340; Saunderson, *op. cit.*, pp. 6–7, 28; *National Live Stock Producer*, **28** (June, 1950), 4; Paul Horn, "The Flint Hills," *American Hereford Journal*, **41** (May 15, 1950), 10–12.

25. Saunderson, *op. cit.*, pp. 5, 9–10, 26–27; Sonnichsen, *op. cit.*, p. 12.

26. Mont H. Saunderson, "What's Ahead for the Western Cattle Ranch," *American Hereford Journal*, **42** (July 1, 1951), 620; Kraenzel, *op. cit.*, p. 328.

27. Sonnichsen, *op. cit.*, pp. 7–8, Quote, pp. 91–92.

28. Sonnichsen, *op. cit.*, p. 91.

29. James R. Gray and Chester B. Baker, *Cattle Ranching in the Northern Great Plains* (Montana Agri. Exp. Sta. Cir. 204, 1953), p. 7; Bureau of the Census, *U.S. Census of Agriculture, 1950*, II (Washington: GPO, 1952), 30; *Statistical Abstract of the United States, 1958*, p. 653; Saunderson, *op. cit.*, pp. 8–9.

30. *Statistical Abstract of the United States, 1958*, p. 675; Orcutt and Jacobsen, Extension Service Report, Montana, 1951, *loc. cit.*, p. 7.

31. *American Cattle Producer*, **37** (Sept., 1955), 8.

32. *Statistical Abstract of the United States* (Washington: U.S. Department of Commerce, 1952 and 1955).

33. *American Cattle Producer*, **32** (Sept., 1950), 18; *ibid.*, **35** (June, 1953), 20; *ibid.*, **36** (Feb., 1955), 29; M. S. Shahan and J. Traum, "Foot-and-Mouth Disease," *Animal Diseases* (USDA Yearbook, 1956), p. 194.

34. Orcutt and Jacobsen, 1951, *loc. cit.*, pp. 45–46; *American Cattle*

Producer, **35** (June, 1953), 21; *ibid.* (Mar., 1954), 5; *ibid.,* **36** (Feb., 1955), 20; *ibid.* (May, 1955), 15.

35. *National Live Stock Producer,* **32** (Mar., 1954), 30; *American Cattle Producer,* **35** (May, 1954), 10; *National Live Stock Producer,* **33** (Dec., 1954), 12; *American Cattle Producer,* **36** (Mar., 1955), 27; *National Live Stock Producer,* **30** (Mar., 1952), 16.

36. Gaines W. Eddy and R. C. Bushland, "Screwworms That Attack Livestock," *Animal Diseases,* p. 174; *American Cattle Producer,* **37** (July, 1955), 16.

37. *National Live Stock Producer,* **30** (May, 1952), 14; *American Cattle Producer,* **36** (Mar., 1955), 26.

38. *American Cattle Producer,* **37** (Sept., 1955), 18; Allred and Nixon, *loc. cit.,* pp. 29–30; Saunderson, *op. cit.,* p. 32; Towne and Wentworth, *op. cit.,* pp. 328–329; *National Live Stock Producer,* **32** (Mar., 1954), 4.

39. Tom Lea, *The King Ranch* (Boston: Little, Brown, 1957), II, 652.

40. *National Live Stock Producer,* **30** (Mar., 1952), 17; *Kansas Stockman,* **39** (Jan., 1954), 44; Orcutt and Jacobsen, *op. cit.,* 1954, pp. 26–27, 32.

41. *American Cattle Producer,* **35** (Feb., 1954), 28; *ibid.,* **37** (Jan., 1956), 20.

42. *American Cattle Producer,* **31** (Feb., 1950), 7; "Federal Grazing Land Tenancy Bill," *ibid.,* **35** (June, 1953), 9; *ibid.,* **36** (Sept., 1954), 7; Samuel T. Dana, *Forest and Range Policy: Its Development in the United States* (New York: McGraw-Hill, 1956), pp. 287, 289–290; *American Cattle Producer,* **31** (May, 1950), 5; *ibid.,* **32** (Feb., 1951), 8.

43. *American Cattle Producer,* **31** (Apr., 1950), 5; *ibid.,* **37** (Sept., 1955), 9; *ibid.,* **34** (Aug., 1952), 5; *ibid.,* **36** (June, 1954), 7.

44. Sonnichsen, *op. cit.,* p. 8; *Kansas Stockman,* **39** (Oct., 1954), 7; Kraenzel, *op. cit.,* pp. 164, 265–266.

45. Kraenzel, *op. cit.,* p. 344.

CHAPTER XV

1. Agricultural Marketing Service, *Livestock and Meat Statistics* (USDA Stat. Bul. 230, 1958), p. 204; Agricultural Marketing Service, *Supplement for 1960 to Statistical Bulletin 230* (Washington: USDA, 1961), p. 107.

2. Quote, *The Cattleman,* **45** (Fort Worth, Dec., 1958), 18; *see also* Harold L. Oppenheimer, "Arithmetic for the Cowman," *American Hereford Journal,* **50** (Jan. 1, 1960), 118, 122.

3. *Livestock and Meat Statistics,* p. 283; *Supplement for 1960 to Statistical Bulletin 230,* p. 137; "Congressman Cites Need for National Beef Campaign," *American Cattle Producer,* **40** (Denver, Jan., 1959), 35; "Meeting Notes," *ibid.,* p. 29; "Meeting Notes," *ibid.* (Apr., 1959), 12; *The Cattleman,* **44** (Apr., 1958), 43.

4. *National Live Stock Producer,* **36** (Chicago, Mar., 1958), 22; Clarence H. Girard, *Protecting the Cattle Industry—Some Current Problems* (Washington: USDA, Agricultural Marketing Service, 1961), pp. 1–3; "Association Notes," *American Cattle Producer,* **41** (Jan., 1960), 7.

5. "Committee Reports at Omaha Meeting," *American Cattle Producer,* 40 (Feb., 1959), 14; "Association Notes," *American Cattle Producer,* 41 (Jan., 1960), 17; *The Cattleman,* 44 (Feb., 1958), 7; "Frozen Food Business Up," *Kansas Stockman,* 42 (Topeka, Mar., 1957), 58.

6. B. W. Allred and J. C. Dykes (eds.), *Flat Top Ranch* (Norman: Univ. of Oklahoma Press, 1957), pp. 67–69; "Relief for Drouth Sufferers," *The Cattleman,* 43 (Sept., 1950), 5; *Kansas Stockman,* 42 (Mar., 1957), 33; Charles Hughes, "Dixie Beef," *American Cattle Producer,* 41 (Oct., 1959), 10–11.

7. *American Cattle Producer,* 37 (Jan., 1956), 7; *ibid.* (Feb., 1956), 9; *The Cattleman,* 43 (July, 1956), 18, 24, 106–110; *Kansas Stockman,* 42 (May, 1957), 8; *The Cattleman,* 44 (Feb., 1958), 16; "Price Supports Announced," *ibid.* (Mar., 1958), 35; *The Cattleman,* 44 (Feb., 1958), 10.

8. *The Cattleman,* 43 (Sept., 1956), 5, 10; *ibid.* (Oct., 1956), 7.

9. Edgar F. Baumann, "Conservation Ranching a 'Must,'" *The Cattleman,* 43 (Oct., 1956), 38 ff., 64; Allred and Dykes, *op. cit.,* pp. 85–87; M. H. McVicker, "April in February," *Breeder's Gazette,* 123 (May, 1958), 10. In the summer of 1961, while taking a trip through California, I happened to camp next to a Texas cattleman who was also on vacation. He told me quite a bit about his business. When I asked his opinion of the several magazines for producers, he said something like this, if I recall rightly: "When I first got into this business about seven years ago I read all of those magazines. But I don't get any of them now. They are all full of science fiction. They tell of gains that never were. They're all just fantastic tales." He may not have been typical.

10. *National Live Stock Producer,* 36 (Feb., 1958), 27; *The Cattleman,* 44 (Apr., 1958), 12; "Rains Cheer Cowmen at ANCA Session," *American Hereford Journal,* 47 (Feb. 1, 1957), 78; "Association Notes," *American Cattle Producer,* 41 (July, 1959), 11.

11. E. P. Orcutt and N. A. Jacobsen, *Annual Report,* Livestock, Extension Service, Bozeman, Montana, 1956, p. 6; "New Ruling to Curb Bang's," *American Hereford Journal,* 47 (Jan. 15, 1957), 70; "Cattlecade," *Breeder's Gazette,* 124 (June, 1959), 21.

12. "Meeting Notes," *American Cattle Producer,* 40 (Jan., 1959), 29; "USDA Announces Program for Brucellosis Tests," *ibid.,* 41 (June, 1959), 12; "Association Notes," *ibid.* (July, 1959), 11.

13. *The Cattleman,* 44 (Feb., 1958), 12; "Feed Additive Report," *Breeder's Gazette,* 124 (Feb., 1959), 9.

14. *National Live Stock Producer,* 35 (Feb., 1957), 18; *ibid.,* 37 (Nov., 1958), 21; John Harms, "Tests Show Malathion Kills Lice, Hornflies and Ticks on Cattle and Has Approval of U.S.D.A.," *The Cattleman,* 45 (Dec., 1958), 48; *ibid.* (Aug., 1958), 94.

15. On screwworms: "Association Notes," *American Cattle Producer,* 41 (Nov., 1959), 12; On bacteria: *The Cattleman,* 45 (Jan., 1959), 28; On herbicides: Allred and Dykes, *op. cit.,* pp. 40, 56–57, 59–61; H. G. Reynolds and F. H. Tschirley, *Mesquite Control on Southwestern Rangeland* (USDA Leaflet 421, 1957), p. 2; *The Cattleman,* 45 (Jan., 1959), 116.

16. *National Live Stock Producer,* 36 (Dec., 1957), 10.

17. "Cattle Gain More with Tranquilizer in Ration," *The Cattleman,* 4 (Mar., 1958), 51; W. M. Beeson, *et al.,* "Combination of an Antibiotic and a Female Hormone for Fattening Steers," *Journal of Animal Science,* 16 (Nov., 1957), 848–849; *National Live Stock Producer,* 36 (May, 1958), 15; *ibid.* (Mar., 1958), 11; "Cattlecade," *Breeder's Gazette,* 123 (Dec., 1958), 21; W. M. Beeson, "Cattle Feeding," *ibid.,* 124 (Apr., 1959), 16; Jay Richter, "Cattle Corral," *American Hereford Journal,* 50 (Jan. 1, 1960), 211; *National Live Stock Producer,* 37 (Dec., 1958), 29.

18. *The Cattleman,* 45 (Feb., 1959), 12.

19. *Kansas Stockman,* 42 (Jan., 1957), 31; "Committee Reports at Omaha Meeting," *American Cattle Producer,* 40 (Feb., 1959), 16.

20. "Artificial Insemination for Beef Cattle," *Breeder's Gazette,* 124 (Apr., 1959), 29; *National Live Stock Producer,* 36 (Nov., 1957), 13.

21. "The Beefmaster," *American Cattle Producer,* 37 (Feb., 1956), 37; *ibid.* (Mar., 1956), 30; Roger B. Letz, "The Claude McCan Cattle," *The Cattleman,* 45 (Dec., 1958), 26–27.

22. Allred and Dykes, *op. cit.,* pp. 42–43, 134–135, 177; "Bringing Pasture to the Cows," *The Cattleman,* 44 (May, 1958), 36–37; Lewis Nordyke, "Cattle Country," *American Hereford Journal,* 50 (Sept. 1, 1959), 108; Quote, "Land," *The Cattleman,* 45 (Jan., 1959), 33.

23. Harold E. Oppenheimer, "Arithmetic for the Cowman," *American Hereford Journal,* 50 (Jan. 1, 1960), 120; *Statistical Abstract of the United States, 1960* (Washington: U.S. Department of Commerce, 1960), p. 681.

24. W. M. Beeson, "Cattle Feeding," *Breeder's Gazette,* 124 (Apr., 1959), 28–29.

25. *Kansas Stockman,* 42 (Mar., 1957), 75; Allred and Dykes, *op. cit.,* p. 77; *Kansas Stockman,* 42 (Jan., 1957), 12; First quote, Allred and Dykes, *op. cit.;* Second quote, H. W. Cooper, J. E. Smith, Jr., and M. D. Atkins, *Producing and Harvesting Grass in the Great Plains* (USDA Farmers' Bul. 2112, 1957), p. 5.

26. Quote, Clarence H. Girard, *Protecting the Cattle Industry—Some Current Problems* (Address before the Texas and Southwestern Cattle Raisers Association, Washington: USDA, Mimeo, 1961), p. 3; "Sam Guard's Roundup," *Breeder's Gazette,* 123 (Feb., 1928), 26; Gerald Engelman, "Vertical Integration in the Cattle Business," *American Cattle Producer,* 40 (Feb., 1959), 29.

27. "Meeting Notes," *American Cattle Producer,* 40 (Apr., 1959), 14; *The Cattleman,* 45 (Apr., 1959), 40–41; "Association Notes," *American Cattle Producer,* 41 (July, 1959), 11.

28. "Association Notes," *American Cattle Producer,* 41 (Jan., 1960), 16.

Bibliography

Annotated bibliographies are peculiarly useless. The casual reader finds the titles hidden in a mass of verbiage, and in despair he will likely turn to his librarian for guidance in further reading. But, at any rate, the citations usually suggest what books the reader may want to examine. The serious scholar will want to check everything, no matter what the authority says. Who would depend entirely on the judgment of any author when undertaking a genuine research project? For the scholar it is enough to have a handy list of all the material his predecessor used. For the general reader such a list is at least easy to scan and comprehend. Probably a bibliography should help readers see what materials the author used, and how he came to know what he claims to know. This revelation of research methods is more readily, and possibly more honestly made, when the sources are merely stated. This bibliography does not contain all the possible sources on the history of the Plains cattlemen in the twentieth century. It does contain all the sources used in the preparation of this narrative.

Bibliographic Guides:

Agricultural Index. New York: H. W. Wilson, 1916–1960.

Annual Report of the Librarian of Congress. Washington: Government Printing Office, 1938–1942.

BRADLEY, MARY A., AND MABEL G. HUNT. *Index to Publications of the United States Department of Agriculture, 1901–1925.* Washington: Government Printing Office, 1932.

BRADLEY, MARY A. *Index to Publications of the United States Department of Agriculture, 1926–1930.* Washington: Government Printing Office, 1935.

————. *Index to Publications of the United States Department of Agriculture, 1931–1935.* Washington: Government Printing Office, 1937.

————. *Index to Publications of the United States Department of Agriculture, 1936–1940.* Washington: Government Printing Office, 1943.

BROWN, STANLEY W., AND VIRGIL E. BAUGH. Preliminary Inventory of Records of the Farmers Home Administration. Manuscript, The National Archives and Records Service. Washington, 1959.

EDWARDS, EVERETT E. *Bibliography of the History of Agriculture in the United States.* USDA Misc. Pub. 84. Washington: Government Printing Office, 1930.

————. References on the Range Cattle Industry Since 1900. Manuscript, USDA Division of Statistics and History. Washington, n.d.

Guide to the Records in the National Archives. Washington: Government Printing Office, 1948.

Harvard Guide to American History. Cambridge, Mass.: Belknap Press, 1954.

International Index to Periodicals. New York: H. W. Wilson, 1920–1960.

Reader's Guide to Periodical Literature. New York: H. W. Wilson, 1900–1960.

RENNER, F. G., EDWARD C. CRAFTS, THEO C. HARTMAN, AND LINCOLN ELLISON. *A Selected Bibliography on Management of Western Ranges, Livestock, and Wildlife.* USDA Misc. Pub. 281. Washington: Government Printing Office, 1938.

United States Office of Experiment Stations. *List of Bulletins of the Agricultural Experiment Stations.* Washington: Government Printing Office, 1924–1944.

Your Government's Records in the National Archives. Washington: Government Printing Office, 1950.

Manuscripts:

Extension Service, Montana, *Annual Reports,* Livestock, Bozeman, 1918–1956.

United States Forest Service. Records of the Division of Range Management, 1905–1937. Record Group 95, National Archives, Washington.

Works Progress Administration. Historical Record Survey, Montana Collection, Bozeman, Montana.

Periodicals:

American Cattle Producer. Denver, 1919–1960. From 1919–1934 title was *The Producer.*

American Hereford Journal. Kansas City, Missouri, 1950–1961.

Breeder's Gazette. Chicago, 1930–1961.

The Cattleman. Fort Worth, 1914–1961.

Dawson County Review. Glendive, Montana, 1920.

Ekalaka Eagle. Montana, 1921–1923.

Farmer and Stockman. Oklahoma City, 1911–1950. 1911–1935 as *Oklahoma Farmer and Stockman.*

The Independent. Miles City, Montana, 1900–1906.
Kansas Stockman. Topeka, 1916–1961.
Miles City American. Montana, 1913–1916.
Montana Stockgrower. Helena, 1929–1934.
Montana Stockman and Farmer. Helena, 1902–1907.
National Live Stock Producer. Chicago, 1922–1960.

Primary Sources:

"A.A.A. Range Program," *American Cattle Producer,* **18** (Nov., 1936), 18–19.
Abstract of the Fourteenth Census of the U.S., 1920. U.S. Department of Commerce. Washington: Government Printing Office, 1923.
Agricultural Marketing Service. *Livestock and Meat Statistics.* USDA Stat. Bul. 230. Washington: Government Printing Office, 1958.
Agricultural Statistics. USDA. Washington: Government Printing Office, 1936–1961.
ALBEE, L. R. "Grass and Cattle in Balance," *Soil Conservation,* **23** (Nov., 1957), 83–85.
ALICOTA, JOSEPH E. "Fluke Treatment—Here's How," *The Cattleman,* **32** (Oct., 1945), 52.
ALLRED, B. W., AND NIXON, W. M. *Grass for Conservation in the Southern Great Plains.* USDA Farmers' Bul. 2093. Washington: Government Printing Office, 1955.
ANDERSON, R. "It's Near: Artificial Breeding for Range Cows," *Farm Journal,* **82** (Apr., 1958), 58.
"Answering the Sportsman," *American Cattle Producer,* **30** (Nov., 1948), 10.
"Argentine Pact," *American Cattle Producer,* **18** (May, 1937), 15.
ARMSBY, HENRY P. *The Nutrition of Farm Animals.* New York: Macmillan, 1917.
"Artificial Insemination for Beef Cattle," *Breeder's Gazette,* **124** (Apr., 1959), 29.
"Bad News from Mexico," *American Cattle Producer,* **29** (Jan., 1948), 9.
BARKER, ROBERT M. "The Economics of Cattle-Ranching in the Southwest," *Review of Reviews,* **24** (Sept., 1901), 305–313.
BARNES, WILL C. "Brahman or Zebu Cattle," *The Producer,* **9** (Apr., 1928), 3–6.
———. "Brahman or Zebu Cattle," *ibid.,* **9** (May, 1928), 3–6.
———. "Looking Backward," *ibid.,* **7** (Apr., 1926), 3–6.
BAUMANN, EDGAR F. "Conservation Ranching a 'Must,'" *The Cattleman,* **43** (Oct., 1956), 38.
"The Beefmaster," *American Cattle Producer,* **37** (Feb., 1956), 37.

BEESON, W. M. "Cattle Feeding," *Breeder's Gazette*, 124 (Apr., 1959), 28–29.

——, *et al.* "Combination of an Antibiotic and a Female Hormone for Fattening Steers," *Journal of Animal Science*, 16 (Nov., 1957), 845–849.

BENTLY, H. L. *Experiments in Range Improvement in Central Texas.* U.S. Bur. Plant Ind., Bul. 13. Washington: Government Printing Office, 1902.

BLACK, W. H., AND V. V. PARR. *Dehorning, Castrating, and Marking Beef Cattle.* USDA Farmers' Bul. 1600. Washington: Government Printing Office, 1929.

——. *Feed-Lot and Ranch Equipment for Beef Cattle. ibid.,* 1584. Washington: Government Printing Office, 1929.

BLACKMAR, FRANK W. "Kansas after the Drought," *Review of Reviews*, 24 (Sept., 1901), 317–318.

BLACKMER, F. M. "West, Water, and the Grazing Laws," *Survey Graphic*, 26 (July, 1937), 387.

BLANKINSHIP, J. S. *Range Improvement.* Montana Agri. Exp. Sta. Annual Report, 1902. Bozeman, 1903.

BOHMAN, V. R., *et al.* "Effect of Chlortetracycline, Stilbestrol and Animal Fat on Fattening Steers," *Journal of Animal Science*, 16 (Nov., 1957), 833–839.

BONNEN, C. A., AND B. H. THIBODEAUX. *A Description of the Agriculture and Type-of-Farming Areas in Texas.* Texas Agri. Exp. Sta. Bul. 544. College Station, 1937.

BORTFELD, C. F. "Livestock Now the Most Important Source of Income for North Dakota Farmers," *North Dakota Agricultural Experiment Bimonthly Bulletin*, 3 (Jan., 1941), 17–18.

BRAYER, HERBERT O. "Colorado's Cattle Industry," *American Cattle Producer*, 27 (Sept., 1945), 8–10.

BREWSTER, M. H. "How We Get Along Without Cowboys; Ranch Family Drives 338 Steers through Rugged Montana," *Saturday Evening Post*, 216 (Sept. 4, 1943), 26–27.

"Bringing Pasture to the Cows," *The Cattleman*, 44 (May, 1958), 36–37.

BRITE, L. C. "Some Problems of the Livestock Industry," *The Cattleman*, 8 (June, 1921), 30–31.

BROSEMER, L. J. "Blizzard over Oklahoma Swept an Intelligent and Dominating Interest in Animal Keeping onto Every Farm in the State," *Breeder's Gazette*, 104 (Feb., 1939), 8–9.

BURDICK, R. T., *et al. Study of Ranch Organization in Eastern Colorado.* Colorado Agri. Exp. Sta. Bul. 327. Fort Collins, 1928.

Bureau of the Census. *Historical Statistics of the United States, 1789–1945.* Washington: U.S. Department of Commerce, 1952.

————. *U.S. Census of Agriculture, 1950.* Washington: Government Printing Office, 1952.

BURNS, JOHN C. "Value of Beef Cattle on Diversified Farms," *The Cattleman*, 12 (June, 1925), 35–38.

CAMPBELL, R. S., AND EDWARD C. CRAFTS. *How to Keep and Increase Black Grama on Southwestern Ranges.* USDA Leaflet 180. Washington: Government Printing Office, 1939; reprinted with some changes, 1948.

"The Cattle Feed Situation," *The Cattleman*, 30 (Feb., 1944), 80.

"Cattle Gain More with Tranquilizer in Ration," *The Cattleman*, 44 (Mar., 1958), 51.

"Cattle Scarcity More Pronounced," *Miles City American* (July 16, 1914), p. 2.

"This City-Farmer Commutes by Air: Robbers Roost Ranch, Wyoming," *House and Garden*, 80 (Nov., 1941), 80–81.

CLANCY, F. H. "Rodeos and Horses," *The Cattleman*, 28 (Sept., 1941), 69–76.

CLARK, ALLEN R. *Cattle Movements and Livestock Auction Markets in Montana.* M.S. thesis, Montana State College, Bozeman, 1947.

CLARK, R. T., *et al. Production Factors in Range Cattle under Northern Great Plains Conditions.* USDA Tech. Bul. 1181. Washington: Government Printing Office, 1958.

CLARK, R. W. *The Relation of Livestock and the Silo to Farm Profits.* Colorado Agricultural College Ext. Bul. 157-A. Fort Collins, 1919.

COCKERILL, P. W. *Freight Rates on New Mexico Livestock and Feed.* New Mexico Agri. Exp. Sta. Bul. 346. State College, 1948.

————, *et al. Type of Farming and Ranching Areas in New Mexico.* New Mexico Agri. Exp. Sta. Bul. 267. State College, 1939.

"Committee Reports at Omaha Meeting," *American Cattle Producer*, 40 (Feb., 1959), 14.

"Conference on the Taylor Grazing Act," *Montana Stockgrower*, 6 (Aug. 20, 1934), 1.

"Conserve All Feed and Water," *The Kansas Stockman*, 20 (Sept. 1, 1936), 3.

CONWAY, H. M. *Animal Livestock Market Review, 1926.* USDA. Washington: Government Printing Office, 1927.

COOPER, H. W., J. E. SMITH, JR., AND M. D. ATKINS. *Producing and Harvesting Grass Seed in the Great Plains.* USDA Farmers' Bul. 2112. Washington: Government Printing Office, 1957.

COTTON, JOHN. "Range Management," *Yearbook, U.S. Department of Agriculture: 1906.* Washington: Government Printing Office, 1907.

CRAFT, W. A. *Survey of Livestock Breeding and Feeding Practices.* Oklahoma Agri. Exp. Circ. 73. Stillwater, 1928.

CULLEY, MATT J. *An Economic Study of Cattle Business on a South-*

western Semidesert Range. USDA Circ. 448. Washington: Government Printing Office, 1937.

"Damaged Land," *American Cattle Producer,* 36 (May, 1955), 20.

DOUGLAS, LYNN H. "Why Public Land Controversies Arise in the West," *American Cattle Producer,* 30 (July, 1948), 17.

"Dude Ranching and Diversification of Ranch Investments," *Montana Stockgrower,* 2 (June 1, 1930), 7.

EDWARDS, J. R. The Cattle Feed Situation," *The Cattleman,* 30 (Feb., 1944), 80.

ENGLEMAN, GERALD. "Vertical Integration in the Cattle Business," *American Cattle Producer,* 40 (Feb., 1959), 29.

————, AND B. S. PENCE. *Livestock Auction Markets in the United States, Development, Volume Handled, and Marketing Charges.* U.S. Agricultural Marketing Research Report 223. Washington: Government Printing Office, 1958.

"The Farm Situation," *The Producer,* 11 (Aug., 1929), 19.

FARROW, J. E. "Making Cowboys into Business Men," *World To-Day,* (Apr., 1911), 456–468.

"Federal Grazing Land Tenancy Bill," *American Cattle Producer,* 35 (June, 1953), 9.

"Federal Meat Inspection and Livestock Health," *American Veterinary Medicine Association Journal,* 132 (Jan. 1, 1958), 38.

"Feed Additive Report," *Breeder's Gazette,* 124 (Feb., 1959), 9.

"Financing the Cattle Industry," *Bankers Magazine,* 90 (Feb., 1915), 232–234.

FREED, SAM. "The Beet-Sugar Industry in Its Relation to Live Stock," *The Producer,* 2 (Dec., 1920), 5–8.

"Fresh Outbreak of Foot and Mouth," *Miles City Independent* (Feb. 12, 1915), p. 3.

"Frozen Food Business Up," *Kansas Stockman,* 42 (Mar., 1957), 58.

FULTS, JESS L. *Blue Grama Grass for Erosion Control and Range Reseeding in the Great Plains and a Method of Obtaining Seed in Large Lots.* USDA Circ. 402. Washington: Government Printing Office, 1936.

GARRETT, GARET. "That Pain in Our Northwest," *Saturday Evening Post,* 197 (Apr. 12, 1924), 3–4.

GIRARD, CLARENCE H. *Protecting the Cattle Industry—Some Current Problems.* USDA, Marketing Service. Washington: Mimeo speech, 1961.

"Government Buying of Drought Live Stock," *American Cattle Producer,* 16 (Aug., 1934), 13.

"Grasshopper Plague," *The Producer,* 3 (Aug., 1921), 21.

"Grass Replacing Grains," *Kansas Stockman,* 30 (Dec., 1944), 6.

GRAY, JAMES R., AND CHESTER B. BAKER. *Cattle Ranching in the*

Northern Great Plains. Montana Agri. Exp. Sta. Circ. 204. Bozeman, 1953.

GUARD, S. R. "Classification Comes to Beef Cattle," *Breeder's Gazette*, 123 (May, 1958), 11.

HALCROW, HAROLD. *The Problem of the Unsuccessful Dry Farm in the Northern Great Plains*. M.S. thesis, Montana State College. Bozeman, 1938.

HAMPSON, C. M. *Some Factors of Success in Cattle Ranch Management, Western South Dakota*. South Dakota Agri. Exp. Sta. Circ. 13. Brookings, 1933.

HANSON, HERBERT C. "Administration of Western State Lands for Grazing," *The Producer*, 8 (May, 1927), 3–5.

———. "Administration of Western State Lands for Grazing," *ibid.*, 9 (June, 1927), 3–6.

HARGER, M. "Modern Methods in the Cattle Industry," *Outlook*, 72 (Sept. 6, 1902), 39–47.

HARGER, C. M. "New Era of the Ranch Lands," *Review of Reviews*, 44 (Nov., 1911), 580–590.

HART, S. H. "Treasury Acquiesces in Capital Gains—with Reservations," *American Hereford Journal*, 42 (May 1, 1951), 18.

HATCHER, AVERLYNE M. "The Water Problem of the Matador Ranch," *Southwestern Historical Quarterly*, 48 (Apr., 1945), 564.

HATTON, JOHN H. "National-Forest Grazing Regulations," *The Producer*, 4 (Apr., 1923), 5–9.

Hearings, Committee on Agriculture, House of Rep., 65th Cong., 2nd Sess., H.R. 9966, Feb. 19, 1918, Part 2. Washington: Government Printing Office, 1918.

HEDGES, H. *Economic Aspects of the Cattle Industry of the Nebraska Sand Hills*. Nebraska Agri. Exp. Sta. Bul. 231. Lincoln, 1928.

HORN, PAUL. "The Flint Hills," *American Hereford Journal*, 41 (May 15, 1950), 10–11.

HOWARD, I. M. "Anchoring Ranches and Ranchers," *The American Cattle Producer*, 18 (Jan., 1937), 4–5.

———. "Let the Prairies Go to Grass," *American Cattle Producer*, 17 (Oct., 1935), 3–5.

———. "More Moisture, More Grass," *American Cattle Producer*, 19 (June, 1937), 3–4.

HUGHES, CHARLES E. "Technological Advances in Cattle Ranching," *Armour's Analysis*, 4 (Jan.–Mar., 1956), 1–8.

———. "Dixie Beef," *American Cattle Producer*, 41 (Oct., 1959), 10–11.

HULT, J. E. "Dry Land Farmers Are Hard Up—But So Is Everybody," *Ekalaka Eagle* (Montana: Nov. 25, 1921), p. 5.

HUNTER, B., P. W. COCKERILL, AND H. B. PINGREY. *Type of Farming and Ranching Areas in New Mexico*. New Mexico Agri. Exp. Sta. Bul. 261. State College, 1939.

HUNTER, BYRON, AND SAMUEL B. NICKOLS. *An Economic Study of Irrigated Farming in Twin Falls County, Idaho*. USDA Bul. 1421. Washington: Government Printing Office, 1926.

"Intermediate Credit Banks," *The Producer*, 6 (Dec., 1924), 11.

Irrigation Agriculture in the West. USDA Misc. Pub. 670. Washington: Government Printing Office, 1948.

JOHNSON, M. B. "Cattle Ranch Operation in Northern Great Plains Region," *The Producer*, 12 (Nov., 1930), 5–9.

———. *Cattle Ranch Organization and Management in Western South Dakota*. South Dakota Agri. Exp. Sta. Bul. 255. Brookings, 1930.

———. *Ranch Organization and Management in Western North Dakota*. North Dakota Agri. Exp. Sta. Bul. 237. Fargo, 1930.

———, AND R. D. JENNINGS. *Cattle Ranching and Range Utilization in Western North Dakota*. USDA Bur. Agri. Econ. Special Report, Mimeo. Washington, 1937.

JOHNSON, SHERMAN E. *An Economic Analysis of Production Problems in the Bitter Root Valley*. Montana Agri. Exper. Sta. Bul. 220. Bozeman, 1929

"Kansas City Mayor Says Meat Dealers Appear to be Profiteering," *The Cattleman*, 8 (Dec., 1921), 11.

KIFER, R. S., AND H. L. STEWARD. *Farming Hazards in the Drought Areas*. Works Progress Administration, Division of Social Research, Mimeo. Washington: Government Printing Office, 1938.

KLEBERG, ROBERT J., JR., "The 'Santa Gertrudis' Breed of Beef Cattle," *The Producer*, 13 (June, 1931), 3–7.

KYLE, E. J., AND A. R. ALEXANDER. *Agriculture in the Southwest*. New York: Scribner, 1940.

LETZ, ROGER B., "The Claude McCan Cattle," *The Cattleman*, 45 (Dec., 1958), 26–27.

"Life Visits an Oklahoma Ranch: Roy Turner Has Prize Herd of Herefords," *Life*, 17 (July 10, 1944), 98–101.

"Live Stock and Grass," *Wallaces Farmer*, 43 (Feb. 22, 1918), 339.

"Livestock Treaty Approved," *The Cattleman*, 14 (May, 1928), 10–11.

LUSH, JAY L. "Conference on Stock Cattle Problem," *Kansas Stockman*, 13 (June 15, 1929), 5.

McCULLY, JOHN D. "1940 Range-Improvement Program," *The Cattleman*, 26 (Nov., 1939), 15.

McGILL, D. P. "Yesterday's Research, Today's Survival," *Crops and Soils*, 10 (Aug., 1958), 14–16.

McVICKER, M. H. "April in February," *Breeder's Gazette*, 123 (May, 1958), 10.

MANTZ, J. W. "The Charollaise Beef Look," *American Cattle Producer*, 37 (Jan., 1956), 32.

MARKS, MAUDEEN. "The Brahmans Go Places," *American Cattle Producer*, 31 (Dec., 1949), 43.

MARTIN, J. H., AND J. C. STEPHENS. *The Culture and Use of Sorghums for Forage*. USDA Farmers' Bul. 1844. Washington: Government Printing Office, 1940.

METZGER, S. S. "Day on the Ranch," *Sunset*, 37 (July, 1916), 47.

MICHAELSON, LEON G. *Some Size, Income and Organization Characteristics of the Ranches of 46 Montana Counties*. M.S. thesis, Montana State College. Bozeman, 1938.

MILLER, C. E. "Good Stockmen and the Badlands," *Breeder's Gazette*, 113 (Sept., 1948), 10.

MIMS, E. H., "Buzzards—Another Foe to Conquer," *The Cattleman*, 34 (Oct., 1947), 25.

MOLLIN, F. E. "Agricultural Adjustment Program as Cattle Producers View It," *The Producer*, 15 (Nov., 1933), 6–9.

————. *If and When It Rains—The Stockman's View of the Range Question*. Denver: American National Livestock Association, 1938.

MONROE, DAY, et al. *Family Income and Expenditures, Pacific Region and Plains and Mountain Region, Part 1, Family Income*. USDA Misc. Pub. 356. Washington: Government Printing Office, 1939.

"Montana," *American Cattle Producer*, 16 (June, 1934), 32.

Montana Agricultural Statistics. USDA Bureau of Agricultural Economics. Helena, 1946.

MOORHOUSE, L. A. "Analysis of Ranch Operations—Factors That Make for Success in the Cattle Business," *The Cattleman*, 14 (Mar., 1928), 83–87.

MURRAY, HENRY T. *State Land Management in Montana*. M.S. thesis, Montana State College. Bozeman, 1942.

MYERS, CHARLES A. "Co-operative Range Ownership," *The Producer*, 2 (Feb., 1921), 5–7.

NELSON, A. G. *Planning Minimum Sized Ranches and Farms for the Hyde County Area in South Dakota*. South Dakota Agri. Exp. Sta. Bul. 346. Brookings, 1940.

————, AND G. E. KORZAN. *Profits and Losses in Ranching, Western South Dakota, 1931–1940*. South Dakota Agri. Exp. Sta. Bul. 352. Brookings, 1941.

————. *Should Farmers Emphasize Wheat or Livestock in North Central South Dakota?* South Dakota Agri. Exp. Sta. Circ. 33. Brookings, 1941.

"New Grazing Policy in Use," *National Live Stock Producer*, 18 (Sept., 1940), 16.

"New State Bills," *American Cattle Producer*, 40 (Mar., 1959), 33.

NOLEN, D. W. "Feeding Pens of William Heuermann Are Practically Empty," *The Cattleman*, 30 (Jan., 1944), 31.

NORDYKE, LEWIS. "Angel of the Range; Wyoming Hereford Ranch," *Saturday Evening Post*, 218 (Nov. 3, 1945), 26–27.

————. "Cattle Country," *American Hereford Journal*, 50 (Sept. 1, 1959), 108.

"Northwest Is Hard Hit," *The Producer*, 1 (Jan., 1920), 32.

NORTON, L. J. "Some Recent Changes in Meat and Feed Crop Production," *Journal of Farm Economics*, 9 (1927), 303–317.

O'BRIEN, H. R. "It Was Livestock or Starve," *Country Gentleman*, 110 (Dec., 1940), 13.

OPPENHEIMER, HAROLD L. "Arithmetic for the Cowman," *American Hereford Journal*, 50 (Jan. 1, 1960), 118, 122.

OSLAND, H. B. *Silage and Trench Silos in Colorado*. Colorado Agricultural College Ext. Serv. Bul. 315-A. Fort Collins, 1931.

"Packing Investigation Develops Surprises," *The Cattleman*, 4 (Feb., 1918), 25–27.

PARR, V. V., G. W. COLLIER, AND G. S. KLEMMEDSON. *Ranch Organization and Methods of Livestock Production in the Southwest*. USDA Tech. Bul. 68. Washington: Government Printing Office, 1928.

"Passing of the South Plains Ranches," *The Cattleman*, 10 (Mar., 1924), 59–61.

PERRY, G. S. "Drought, Varmints and Rollbacks," *Country Gentleman*, 121 (July, 1951), 21.

PETERSON, ROALD. "Crested Wheat Grass for Northern Plains," *American Cattle Producer*, 20 (Aug., 1938), 12.

PETERSON, V. V. "Cattle in Wyoming," *American Cattle Producer*, 27 (Aug., 1945), 8.

————. "Oklahoma's Cattle Industry," *American Cattle Producer*, 28 (Sept., 1946), 9–11.

————. "Range History of Nebraska," *American Cattle Producer*, 27 (Jan., 1946), 12–14.

PETERSON, W., P. V. CARDON, K. C. IKELER, G. STEWART, AND A. C. ESPLIN. *Cattle Ranching in Utah*. Utah Agri. Exp. Sta. Bul. 203. Logan, 1927.

PETERSON, W. M. "Stock-Feeding and Soil-Building," *The Producer*, 1 (June, 1919), 18–20.

PICKETT, E. "White Faces," *Country Gentleman*, 84 (Jan. 18, 1919), 5.

PINGREY, H. B. *Cattle Ranching in Southeastern New Mexico*. New Mexico Agri. Exp. Sta. Bul. 336. State College, 1948.

————. *Combination Ranching in Southeastern New Mexico*. New Mexico Agri. Exp. Sta. Bul. 332. State College, 1946.

PIPER, C. V. *Forage Plants and Their Culture.* New York: Macmillan, 1947.

POOLE, JAMES K. "Cattle Business out of Woods," *The Producer,* 12 (Sept., 1930), 11.

PRATT, W. H. "Case of a Small Rancher," *Agricultural Journal of British Columbia,* 5 (May, 1920), 76–77.

"Price Supports Announced," *The Cattleman,* 44 (Mar., 1958), 35.

PRIESTMAN, M. T. "Model Stock and Dairy Farm," *Country Life,* 15 (Feb., 1909), 368–369.

PRYOR, IKE T. "How Texas Came Back," *The Producer,* 1 (July, 1919), 14–15.

"Public Land Legislation," *Montana Stockgrower,* 6 (Jan. 15, 1934), 9.

"Ranchers Winter Calves on Alfalfa," *Successful Farming,* 56 (Oct., 1958), 112.

"Range Cattle Sold in East," *Miles City Independent* (Aug. 4, 1916), 5.

The 1938 Range Conservation Program—Western Region. U.S. Agricultural Adjustment Administration Leaflet 202. Washington: Government Printing Office, 1938.

READ, A. D. "I Like Ranching in the Rockies," *Breeder's Gazette,* 89 (Mar. 4, 1926), 264.

"Record Price Paid for Cattle Off Range," *Miles City American* (Nov. 5, 1914).

REEVES, FRANK. "West Texas Becoming 'Feed Minded,'" *The Cattleman,* 23 (Mar., 1937), 61–64.

REEVES, GEORGE S. *Man from South Dakota.* New York: Dutton, 1950.

REES, H. "Story of a Ranch," *American Cattle Producer,* 25 (Sept., 1943), 7–11.

"Reindeer Competition," *The Producer,* 14 (Mar., 1933), 18.

"Relief for Drouth Sufferers," *The Cattleman,* 43 (Sept., 1956), 5.

REYNOLDS, H. G., AND H. W. SPRINGFIELD. *Reseeding Southwestern Range Lands with Crested Wheatgrass.* USDA Farmers' Bul. 2056. Washington: Government Printing Office, 1953.

REYNOLDS, H. G., AND F. H. TSCHIRLEY. *Mesquite Control on Southwestern Rangeland.* USDA Leaflet 421. Washington: Government Printing Office, 1957.

ROATH, C. W. *Steer Feeding in Southeastern Wyoming.* Wyoming Agri. Exp. Sta. Bul. 212. Laramie, 1935.

ROCHFORD, L. H. *Influence of California Demand on Colorado Beef-Cattle Prices.* Colorado Agri. Ext. Serv. Bul. 316-A. Fort Collins, 1932.

ROPE, L. S. "Pellets for Cattle and Sheep," *Breeder's Gazette,* 125 (Jan., 1960), 8.

ROTH, ARTHUR H., JR. *A Study of the Comparative Advantages of Raising Beef Cattle in the Corn Belt and on Montana Ranges.* M.S. thesis, Montana State College. Bozeman, 1936.

RULE, GLENN K. *Crops against the Wind on the Southern Great Plains.* USDA Farmers' Bul. 1833. Washington: Government Printing Office, 1939.

———. *Toward Soil Security on the Northern Great Plains.* USDA Farmers' Bul. 1864. Washington: Government Printing Office, 1941.

RUSSELL, CHARLES M. *Trails Plowed Under.* New York: Doubleday, 1927.

SALLEE, G. A., et al. *Economic Study of Livestock Possibilities in the Red River Valley of Minnesota.* Minnesota Agri. Exp. Sta. Bul. 283. Minneapolis, 1931.

SAMPSON, ARTHUR W. *Livestock Husbandry on Range and Pasture.* New York: John Wiley, 1928.

SAMPSON, A. W. *Native American Forage Plants.* New York: John Wiley, 1924.

SAUNDERS, A. DALE. *Trends in Size, Land Tenure, Income, Organization, and Management of Selected Cattle Ranches in Southeastern Montana, 1924–48.* M.S. thesis, Montana State College. Bozeman, 1949.

SAUNDERSON, MONT H. "Ranch Prices—Whither Bound?" *American Cattle Producer,* **31** (Sept., 1949), 12.

———. *Western Stock Ranching.* Minneapolis: University of Minnesota Press, 1950.

———, AND D. W. CHITTENDEN. *Cattle Ranching in Montana.* Montana Agri. Exp. Sta. Bul. 341. Bozeman, 1937.

SCOTT, DUNCAN. "Keeps Grass Up and Erosion Down," *American Cattle Producer,* **24** (June, 1942), 8–9.

SHORT, L. R., AND E. J. WOOLFOLK. *Reseeding to Increase the Yield of Montana Range Lands.* USDA Farmers' Bul. 1924. Washington: Government Printing Office, 1943; Revised, 1952.

SIEGLINGER, JOHN B. *Grain-Sorghum Experiments at the Woodward Field Station in Oklahoma.* USDA Department Bul. 1175. Washington: Government Printing Office, 1923.

"Small Cattle Ranch the More Efficient," *The Producer,* **6** (Sept., 1924), 29.

SMITH, H. H. "How to Live 70 Miles from Town," *Saturday Evening Post,* **217** (Sept. 23, 1944), 26–27.

"Socialism for U.S. Farms," *National Live Stock Producer,* **27** (May, 1949), 12.

"Soil and Range Practices for West," *American Cattle Producer,* **18** (Feb., 1937), 17.

"South Dakota Farms," *New York Produce Review and American Creamery*, **12** (May 8, 1901), 10.

SPAFFORD, R. R. *Farm Types in Nebraska, As Determined by Climate, Soil, and Economic Factors.* Nebraska Agri. Res. Exp. Bul. 15. Lincoln, 1919.

"The Stanfield Grazing Bill," *The Producer*, **8** (June, 1926), 3–7.

STARVIS, J. T. *Effects of Different System and Intensities of Grazing upon the Native Vegetation at the Northern Great Plains Field Station.* USDA Department Bul. 1170. Washington: Government Printing Office, 1923.

STATEN, GLEN, R. S. STROUD, AND JOHN CARTER. *Alfalfa Production Investigations in New Mexico.* New Mexico Agri. Exp. Sta. Bul. 323. State College, 1945. *Statistical Abstract of the United States.* United States Department of Commerce, 1890–1961. Washington: Government Printing Office, 1890–1961.

STEPHENS, J. C., J. H. MARTIN, AND H. N. VINALL. *Identification, History, and Distribution of Common Sorghum Varieties.* USDA Tech. Bul. 506. Washington: Government Printing Office, 1936.

STEPHENS, J. M., *et al. Report of the Northern Great Plains Field Station for the 10 Year Period, 1913–22 Inclusive.* USDA Department Bul. 1301. Washington: Government Printing Office, 1925.

STEWART, T. G. *Pasture and Feed Crops for Plains Area of Colorado.* Colorado Agricultural College Ext. Serv. Bul. 315-A. Fort Collins, 1932.

STEWART, T. G., D. W. ROBERTSON, AND D. KOONCE. *Pasture and Feed Crops for Irrigated and Mountain Areas.* Colorado Agricultural College Ext. Bul. 318-A. Fort Collins, 1932.

"Stockmen Object to Elimination of National Forest," *Miles City American* (Nov. 20, 1913), 1.

"Storms Batter West," *American Cattle Producer*, **30** (Feb., 1949), 20.

"Teen-Agers Could Boost Meat Use," *American Cattle Producer*, **36** (May, 1955), 26.

"Term Permits on Forests Still Available," *American Cattle Producer*, **19** (Oct., 1937), 15.

THOMAS, A. R. "On a Powder River Ranch," *Overland*, **58** (Oct., 1911), 334–341.

TOWNE, CHARLES W. *Her Majesty Montana.* Butte: Standard Press, 1939.

"Tranquilizer in Feed Ok'd for Beef," *Farm Journal*, **82** (Oct., 1958), 54.

United States Census. 12th Census to the 16th Census. Washington: Government Printing Office, 1902, 1913, 1922, 1932, 1942.

"USDA Announces Program for Brucellosis Tests," *American Cattle Producer*, 41 (June, 1959), 12.

"United States, Statistics, Shifts in Production Areas Trend toward the East," *American Cattle Producer*, 39 (Apr., 1958), 12–14.

"The Uninvited Guest," *The Producer*, 2 (Feb., 1921), 23.

VAN HOUWELING, C. D. "Our Battle against Animal Diseases," *Animal Diseases*. USDA Yearbook, 1956. Washington: Government Printing Office, 1956.

WADDELL, W. N. "The Drouth and the Tick," *The Cattleman*, 3 (June, 1916), 20.

WALKER, A. H. "Soil and Water Conservation in Culberson County," *The Cattleman*, 26 (Nov., 1939), 65–68.

"War Finance Corporation Opens Cattle Loan Agencies," *The Cattleman*, 5 (Sept., 1918), 13–15.

WENTWORTH, E. N. "Changes in the Center of Beef Production," *The Cattleman*, 8 (Nov., 1921), 16.

————. "Outlook for Beef Consumption," *Montana Stockgrower*, 3 (Dec. 1, 1931), 9.

————. "Shifting Regions of Live Stock Growing," *American Cattle Producer*, 20 (Feb., 1939), 3–6.

WILSON, M. L., R. H. WILCOX, G. S. KLEMMEDSON, AND V. V. PARR. *A Study of Ranch Organization and Methods of Range-Cattle Production in the Northern Great Plains Region*. USDA Tech. Bul. 45. Washington: Government Printing Office, 1928.

WRENN, J. E. "Marketing of American Meat Products in Export Trade," *The Cattleman*, 12 (June, 1925), 39–45.

"Wyoming Stockmen to Receive Federal Money," *The Producer*, 13 (Apr., 1932), 31.

YOUNGBLOOD, BONNEY. *An Economic Study of a Typical Ranching Area*. Texas Agri. Exp. Sta. Bul. 297. College Station, 1921.

Secondary Sources:

AITKEN, W. A. "Shipping Fever," *Animal Diseases*. USDA Yearbook, 1956. Washington: Government Printing Office, 1956.

ALLRED, B. W. *Range Conservation Practices for the Great Plains*. USDA Misc. Pub. 410. Washington: Government Printing Office, 1940.

————, AND J. C. DYKES (eds.). *Flat Top Ranch*. Norman: University of Oklahoma Press, 1957.

ANDERSON, HARRY G., AND ALVA H. BENTON. *Cattle Marketed in North Dakota, 1929–30–31 and Some Factors Underlying Their Production*. North Dakota Exp. Sta. Bul. 275. Fargo, 1933.

ANDERSON, OSCAR E., JR. *Refrigeration in America.* Princeton: Princeton University Press for the University of Cincinnati, 1953.

ATWOOD, A. W. "Passing of the Ranches," *Saturday Evening Post,* 198 (Nov. 28, 1925), 12–13.

BARGER, HAROLD, AND H. H. LANDSBERG. *American Agriculture, 1899–1939: A Study of Output, Employment, and Productivity.* New York: National Bureau of Economic Research, 1942.

BENEDICT, MURRAY R. *Farm Policies of the United States, 1790–1950.* New York: Twentieth Century Fund, 1953.

————, AND OSCAR STINE. *The Agricultural Commodity Programs.* New York: Twentieth Century Fund, 1956.

BIDWELL, P. W., AND J. I. FALCONER. *History of Agriculture in the Northern United States, 1620–1860.* New York: Peter Smith, 1941.

BIERER, B. W. *A Short History of Veterinary Medicine in America.* East Lansing: Michigan State University Press, 1955.

BILLINGTON, RAY A. *Westward Expansion: A History of the American Frontier.* New York: Macmillan, 1949.

BOLINO, AUGUST C. *The Development of the American Economy.* Columbus: Charles E. Merrill, 1961.

"Brahma Cattle Increasing—A Little of Their Early History in Texas," *The Cattleman,* 6 (July, 1919), 21–23.

BRIGGS, HAROLD E. *Frontiers of the Northwest.* New York: Appleton-Century, 1940.

BRINKMANN, THEODORE. *Economics of the Farm Business.* Translation and notes by Elizabeth T. Benedict, H. H. Stippler, and M. R. Benedict. Berkeley: University of California Press, 1935.

BRITTAIN, ROBERT. *Let There Be Bread.* New York: Simon and Schuster, 1952.

BURLINGAME, MERRILL G., AND K. ROSS TOOLE. *A History of Montana.* 3 Vols. New York: Lewis Historical Publishing Company, 1957.

BURMEISTER, CHARLES A. "Six Decades of Rugged Individualism: The American National Cattlemen's Association, 1898–1955," *Agricultural History,* 30 (Oct., 1956), 143–149.

BURSON, FLOSSIE. *The Transition of Agriculture in the Great Plains from 1920 to 1929.* M.S. thesis, Iowa State University. Ames, 1934.

CARPENTER, F. R. "Problem of Grazing on Public Lands," *American Cattle Producer,* 21 (Dec., 1939), 16–17.

CLARK, THOMAS D. *Frontier America.* New York: Scribner, 1959.

CLAWSON, MARION. *The Western Range Livestock Industry.* New York: McGraw-Hill, 1950.

CLEMEN, R. A. *The American Livestock Industry.* New York: Ronald Press, 1923.

COHEN, I. BERNARD. *Science, Servant of Man.* Boston: Little, Brown, 1948.

COREY, LEWIS. *Meat and Man: A Study of Monopoly, Unionism, and Food Policy.* New York: Viking Press, 1950.

CULBERT, JAMES I. "Cattle Industry of New Mexico," *Economic Geography,* 17 (Apr., 1941), 155–168.

CUMMINGS, RICHARD O. *The American and His Food.* Chicago: University of Chicago Press, 1941.

DALE, EDWARD E. "The Cow Country in Transition," *Mississippi Valley Historical Review,* 24 (June, 1937), 3–20.

————. *The Range Cattle Industry: Ranching on the Great Plains 1865 to 1925.* Norman: University of Oklahoma Press, 1960.

DANA, SAMUEL T. *Forest and Range Policy: Its Development in the United States.* New York: McGraw-Hill, 1956.

DEGRAFF, HERRELL. *Beef Production and Distribution.* Norman: University of Oklahoma Press, 1960.

DERICQUES, A. E. "Forty Years' Evolution in Range Cattle," *Breeder's Gazette,* 97 (Mar., 1932), 12–19.

DOUGLAS, C. L. "How the Hump-Backed Brahma Cattle Found Their Way to Texas," *The Cattleman,* 22 (Apr., 1936), 20–26.

DUPREE, A. HUNTER. *Science in the Federal Government.* Cambridge, Mass.: Belknap Press, 1957.

EDDY, GAINES W., AND R. C. BUSHLAND. "Screwworms That Attack Livestock," *Animal Diseases.* USDA Yearbook, 1956. Washington: Government Printing Office, 1956.

ELY, RICHARD T., AND GEORGE S. WEHRWEIN. *Land Economics.* New York: Macmillan, 1940.

DUSENBERRY, WILLIAM. "Foot and Mouth Disease in Mexico, 1946–1951," *Agricultural History,* 29 (Apr., 1955), 82–90.

FITE, GILBERT C., AND JIM E. REESE. *An Economic History of the United States.* Boston: Houghton Mifflin, 1959.

FITZ-GERALD, D. A. *Livestock under the A.A.A.* Washington: Brookings Institution, 1935.

FLETCHER, ROBERT S. "The End of the Open Range in Eastern Montana," *Mississippi Valley Historical Review,* 16 (Sept., 1929), 205–211.

————. *Organization of the Range Cattle Business in Eastern Montana.* Montana Agri. Exp. Sta. Bul. 265. Bozeman, 1932.

FOSS, PHILIP O. *Politics and Grass: The Administration of the Public Domain.* Seattle: University of Washington Press, 1960.

FOSTER, AUREL O. "Chemotherapeutic Agents for Internal Parasites," *Animal Diseases.* USDA Yearbook, 1956. Washington: Government Printing Office, 1956.

FOWLER, BERTRAM B. *Men, Meat and Miracles*. New York: Messner, 1952.

GENUNG, A. B. "Agriculture in the World War Period," *An Historical Survey of American Agriculture*. USDA Yearbook Separate, 1783. Washington: Government Printing Office, 1941.

GOODING, C. L. "Quarantining," *Animal Diseases*. USDA Yearbook, 1956. Washington: Government Printing Office, 1956.

Grass, Yearbook of Agriculture, 1948. USDA Yearbook. Washington: Government Printing Office, 1948.

HAGG, MAURICE (ed.). *The Range Lands of Wyoming*. Wyoming Agri. Exp. Sta. Bul. 289. Laramie: 1949.

HARDING, T. S. *Two Blades of Grass*. Norman: University of Oklahoma Press, 1947.

HARGREAVES, MARY W. *Dry Farming in the Northern Plains, 1900–1925*. Cambridge, Mass.: Harvard University Press, 1957.

HARMS, JOHN. "Tests Show Malathion Kills Lice, Hornflies and Ticks on Cattle and Has Approval of U.S.D.A.," *The Cattleman*, 45 (Dec., 1958), 48.

HARRIS, L. E., *et al.*, "Method of Feeding Supplements to Individual Cattle on Winter Range," *Journal of Animal Science*, 16 (Nov., 1957), 872–876.

HARRIS, SEYMOUR (ed.). *American Economic History*. New York: McGraw-Hill, 1961.

HATTON, JOHN H. "Livestock Vicissitudes and Rainbows," *American Cattle Producer*, 22 (Sept., 1940), 5–7.

HAYES, WILLIAM E. *Iron Road to Empire*. Published by the Author, 1953.

HELBURN, NICHOLAS. *Land Use Adjustments in Blaine, Phillips, and Valley Counties, Montana, 1934 to 1940*. M.S. thesis, Montana State College. Bozeman, 1941.

HENLEIN, PAUL C. *Cattle Kingdom in the Ohio Valley, 1783–1860*. Lexington: University of Kentucky Press, 1959.

HOPKINS, JOHN A. *Economic History of the Production of Beef Cattle in Iowa*. Iowa City: Iowa Historical Society, 1928.

HOWARD, JOSEPH K. *Montana: High, Wide, and Handsome*. New Haven: Yale University Press, 1943.

HOWARD, RANDALL R. "The Passing of the Cattle King," *Outlook*, 98 (May 27, 1911), 195–204.

HULTZ, FRED S. *Range Beef Production in the Seventeen Western States*. New York: John Wiley, 1931.

Indexes of Prices Paid by Montana Farmers and Ranchers, 1935–1952. Montana Agri. Exp. Sta. Bul. 492. Bozeman, 1953.

JOHNSON, HOWARD W., AND ALBERT F. RANNEY. "Tuberculosis and

Its Eradication," *Animal Diseases.* USDA Yearbook, 1956. Washington: Government Printing Office, 1956.

KELSO, M. M. "The Place of Grassland Farming," *Grass, Yearbook of Agriculture, 1948.* USDA Yearbook, 1948. Washington: Government Printing Office, 1948.

KLOSE, NELSON. *The Introduction, Improvement, and Adaptation of Sorghum Varieties in Texas.* M.A. thesis, University of Texas. Austin, 1937.

KRAENZEL, CARL F. *Great Plains in Transition.* Norman: University of Oklahoma Press, 1955.

LARSEN, AUBREY B., AND HOWARD W. JOHNSON. "Paratuberculosis (Johne's Disease)," *Animal Diseases.* USDA Yearbook, 1956. Washington: Government Printing Office, 1956.

LAVENDER, DAVID. *One Man's West.* New York: Doubleday, 1943.

LEA, TOM. *The King Ranch.* 2 Vols. Boston: Little, Brown, 1957.

LOTZE, JOHN C., DANIEL W. GATES, AND T. O. ROBY. "Anaplasmosis of Cattle," *Animal Diseases.* USDA Yearbook, 1956. Washington: Government Printing Office, 1956.

MALIN, JAMES C. "The Adaptation of the Agricultural System to Sub-Humid Environment," *Agricultural History,* 10 (July, 1936), 118–141.

MANSFIELD, HARVEY C., et al. *A Short History of OPA.* Office of Price Administration. Washington: Historical Reports on War Administration, 1947.

MANTHEI, C. A., A. K. KUTTLER, AND E. R. GOODE, Jr. "Brucellosis," *Animal Diseases.* USDA Yearbook, 1956. Washington: Government Printing Office, 1956.

MOSK, S. A. "Land Policy and Stock Raising in the Western United States," *Agricultural History,* 17 (Jan., 1943), 14–30.

NELSON, BRUCE. *Land of the Dacotahs.* Minneapolis: University of Minnesota Press, 1946.

NORDYKE, LEWIS. *Great Roundup.* New York: William Morrow, 1955.

Northern Great Plains Agricultural Council Sessions. Lincoln: The Council, 1951.

OLIVER, JOHN W. *History of American Technology.* New York: Ronald Press, 1956.

OSGOOD, ERNEST S. *The Day of the Cattlemen.* Minneapolis: University of Minnesota Press, 1929.

PATTERSON, W. C., AND L. O. MOTT. "Vesicular Stomatitis—V.S.," *Animal Diseases.* USDA Yearbook, 1956. Washington: Government Printing Office, 1956.

PEFFER, E. LOUISE. *The Closing of the Public Domain; Disposal and Reservation Policies, 1900–1950.* Stanford: Stanford University Press, 1951.

PELZER, LOUIS. *The Cattlemen's Frontier*. Glendale: Arthur H. Clark, 1936.

PIPER, C. V., *et al.* "Our Forage Resources," *Yearbook, United States Department of Agriculture, 1923*. Washington: Government Printing Office, 1923.

POLLOCK, J. M. *The Unvarnished West: Ranching As I Found It*. London: Palmerston Press, 1907.

Prices Received by Montana Farmers and Ranchers, 1910–1952. Montana Agri. Exp. Sta. Bul. 503. Bozeman, 1954.

RIGGS, J. K. "Fifty Years of Progress in Beef Cattle Nutrition," *Journal of Animal Science*, 17 (Nov., 1958), 981–1006.

ROBBINS, ROY M. *Our Landed Heritage: The Public Domain, 1776–1936*. Lincoln: University of Nebraska Press, 1962.

SAVAGE, D. A., AND D. F. COSTELLO. "The Southern Great Plains," *Grass, Yearbook of Agriculture, 1948*. Washington: Government Printing Office, 1948.

SCHLEBECKER, JOHN T. "Grasshoppers in American Agricultural History," *Agricultural History*, 27 (July, 1953), 85–93.

———. "Pliant Prairie: One Plant's Influence on One Prairie State," *Montana, the Magazine of Western History*, 8 (Winter, 1958), 30–41.

———. "The World Metropolis and the History of American Agriculture," *Journal of Economic History*, 20 (June, 1960), 187–208.

———, AND A. W. HOPKINS. *A History of Dairy Journalism in the United States, 1810–1950*. Madison: University of Wisconsin Press, 1957.

SCHELL, HERBERT S. "Adjustment Problems in South Dakota," *Agricultural History*, 14 (Apr., 1940), 65–74.

SEARS, ALFRED B. "The Desert Threat in the Southern Great Plains," *Agricultural History*, 15 (Jan., 1941), 1–11.

SEARS, PAUL B. *Deserts on the March*. Norman: University of Oklahoma Press, 1935.

SELBRY, H. E., AND D.T. GRIFFITH. "Western Range Livestock Production," *American Cattle Producer*, 28 (Aug., 1946), 11–14.

SHAHAN, M. S., AND J. TRAUM. "Foot-and-Mouth Disease," *Animal Diseases*. USDA Yearbook, 1956. Washington: Government Printing Office, 1956.

SHANNON, FRED A. *The Farmers' Last Frontier*. New York: Farrar and Rinehart, 1945.

SHEPHERD, GEOFFREY S. *Marketing Farm Products*. Ames: Iowa State University Press, 1946.

SHIDELER, JAMES H. *Farm Crisis, 1919–1923*. Berkeley: University of California Press, 1957.

SMITH, HOWARD. *American Economic History.* New York: Ronald Press, 1955.

SONNICHSEN, C. L. *Cowboys and Cattle Kings; Life on the Range Today.* Norman: University of Oklahoma Press, 1950.

SOULE, GEORGE, AND VINCENT P. CAROSSO. *American Economic History.* New York: Dryden, 1957.

STEELE, HARRY A. *Mortgage Foreclosures in South Dakota, 1921–32.* South Dakota Agri. Exp. Sta. Cir. 17. Brookings, 1934.

STEIN, C. D. "Blackleg," *Animal Diseases.* USDA Yearbook, 1956. Washington: Government Printing Office, 1956.

"30 Years Ago," *American Hereford Journal,* **45** (Sept. 15, 1954), 122, 219.

THORNTHWAITE, C. W. "The Great Plains," in C. Goodrich, *Migration and Economic Opportunity.* Philadelphia: University of Pennsylvania Press, 1936.

TOWNE, CHARLES, AND E. N. WENTWORTH. *Cattle and Men.* Norman: University of Oklahoma Press, 1955.

WAGONER, JUNIOR J. *History of the Cattle Industry in Southern Arizona, 1540–1940.* Tucson: University of Arizona Press, 1952.

WARWICK, E. J. "Fifty Years of Progress in Breeding Beef Cattle," *Journal of Animal Science,* 17 (Nov., 1958), 922–943.

WEBB, WALTER P. *The Great Plains.* Boston: Ginn, 1931. *The Western Range.* Senate Document 199, 74th Cong., 2nd Sess. Washington: Government Printing Office, 1936.

WINTHER, O. O. *The Great Northwest.* New York: Knopf, 1952.

Index

Abortion. *See* Brucellosis

Acreage: declines, 87; size, farms, ranches, 15, 25–26, 185; under Stock Raising Homestead Act, 70; wheat, decline, 148

Adamson, Dan: prices received, 60

Additives, feed: antibiotics, 217; general, 229–230, 235

Advertising: campaigns, 224

Africander: cattle introduced, 132

Agricultural Adjustment Act: 1933, passed, 136; replaced, 1936, 159

Agricultural Adjustment Administration: destroyed, Supreme Court, 159; feed grains under, 178

Agricultural Credit Corporation, 91

Agricultural Marketing Act: 1929, work, 125–126; dead, 126. *See also* Federal Farm Board

Agricultural Stabilization and Conservation Committee: cactus program, 230

Agriculture, Department of: battles screwworm, 181, 217–218; beef grading, 118; breeds Nordan wheatgrass, 211; brucellosis campaign, 228–229; conservation payments, 176, 227; Farm Security Administration, 177–178; eradication, foot-and-mouth, 196, 216; fights anaplasmosis, 216, 217; fights diseases, 65, 124–125, 196, 216–217, 228–229; finds cause, X-disease, 217; finds systemic insecticide, 229; operates Resettlement Administration, 160; supervises packers, 188–189; support-beef buying, 207–208; tick fever work, 88; tuberculosis eradication, 125

Agriculture, Secretary of: Packers and Stockyards Act, 91; can regulate chain stores, 189; Forest fees, 102; sets charges, marketing agencies, 123. *See also* Wallace, Henry A.; Wilson, James

Aldrin: insecticide, grasshoppers, 208

Alfalfa: grasshopper control, 208; in-

creased use, 23, 37, 83, 98–99; as legume, 182, 227; comes to Plains, 13; production, 182, 227; use declines, 112; use, North, 129. *See also* Supplemental feeding

American Brahman Breeders Association, 100

American Cattle Growers' Association, 28

American National Cattlemen's Association, 28

American National Livestock Association: anaplasmosis, 217; brucellosis, 228; conservation, 160; founded, 28; price controls, 205; program, public domain, 102, 156

Anaplasmosis: growing seriousness, 110; nature, 216–217; vaccine, 216

Anderson, Clinton P.: rationing, 174

Anderson, Mark: co-author, *Range Management on the National Forests*, 84

Animal Husbandry, Division of, 27

Animal Industry, Bureau of: against Argentine beef, 126; blackleg eradication, 48–49, 65; brucellosis work, 164; tick fever work, 12, 27–28, 39; general disease work, 164; meat inspection, 18; recognizes Santa Gertrudis, 184

Antibiotics: appear, 181; feed additive, 217, 229

Anthrax: outbreak, South Dakota, 164

Argentina: competition with, 18, 126, 167; sanitary convention, 147; convention killed, 202

Armour Company: merged, Morris, 92

Artificial insemination, 232–233

Auction markets: supervision, 206, 224; trucks influence, 206; used more, 188, 206, 224

Automobiles: influence cattlemen, 214, 221; reduce horses, 93

Aureomycin: feed additives, 217; uses, 229

Australia: competition with, 126

311

Baby beef: consumers prefer, 73, 213; production, 98, 213; in war, 190. *See also* Consumption

Bacteria: fertilizers innoculated, 227; insecticide, 230. *See also* Disease

Bang's Disease. *See* Brucellosis

Bankers: depression, 121; Federal Reserve controls, 75–76; failures, 91, 106–107; offer credit, 106–107; wartime, 60. *See also* Credit

Barnes, Will C.: depression, 76; founder, American National Cattlemen's Association, 28

Beef: boycott, 104, 153; Plains as source, 151; shortage, 170, 172. *See also* Consumption

Beefmaster: new breed, 233

Beef Trust. *See* Trust, beef; Big Five

Benson, Ezra T.: Farm Bureau, 226; drouth relief, 207; soil bank, 225

Big Five: becomes Big Four, 92; cattlemen assail, 76–77

Biochemistry: against weeds, brush, 218–219, 230–231; animal husbandry, 229–230, 231

Biological Survey: prairie dog extermination, 47–48, 64, 79; predator control, 64, 80, 110

Black grama: range grass, 195

Blackleg: Bureau of Animal Industry attacks, 48–49; Extension Service attacks, 65; federal efforts, 80, 109; free vaccine, 65, 80

Black Markets: cattle feeds, 172; increases rustlers, 185; rationing, 173

Black stem rust: damages wheat, 65–66

Blizzard: description, results, 7, 9, 40–41, 123–124, 153–154, 180, 193–194; federal relief, 187, 193–194; feed shortages, 195

Borden, O. P.: goes to India, 24; imports Brahmans, 37–38

Boston: beef boycott, 104

Boycott: meat, 104, 153, 187; effectiveness, 153, 187

Braceros: pay scale, 236

Brahma. *See* Brahman

Brahman: cattle, into Texas, 24, 37–38; bulls, Brazil to Mexico, 196; more used, 68, 84–85, 99–100; basis, Santa Gertrudis, 85

Brangus: new cattle breed, 233

Brannan, Charles F., offers plan, 188

Brannan Plan: description, 188; opposition, 188, 207

Brazil: source, foot-and-mouth, 196

Breeding: of cattle, advantages,

southern Plains, 5, 192; artificial insemination, 232–233; cattle improved, 37–39, 54, 99–100, 132, 184, 202, 219–220, 232; Charolaise, used, 84, 220; dwarfism, Herefords, 219–220, 233; fertility hormone, 217, greater use, purebreds, 84, 202; Herefords preferred, 24; new breeds, 37–39, 132, 184, 220, 233; Santa Gertrudis, 184, 219, 233

Bridges, B. W.: quoted, drouth, 180

Brucellosis: calf vaccination, 165, 181, 216, 228–229; control efforts, 108–109; diagnosis, 164, 181; effects, Plains cattle, 49; eradication programs, 144–145, 181, 216, 228–229; quarantine, 228; vaccine, 49, 124–125, 165, 181

Bulldozers: use, 194, 214, 219

Bull Moose: reform group, 44

Bulls. *See* Breeding

Burdick, Usher L.: quoted, 91

Burroughs, Wise: co-discoverer, stilbestrol, 217, 231

Buzzards: predators, 80, 198

Cactus: burning spines, feed, 163, 219; eradication methods, efforts, 199, 219, 230; herbicides, 219, 230

California: foot-and-mouth outbreak, 88; rise, urban market, 106, 121

Calves: crop rises, 98, 202; feeding, 98, 113

Campbell, Hardy W.: dry farming, 22

Canada: strip cropping begins, 66

Cancer: linked, stilbestrol, 232

Capital gains. *See* Taxes

Carey Act: influence, 14–15

Carpenter, Farrington, R.: director of grazing, 144; Ickes fires, 157

Casement, Dan: investigates forest grazing fees, 115

Casement Report, forest fees, 115–116

Cattle: condition, 46, 62–63, 92, 107; numbers, Plains, 6, 26, 42, 47, 52, 73, 81, 100, 105–106, 130, 151, 165, 184, 193, 215, 234; numbers, U.S., 52, 81, 105, 151

Chain stores: compete, Packers, 122, 175, 224; control efforts, 189, 236; feeding operations, 236; reactions, cattlemen, 122–123, 175, 224, 236; spread frozen foods, 225

Chapman, Oscar, 144

Charbray: new crossbreed, 233

Charolaise: cattle imported, 84; International Charolaise Cattle Raisers Association begun, 220

Chemistry. See Biochemistry

Chicago: packers move out, 220

Chlordane: against grasshoppers, 198, 208

Chutes: increased use, 132

Civilian Conservation Corps: activities, 147, 160–161, 176; cooperates, other agencies, 147, 160–161; ended, 176

Civil War: effect, Plains cattle industry, 4

Clark-McNary Act, 102

Clawson, Marion: quoted, ranch scarcity, 129; quoted, ranch feudalism, 191

Colorado: cattlemen's convention, 207; conditions, 45, 62

Colorado Stock Growers and Feeders Association: voluntary brucellosis control, 181

Combine: wheat, causes expansion of industry, 51–52

Commodities: organization along lines, 222. See also Beef; Meat; Wheat

Commodity Credit Corporation: subsidize beef producers, 178

Connally, Thomas: Senator, Texas, kills Sanitary Convention, 147, 167

Consent Decree: cattlemen's reaction, 77, 92, 117, 122; court action, 92, 117, 122; origin, 77; packers ignore, 117, 122

Conservation: cattlemen oppose, 159; CCC, 147; contour ridging, 164; effects, industry, 226–227; Forest Service, 56; interest declines, 176, 194, 227; payments, cattlemen, 175–176; permanent, 158–160, 161, 175–176; 226–227; soil, methods, 210; soil bank, 226

Conservationists: disliked, 117

Consumers: boycott beef, 104, 153; want light, lean meat, 204, 232

Consumption: beef, per capita, 16, 17, 30, 53, 59, 72, 90, 104, 119, 134, 139, 145, 152, 169–170, 187, 204, 224; beef, rises, 58–59, 169–170; declines, 119–120, 187, 224; Beefless Days, 59

Contour furrowing, 210. See also Contour ridging

Contour ridging: described, 164; devised, urged, 161; increases pasturage, 164; C. Kraenzel, quoted, 214; use extended, 175

Contract feeding: appears, 131–132. See also Vertical integration

Cook, A. W.: Forest Supervisor, 44–45; quoted, range management, 53

Coolidge, Calvin: petitioned to lease public domain, 102

Cooperation. See Grazing districts

Cooperatives: under Agricultural Marketing Act, 125–126; financing cattle shipments, 75; marketing, 73

Cooperative Grazing Districts: use, 200. See also Grazing Districts

Co-Ral: systemic poison, 230

Corey, Lewis: ranches, ranch farms, 193

Corn: silage, 99, 112

Corn Belt: actions of feeders, 72; feeders affected by trucks, 206; not prosperous, 223; production controls, 223; Plains compete, 156, 195

Costs: living, rises, 153, 171

Costs: production, types, causes, 19, 53, 74, 90, 120, 187, 206, 223–224; efforts to reduce, 152; favor baby beef, 190; income covers, 105; inflate, 187; taxes as, 90, 206

Cotton: dry farming, 94; expands, southern Plains, 166

Cottonseed: cake, 162; Plains feed, 67–68, 84, 129; price regulations, 58. See also Supplemental feeding

Cowboys: work changes, 7–9; tasks, 113, 214

Coyotes: predators, 181

Credit: difficulty of securing, 74–75, 90, 120–121, 136; easy to get, 106, 187; feed loans, 141, 146; Farmers Home Administration, 187; federal agencies, 60–61, 76, 90, 91, 126, 136, 141, 146, 187; Federal Land Banks, 60–61; Federal Reserve, 75–76; Intermediate Credit Banks, 90–91; loans forced on cattlemen, 60; New Deal, 136; for poorest, 138–139; Reconstruction Finance Corporation, 126, 136; War Finance Corporation, 61, 76, 90

Creep feeding, 113. See also Feeding

Crested wheatgrass: in grassland farming, 183; introduced, U.S., 14, 67; used more, 36–37, 83–84, 183, 210–211; used, North, virtues, 36–37, 83–84, 99; South, 195, 210–211. See also Siberian wheatgrass; Nordan wheatgrass

Crisp Act, 110

Crops: failures, 45–46, 139; changes,

Crops (*continued*)
112; feed, 162–163; pests, 198.
See also Feeding
Culbertson, C. C.: co-discoverer, stilbestrol, 217
Curacao: screwworms eradicated, 218

Dahmen, Robert: discovered foot-and-mouth bacteria, 88
Dairymen: beefmen join against oleo, 128; success, disease eradication, 216
Darling, Ding: wants to abandon Plains, 156
DDT: against heel flies, 197; fails against grasshoppers, 198
Debts: adjustment, 138; burden unbearable, 91, paid off, 187
Deferred grazing: cattlemen continue, 175; demonstration farms, 161; practice grows, 53–54, 92–93, 194–195, 202; related, water supply, 227. *See also* Range management
Demonstration areas: erosion control, 140, 161
Depression: cattlemen, 72, 73–74; Plains, 91; postwar ends, 105; causes, 119
Dipping: opposition, 39; scabies, 109; tick fever, 109
Disease: antibiotics against, 181; cattle, general, 48–50, 65, 80, 88–89, 108–109, 124–125, 144–145, 164–165, 181–182, 196–198, 216, 228–230; disrupts cattle imports, 37–38; efforts against, 228; plants, 89; problems increased, irrigation, 210. *See also* Brucellosis; Tuberculosis
Distribution. *See* Marketing; Rationing
Diversified farming: failure, 95. *See also* Ranch farming; Pasture farming
Drought Relief Service, 141
Drouth: descriptions, 9, 20, 32–33, 40, 41, 44, 45, 58, 61, 62, 78, 123, 135, 139–140, 145, 154, 155, 180, 207–208, 225–226; federal relief, 141, 146, 156, 180, 207–208, 225–226; results, responses, 32–33, 41, 62, 140, 145, 154, 156, 184, 208, 209, 210
Dry farmers: benefit Plains, 95; fail to push cattlemen out, 66, 183, 201; failure, 81, 82, 129, 130, 148–149, 166, 183, 201; leave Plains,

95, 148, 166, 183; some shift, cattle, 66, 83, 94–95, 129, 149, 183
Dry Farming: development, 22, 52, 93–94; expansion, 22–23, 32, 33, 81, 94, 124, 129, 184; part, cattle complex, 22, 32, 52, 66, 97, 130, 212–213; land used, 32, 66; railroads spread, 21, 52; success, elements, 149, 184; troubles, 148–149, 184; wheat failures, 32–33, 65–66; wheat production, 66, 129; general, 184, 215
Dry Land Agriculture, Bureau of, 32
Dude ranches: interest in, 130
Dust storms, 135, 140, 145, 154, 162, 208, 210; still threaten, 227
Dwarfism: breeders' attitude, 233; avoiding, 220; general, 219–220, 233; method to find carriers, 233

ECP: hormone, cow fertility, 217
Eisenhower, Dwight D.: policies, 223; public domain, 228; price policies, 205; tariff policies, 220–221
Emergency Price Control Act, 170
Emergency Soil Conservation Act: methods, objectives, 136
Enlarged Homestead Act: results, 32, 51
Entomologists. *See* Grasshoppers; Heel flies; Insecticides
Entomology, Bureau of: combats grasshoppers, 155
Ergot: disease, grasses and grains, 89
Erosion: reduced by strip cropping, 66. *See also* Dust storms
Extension Service: disease control, 65, 80; changes, duties, 212; irrigation, 209; reports blizzard, 194; reports, dwarfism, 219

Failures: cattlemen, 91, 121. *See also* Foreclosures
Fall, Albert: wants Forests, 102
Farm Bureau: criticized, 224; criticizes Benson, 226
Farm Credit Administration: feed loans, 146; seeks debt adjustment, 138; set up, 136; absorbed, Farmers Home Administration, 187
Farmers: effects, cattlemen, 19, 50–51; early failures, 9; move on Plains, 21–22, 32, 70; sell out, 201; some shift to cattle, 23; take range land, 7. *See also* Dry farming
Farmers Home Administration: drouth relief, 207–208; credit, after 1946, 187

Farming. *See* Diversified farming; Dry farming; Grassland farming; Ranch farming

Farms: numbers, Plains, 43, 100, 129; sizes, 100, 129, 165–166

Farm Security Administration: activities, 177–178; set up, 160; lumped, Food Production Administration, 177–178

Federal Emergency Relief Administration: early activities, 137; ended, 146

Federal Farm Board: set up, 125–126

Federal government: blizzard relief, 193–194; cattlemen ask for help, 44, 85, 102–103, 125, 135–136, 207, 232; element, Plains unity, 222; increasing involvement, 28–29, 40, 56, 102–103, 120–121, 146, 169, 183, 197, 226, 235

Federal Land Banks: activities, 60–61; mentioned, 136

Federal Reserve System: dominates Agricultural Credit Corporation, 91; results, rediscount rates, 75–76

Federal Surplus Relief Corporation, 137

Federal Trade Commission: investigates packers, 76

Feeders: direct buying suggested, 73; bounties, 178–179; object to cattlemen using hormones, 232; problems, plainsmen, 60

Feeding, to a finish: needed for quality, 212; more, chain stores, 236; ranchers sometimes try, 67, 163, 195, 212, 236

Feeds: effects, stilbestrol, 217; improvements, 234–235. *See also* Supplementary feeding

Fencing: illegal, public domain, 36, 54; Ickes orders fences off, 138

Fertilizers: bacteria innoculated, 227; first interest, 209

Field Inspection Division: tick eradication, 48

First World War: beginning, early consequences, 56, 81

Fish and Wildlife Service: activities against predators, 181

Flat Top Ranch: irrigation, 235; regrassing efforts, 211

Flint Hills: role in industry, 192, 208, 213

Florida: screwworms eradicated, 230

Fodder: substitute, wheat, 66–67; abundant, 107–108

Folklore: Plains life, 221

Food Administraton: First World War, 59, 67–68

Food and Drug Administration: clears feed additives, 229, 231; clears sprays, systemic poisons, 230

Food Production Administration: includes Farm Security Administration, 177–178

Food, technology, 127–128

Foot-and-mouth disease: causal bacteria found, 88; cost of ending, 88; effect, import laws, 84, 196; eradication methods, 49–50; federal efforts, 50, 65, 109–110, 126; plagues, 49–50, 65, 88, 89, 124; plague, Mexico, 196, 216; threat continues, 109–110; vaccine, 109–110

Foot-Rot: aureomycin effective, 229

Foreclosures: rash of, 90, 95, 121; rate down, 105

Foreign Relations Committee: kills Argentine Sanitary Convention, 147

Foreign trade: beef exports, relative decline, 18, 42; nearly cease, 53, 74, 119; element, marketing, 224–225; European restrictions, 42; imports, beef, 179, 202, 220–221; export market, 56, 57; wartime, 57, 59. *See also* Tariff; Marketing

Forest Homestead Act, 34, 51

Forest Service: breeding rules, 69; buy land, 102; cattlemen's reaction, 34–35, 54, 55–56, 69–70, 102, 116, 144, 147–148, 158, 199, 220; competition, Department of Interior, 143, 158, 220; disease, predator control, 39, 47–48, 64; drouth, blizzard aid, 40–41, 58, 68–69, 194; encourage ranch farming, 54–55, 69; functions, 68–69, 158, 220, 228; grazing fees, 33, 34, 35, 69, 85, 102, 115–116, 126, 127, 137, 138, 144, 147, 158, 177; lease controversy, 102; model, grazing districts, 115, 127; policies, grazing, 27, 35, 38–39, 54–55, 68–69, 85, 102, 115, 127, 138, 158, 177, 199; restricts settlement, 33, 51

Forsch, Heinrich: discovers foot-and-mouth bacteria, 88

4-H Clubs: significance, 132–133

Fraud: price support, 141–142; buyers, 224

French, H. E.: quoted, 50–51

Frozen beef: Argentine, 126; quick frozen, marketed, 128, 167

Frozen food: more important than beef, 167; effects, cattle industry, 225

Gage, Lyman: Secretary of Treasury, 38
General Maximum Price Regulation, 170
Gordon, B. F.: quoted, 80–81
Government. *See* Federal government
Grading, of beef, 118
Grain. *See* Wheat; Corn; Sorghum
Grange-Thye Act, 220
Grasses: native inferior, 99, 131; native, reliance, 131; native, reseeding, 146; shortcomings, 196
Grassland farming: use fertilizers, 209; general, 183, 211; pasture farming, 96; use silage, 211–212
Grasshoppers: decline, 155, 180, 208; controlled, 208; hurt dry farmers, 155; plagues, 79, 111, 135, 139, 155, 198, 208; reject sorghum, 155, 163; resist insecticides, 198, 230
Grazer. *See* Herdsmen
Grazing: cattlemen want supervised, 102; less dependence, 130–131, 150; tenure, Plains, 3–4; soil bank, 226
Grazing, Director of: Taylor Act, 144; duties, 156
Grazing Districts: cooperative, 114–155; Taylor Act, 144, 147, 157
Grazing, Division of: CCC assigned, 147, 160–161, 176; competes, Forest Service, 158; control works, 176–177; criticisms, 177. *See also* Land Management, Bureau of
Grazing fees: allocation, 85, 156; comparison, Forest Service, Division of Grazing, 177; controversy, 56, 147, 177; Division of Grazing, 144, 156
The Great Plains, 2–3
The Great Plains in Transition, 214
Greeley, William B.: Chief Forester, 116
Grubs: damage, 196–197, 229; efforts to eradicate, 197, 218, 230; life cycle, 196–197, 218. *See also* Warbles

Hagenbeck, Carl: Zebu cattle, 24
Hammond, R. R.: cattle baron, 94
Handling: cattle, changes, 132
Harding, Warren G.: signed Packers and Stockyards Act, 77

Hargreaves, Mary: quoted, Dakota, 66
Hawley-Smoot Tariff: effects, 126, 132
Hay: acreage increases, 82; drouth, 78–79, 124, 208; production, preparation, 99, 112; special rail rates, 78–70. *See* Supplemental feeding
Health, Education and Welfare, Department of: stilbestrol use, 232
Heel fly: adult warbles, life, 196–197, 218; try to eradicate, 197, 229–230
Herbicides: promise, 199, 202, 230–231; uses, 199, 218–219, 230–231
Herdsmen: called tramps, 34; open range grazers, 9, 23; shoved aside, 53
Hereford: cattle, introduced, 6; dwarfism, 219, 233; favored, 24, 84, 184, 202; virtues, improvements, 184, 202
Higgins, Jay: Forest official, quote, 73
Hill, James J.: dry farming, 21, 22
Homestead Act: dummy claims, 7. *See also* Enlarged Homestead Act; Stock Raising Homestead Act
Hoover, Herbert C.: action, Food Administrator, 59; farm bills, 125
Hormones: assure conception, 217; objections, 232; synthetic, growth, 217, 231–232. *See also* Stilbestrol
Horses: decline, 93; wild, damage, 110
Hughes, Greely: rancher, quoted, 154
Hull, Cordell: Sanitary Convention, Argentina, 147
Humphrey, J. L.: ranch farming, 83
Hyperkeratosis. *See* X-disease

Ickes, Harold I.: changes Director of Grazing, 157; orders range fences off, 138; views, public domain, 143
Immigration: amount, Plains, 4; restricted, 87
Income: average, American, 10–11, 119, 134, 169, 187; cattlemen, 105, 106, 120, 135, 152, 153, 171, 187; effects, beef consumption, 169, 187
Inflation: control efforts, World War II, 169, 170; Korean War, 204, 205; postwar, 186–187; price controls, 170, 205
Insecticides: cattle, 181, 197, 230; grasshoppers, 198, 208; no new ones, 111; improvements, 181, 230

Insects: bacteria, attack, 230; damages, 198, 217–218, 229–230
Insulin: test, dwarfism, 233
Intensification: cattle production, 182, 201, 229, 232, 234; antibiotics, 229; tranquilizers, 232
Interior, Department of: Taylor Act, 143, 157; seeds range, 176; subsistence homesteads, 138; tries to get Forests, 102. *See also* Grazing, Division of
Intermediate Agricultural Credit: agency proposed, 76
Intermediate Credit Banks, 90–91, 136
International Charolaise Cattle Raisers Association, 220
International Harvester, 126
Interstate Commerce Commission: lower rates suggested, drouth, 79; regulations, 100–101
Irrigation: alfalfa used, 99, 182–183; beginnings, 3; cattlemen use, 13, 14, 25, 184, 209; pastures, 209; problems, congestion, 210; sprinklers, 209–210, 235. *See also* Sprinkler irrigation
Itch. *See* Scabies

Jardine, James: co-author, *Range Management on the National Forests,* 84
Jardine, William: Secretary of Agriculture, Forest fees raised, 116
Jeeps: ranch use, 214
Johne's Disease. *See* Paratuberculosis
Johnson grass: crossed, sorghum, 211
Jones-Connally Act, 140

Kansas: anaplasmosis, 110; blizzard, 123; DDT used, 197; Herefords used, 6; pastures, 162, 183; quarantines, 6–7; sorghum, 13; sprinkler irrigation, 235
Kansas Livestock Association: denounce Brannan Plan, 207
Kavanagh, E. N.: Forest supervisor, 41
Keynes, John M.: economic theory, 139
King Ranch: breed Brahmans, 38; cross Brahmans, Shorthorns, 68; develop Santa Gertrudis, 85, 100, 219; leads, silos, 68; losses, 60, 62; some holdings sold, 191
Kinkaid Act, 50
Kleberg, Robert J., Sr.: King Ranch, 38

Klebergs: breed Santa Gertrudis, 84, 100
Kraenzel, Carl: author, *The Great Plains in Transition,* 214

Labor: costs, 187–188, 224, 236; migratory, camps, 178
Labor unions: resist meat prices, 153
LaFollette, Robert F.: reformer, 44
Land: cattlemen own, 113, 214, 234; leased, 92–93, 101–102, 182, 234; prices, 91, 191, 234; problem of securing, 182, 234. *See also* Land tenure
Land Management, Bureau of: blizzard aid, 194; cattlemen's attitude, 199, 220; grazing fees, 200, 220; land under, 200; suggested it absorb Forests, 220. *See also* Grazing, Division of
Land speculation: big ranchers, 191; use federal laws for, 50–51
Land tenure: new patterns, 15, 200–201; problems, 113, 114
Lasley, John: finds insulin test, 233
Land Utilization Division, 146
Leases: grassland, 107, 149; problems, 115, 182
Legge, Alexander, 125–126
Legumes: alfalfa valued, 182; used more, 195, 209, 227
Lend-lease: results, 169
Life: plainsmen, 113, 130, 221–222
Light, Fred: resists Forest Service, 55
Liquidation: cattle, for profit, 105; during drouth, 139, 154
Livestock Reporting Service, 74
Long drive: begun, continued, 5

McBurney, R. W., 163
McCan: new breed, cattle, 233
McCarran, Patrick: Taylor Act, 143
McCoy, Joseph: begins long drive, 5
McFaddin, Al: Brahman breeder, 24
Machinery: cattle husbandry, 112, 214; wheat industry, 51–52
Mackenzie, Murdo, 28
McNary-Haugen Bill: cattlemen favor, 91, 117; dead, 125
Mange. *See* Scabies
Mangels: feed, 112
Marketing: cattle, young, 90, 98, 112–113, 152–153, 189–190, 193, 204; decline, terminal markets, 152, 175, 188, 206, 224; food research, 128; direct selling, 106; trucks change, 101, 190–191, 206; wartime, 173, 175. *See also* Black

Marketing (*continued*)
   markets; Foreign trade; Tariffs;
   Advertising
Markets: domestic, 10–11, 57–58,
   72–73; foreign, 10, 18; metropoli-
   tan, 100–101
Matador Land and Cattle Company,
   191
Meat: inspection, domestic, 166–
   167; inspection, foreign trade, 18.
   See also Consumption
Meatless days: World War I, 172
Mesquite: advancing, 36, 199, 219,
   231; grubbing, 199, 219; 2,4,5-T,
   230–231
Mexico: foot-and-mouth, 196, 216;
   Charolaise, 220; sanitary treaty,
   110, 196
Middlemen: conflict, cattlemen, 106,
   122–123, 188
Missouri: quarantine, 6–7
Mizpah-Pumpkin Creek: grazing district, 114–115
Mollin, F. E.: American National
   Livestock Association, secretary,
   137; Forest fees, 138; quoted, controls, 137; Taylor Act, comment,
   156
Montana: brucellosis ended, 228;
   cattle prices, 89; cooperative grazing, 114–115; drouth, 61, 124,
   154; dry farmers, 66, 95; foot-and-
   mouth, 50; grasshoppers, 79; loans,
   cattlemen, 74; small outfits, 192;
   wheat yields, 66
Morris Company: absorbed by Armour, 92
Mowers: influence, 112

Nordan wheatgrass, 211
North Dakota: bank failures, 106;
   drouth, 61, 124; Nordan developed, 211; dust storms, 140; nonfarm jobs, 153; wheat yields, 66
Northern Plains: advantages, feeding, 5, 195, 196; crested wheatgrass, 67; dry farmers, 95, 148,
   160; grasshoppers, 79; land tenure, 101; ranch farming, 83, 95,
   129–130; Resettlement Administration, 160; weather, 62, 78, 87–
   88, 123, 124, 154, 180, 208; winter feeding, 111
Nutrition: deficiencies overcome,
   209; element, feeding, 235; silage,
   235
National Cattlemen's Association, 28
National Forests. *See* Forest Service
National Wool Growers Association,
   199

Nebraska: small outfits, 192; drouth,
   45; dry farmers, 95; moisture, 61,
   208
Nelson, Elias: rotation grazing, 25
Nesters. *See* Farmers; Dry farming
New Dealers: accomplishments, 139,
   161; attack depression, 136; conservation, 175–176; dead, 202;
   long-range programs, 146–147,
   152, 175–176, 177–178; shelter-
   belts, 161. *See also* Federal government
Newlands Act: influence, 15, 184
New Mexico: hay, 163, 182; small
   outfits, 192; start, range industry,
   4; weather, 45, 62
Newspapers: blamed, boycott, 104–
   105
New Zealand: meat from, 221

O'Connor, Tom: gets Brahmans, 38
Oil: royalties, big ranches, 191
Oklahoma: cattle prices, 89; drouth,
   45, 62, 155; leased pastures, 162
OPA. *See* Price Administration, Office of
Open range: beginning, growth, 4–
   9; decline, 7–11; flaws, 11; railroads ruin, 21; reliance, 15
Oleomargarine, 128
Overgrazing: Division of Grazing,
   176–177; deny had been, 154;
   encouraged, leasing, 115; reduced,
   drouth, 46–47. *See also* Ranch
   farming
Overstocking, 82, 194–195

Pacific Coast: markets, 189, 191
Packers: business practices, 31, 48,
   76, 77, 136, 174, 188, 224, 236;
   cattlemen's attitude, 28, 77, 91–
   92, 121–122, 166–167, 188, 220;
   competition, chain stores, 122,
   175, 189; decentralization, 167,
   220, 224; defy government, 92,
   117, 122; development, central,
   18–19; feed to finish, 236; subsidies, 178; regulation efforts, 77,
   78, 91–92, 122, 150–151, 166–
   167, 174, 224; vertical integration,
   236. *See also* Marketing
Packers and Stockyards Act: content, 77–78; more effective, 91;
   regulates auction markets, 206;
   producers want stronger, 224–
   225, 236
Packers and Stockyards Division,
   188–189
Palmer, A. Mitchell: Consent Decree, 77

Panic of 1907, 42
Parasites: attacks on, 181, 229–230; losses, 181–182, 210; problems, insect, worm, 165, 181–182, 210
Paratuberculosis: in U.S., 39–40
Parity, 170–171, 204. *See also* Prices
Pasture farming: development, spread, 87, 95–98, 107, 111–112, 150, 162, 181–184; methods, 95–97, 111, 113, 131, 150, 162–163, 181–184, 209, 210–211; urged, federal agencies, 162. *See also* Ranch farming
Pastures: improvements, 164, 209–210, 212; replace range, 162, 195–196, 212; Soil Bank, 226
Peck, Allen S., quoted, 160
Petit, Charles: Flat Top Ranch, 211; quoted, irrigation, 235
Pharmaceuticals: regulation, 48–49
Phenothiazine: vermicide, 165, 181, 198, 218
Pierce Act, 157
Pioneers. *See* Farmers; Dry farmers
Pitting. *See* Contour ridging
The Plow That Broke the Plains, 166
Plum Island: disease research, 216
Population: total, U.S., 10, 17, 30, 87; Plains, 22, 148, 166; urban, 10, 30, 59, 169, 204; West Coast, 175, 189
Potter, Albert F.: Forest Service, 35
Power, T. C.: Montana cattleman, 13
Prairie dogs: damage, 48, 79, 139, 180; effort, exterminate, 47–48, 64, 79. *See also* Biological Survey
Predators: federal attack, 63–64, 80, 145–146, 180–181; general, 110, 181, 198; killed, 64, 146; value, control, 64. *See also* Biological Survey; Wolves; Buzzards
Price Administration, Office of: difficulty administering, 172; operations, 171–175; price roll back, 178; rationing, 172, 173; War Food Administrator, conflict, 173. *See also* Federal government
Price Stabilization, Office of, 205
Price controls: effects, cattlemen, 171, 186, 206; general, World War II, 170, 171, 186, 205–206; feeds, 58
Prices: cattle, 6, 19, 41–42, 52–53, 60, 62, 74, 89, 104, 119, 135, 139, 145, 152, 172, 186–187, 205, 223; consumers' protest, 104, 153, 187; land, 91, 191, relief purchases, 141, wartime, 60, 169, 171, 205–

206; wheat, 51, 65. *See also* Consumption
Price supports: Brannan Plan, 188; cattlemen want, 117; cattlemen oppose, 136, 141–142, 188; cattlemen receive, 137, 140, 141, 142, 162, 178–179, 207–208, 226; dry farmers, 166; fraud, 141–142; rules, 140–141; unifies Plains, 222; Agricultural Marketing Act, 125
Pricklypear. *See* Cactus
The Producer: wants federal aid, 86
Production: beef, declines, 121, 146, 165, 193; beef, fluctuations, 174, 198, 209, 217; beef, more intensive, 17, 30, 70–71, 93, 100, 111–112, 129, 182, 201, 215, 232, 235; rises, 58–59, 173, 184, 235; controls, 140–141, 146, 207, 223; demand, 169, 170, 186; effects, biochemistry, 217; free market, 226
Production Credit Corporations, 136
Production Management, Office of, 172
Progressives: reform group, 44
Promotion. *See* Advertising
Prosperity: causes, 105, 187, 224; war produced, 57, 187; for whom, 82–83, 105, 224
Proteins: Americans get more, 204; cottonseed, 67–68; effects, antibiotics, 229
Public domain: attitudes, cattlemen, 26, 31, 33–34, 70, 101–102, 116–117, 127, 138, 143, 199, 228, 236; controlled use, 15. 36, 70, 85, 143–144, 156, 176–177; under Eisenhower, 228; Forests protect, 85, 138; improved, CCC, 176; leasing, 26, 33–34, 117; misuse, 70, 101–102; release, private, suggested, 199; release, states, suggested, 127, 143; Stanfield Bill, 116–117; use, range management, 36, 101–102. *See also* Wilderness Bill
Public Land Commission, 127

Quality: consumers demand higher, 11, 17–18, 90, 190; efforts, improve, 47, 73, 190
Quarantines: brucellosis, 228; foot-and-mouth, 50, 110, 196, 216; general rules, 27; Mexican cattle, 110, 196, 216; screwworms, 218; tick fever, 6–7, 12, 80, 182; tuberculosis, 125. *See also* Disease

Railroads: attitudes, cattlemen, 21, 48, 101, 167, 225; use declines,

Railroads (*continued*)
151, 167; drouth rates, 78–79; expansion, Plains, 21; government operates, 58, 78; service, 58, 118, 150, 190, 225; trucks compete, 101, 118, 150, 225; urge dry farming, 31. *See also* Federal government

Rainfall: good enough, 154, 155, 180, 193, 208. *See also* Drouth

Ranches, large: dissolution, 94, 113–114, 191; Forest Service, 199; general, 191; inferiority, 212–213; reason for survival, 193

Ranch farming: characteristics, 11, 54, 68, 83–84, 94–95, 111–112, 129, 131, 150, 163, 192, 212, 213–214, 234–235; displaces large ranches, 83, 94, 193; dude ranches, 130; extent, 96, 131, 213–214; evolution, spread, 11, 20, 23, 35–36, 67, 82–83, 84, 87, 94–95, 129, 150, 163, 182–183, 201–202, 212–213; federal agencies encourage, 35, 161, 178; overgrazing, 93; railroads push, 21, 190; supplemental feeds, 96, 150, 184, 195, 212–213; World War II, 184

Ranch farmers: appear, 9–10; failures, 149; land investment, 191, 201; pasture farming, 107, 201; survival powers, 40, 41, 60, 68, 109, 201, 234; Taylor Act favors, 157

Ranch farms: cattle, 130, 191; large ranches, 129; life, 113; number, 129, 184–185, 215; sizes, 100, 129, 149–150, 165–166, 185, 191, 215

Ranching, cow and calf, 192

Range management: Bureau of Land Management, 220; Cooperative Grazing Districts, 200–201; little progress, 36, 220, 228; methods, 24–25, 36, 53–54, 84, 92–93, 200–201; Soil Conservation Districts, 200. *See also* Taylor Grazing Act; Forest Service

Ratchford, C. E., 138

Ratchford Report, 115

Rationing: black markets, 173; details, 172–174; hampers truck transport, 190; meat, 173; popular clamor against, 186; producer reaction, 174–175; stamp counterfeiting, 174; steps toward, 172–173. *See also* Price Administration, Office of

Recession: late 1950's, 223

Reciprocal Trade Agreements Act: activities, effects, 147, 179; cattlemen oppose, 179

Reclamation, Bureau of, 184

Reconstruction Finance Corporation: credit, cattlemen, 126

Reeves, George: quoted, drouth, 124; on soil erosion, 166

Refrigeration: mechanical needed, 128; no packer monopoly, 150; used, transport, 77, 150–151

Regional Agricultural Credit Corporations: under RFC, 126

Rehabilitation Division, 146

Relief: cattle program, 136, 139, 141, 145, 152, 160–162, 225; confused, drouth relief, 225–226; element, farm income, 153; predator control, as aspect, 145–146

Reseeding: Forest Service, 200; individuals, 202; native grass, 140, 176

Resettlement Administration, 146, 160

Resettlement Division: activities, 146; labor camps, 178

Retailers: attitude, cattlemen, 122–123, 188, 236

Retailing: cattlemen hope packers will, 117, 122

Ridging. *See* Contour ridging

Riley, Smith: predatory animals, 64

Rinderpest, 38

Roads: improvements, 101

Rock Island Railroad: rates, drouth, 79

Roll Back Order: World War II, 178; Korean War, 205

Roosevelt, Franklin D.: Agricultural Marketing Act, 126; price controls, 171; public domain, 127; rationing, 172. *See also* New Dealers

Roosevelt, Theodore: lets Brahmans in, 38; reformer, 44; protects Forests, 34

Roubicek, Carl B., 219

Rule, Glenn: quoted, sorghum, 164

Rural Rehabilitation Division, 138

Russell, E. C.: Forester, 34

Russian thistles. *See* Tumbleweed

Rustlers: activities, 48, 165, 185; federal law, 185

Rutledge, Richard H.: director grazing, 157

Sampson, Arthur W.: *Plant Succession in Relation to Range Management*, 84; shows advantages deferred grazing, 53–54

Sand Hills: Nebraska, 213

Sanitary Convention: Argentina, 147, 167; killed, 202

Sanitary treaty: Mexico, 110, 196

Santa Fe Railroad: drouth rates, 79

Santa Gertrudis: association, 219; developed, 84; characteristics, 85, 184; established, 100; increase, 132; recognized, Bureau Animal Industry, 184; stimulates breed experiments, 233
Saunderson, Mont: large ranches, 212
Scabies: causes, control, 109
Screwworms: characteristics, 110; control efforts, 181–182, 217–218; seriousness, 110; sterilization method, success, 218, 230
Second World War: employment, 170
Shaw, Thomas: urges more livestock, 32
Shelterbelts: trees on Plains, 140, 146, 161
Shipping fever: antibiotics against, 181; tranquilizers against, 232
Shorthorns: crossed, Brahman, 68, 85; second favorite breed, 84
Siberian wheatgrass, 211
Silage: advantages, 99, 112, 150, 211; during drouth, 150, 208; increased use, 112, 131, 183, 195, 208, 212; plants used, 112, 195, 212; preservatives, 212. See also Supplemental feeding
Silos: cattlemen interested, 68, 83, 99, 112, 131, 150; replaces hay, 99; types, virtues, 211–212
Smith, Theobald: tick fever, 12
Smut: disease, wheat, sorghum, 89
Snow. See Weather
Soapweed: sometimes hay, 112
Soil bank, 225–226
Soil conservation. See Conservation
Soil Conservation and Domestic Allotment Act, 159–161
Soil Conservation Districts, 200
Soil Conservation Service, 161, 176, 210
Soil erosion: contour ridging, 164; Demonstration Areas, 140; Emergency Soil Conservation Act, 136; control efforts, 136, 140, 164, 166, 210; continues, 208; Soil Conservation Act, 136; Soil Conservation Districts, 210; sorghum retards, 164
Soiling: feeding fresh fodder, 234
Sonnichsen, Carl: quoted, 214
Sorghum: characteristics, varieties, 13–14, 24, 50, 155, 163, 164, 211; crossed, Johnson grass, 211; Plains unifier, 221–222; price supports, 226; production, 37, 99; silage, 112, 183; use expands, 13–14, 24, 37, 82, 83, 99, 112, 129, 131, 163–

164, 183, 221, 227. See also Supplemental feeding
South Africa: Africander cattle, 132; anaplasmosis vaccine, 217
South Dakota: bank failures, 106; drouth, 45, 61, 124; dry farmers hurt, 66, 82; small farms, 192; ranch farmers, 150
Southern Plains: breeding area, 5, 99, 100; cottonseed, 67–68; credit problems, 74–75; dry farming, 94; grasses, 92, 162, 211; land tenure, 101; ranch farming, 83, 94–95, 129–130; Santa Gertrudis, 219; weather, 62, 78, 87–88, 123–124, 162, 180, 208–209
Soybeans: feed, 183
Sportsmen: influence, 117, 194
Sprinkler irrigation: Plains lack, 184; advantages, 209–210, 235
Stabilization Corporations, 125
Stanfield, R. N.: Senator, 116–117
Stanfield Bill, 117
State lands: use, management, 36; public domain, 127; tenure, 115. See also Land
Steer ranch: described, 192
Sterilization: screwworms, 218, 230
Stilbestrol: use, effects, 217, 232
Stockmarket: crash, 1929, 120
Stock Raising Homestead Act, 70, 85
Stock Growers' Finance Corporation, 75
Strain 19: brucellosis vaccine, 124–125
Strip cropping, 66
Subsidies: cattlemen get, 160, 178–179, 188, 206–208, 226; conservation program, 160, 226; feed grain, 178–179, 188; soil bank, 226. See also Brannan Plan, Soil bank; Taxes
Subsistence Homesteads, Division of, 138
Sudangrass: introduced, spread, 37. See also Sorghum
Sugar beets: feed, 84, 112
Sunflowers: silage, 112
Supermarkets: impact, 224
Supplemental feeding: crops, 9, 23, 162, 213–214; dry farming an element, 22; emergency, 12–13; grass instead, 82, 97, 164; nutrition, 235; price regulations, 58; problems, 139, 213; profit, 106; range management, 54; ridging, 164; use, growth, 23, 35, 67–68, 83–84, 98–99, 108, 111, 129, 130–131, 150, 195–196, 212, 215, 234; young cattle, 190, 213
Supreme Court: invalidates AAA,

Supreme Court (*continued*) 159; upholds Forest Service, 55; upholds Packers and Stockyards Acts, 77–78; sustains Consent Decree, 117

Surra: disease, 38

Swan Land and Cattle Company, 101

Sweet clover: experiments, 37; silage, 112

Systemic poisons: uses, effects, 218, 229–230

Tariffs: Argentine beef, 167, 202; cattlemen want higher, 126, 128, 144, 147, 179, 202, 220–221, 224–225; effects, 121. *See also* Reciprocal Trade Agreements Act; Sanitary Convention

Taxes: capital gains, 206; part, high costs, 90, 206; as subsidy, 206, 225

Taylor, Edward T.: Congressman, Colorado, 143

Taylor Grazing Act: effects, terms, 143–144, 146–147, 156–157, 176–177; flaws, 156–157; cattlemen support, 143. *See also* Grazing, Division of

TCA: herbicide, effects, 199

Television: possible influence, 221

Tenant Purchase Division, 182

Tenure. *See* Land tenure

Texas: drouth, 45, 61–62, 155; dust storms, 140; feed, finish, 183; foot-and-mouth, 88–89; oppose humane slaughter, 224; origin, range industry, 4–5; screwworm eradication, 230; silos, 68, 150; sorghum, 13; ticks, 65; wheat, 66

Texas and Southwestern Cattle Raisers Association: Reciprocal Trade Act, 179; oppose Brannan Plan, 188

Theiler, Arnold: anaplasmosis, 40

Thomas, Karl: importer, Charolaise, 84

Tick Eradication, Division of: set up, 65

Tick fever: cause, 12; Division of Tick Eradication, 65; Crisp Act, 110; eradication efforts, 12, 27–28, 39, 48, 65, 80, 88, 109, 124; obstruct eradicaton, 48; vaccine, 109

Toxophene: kills grasshoppers, 208

Tractor: entice settlers, 51–52; expanding use, 112, 214; influence feeds, 112; reduce horse numbers, 93

Trailers: carry horses to work, 214

Tranquilizers: cattle, 229, 231, 232

Transport: costs, 4, 89–90; importance, 100–101, 118, 128, 150–151, 190–191, 206, 225; shapes Plains life, 221; trucks *v.* railroads, 167

Trolene: use, effects, 230

Trucks: auction markets, impact, 206; blizzard relief, 194; cattle, better condition, 150; compete, railroads, 118, 150, 167; used more, 101, 118, 128, 150–151, 167, 190–191, 206; meat shipped, 128, 150–151; pickups, 206; ranch loading docks, 132; gas rationing, 190; refrigeration, 128, 150–151; superiority, 101, 150, 190, 225

Truman, Harry S.: price controls, 186; tariff, 220

Trust, beef: 19, 20, 48

Tuberculosis: bovine, battle, 89, 108, 125, 145; decline, 89

Tugwell, Rexford G.: drouth relief, 141

Tumbleweed: hay, silage, 112, 131

Turner, Fred W.: imports Charolaise, 84

2,4-D: effect, 199, 219, 230. *See also* Herbicides

2,4,5-T: herbicide, effect, 219; against mesquite, 230–231

Understocking: northern Plains, 100; general, 108

Unemployment: extent, 120, 134, 152, 169, 223; plainsmen, 153

United Automobile Workers: meatless weeks, 153

Urbanites: element, Plains prosperity, 187, 204, 224; compete, land, 234, 236; object, prices, 153

Urban workers: Brannan Plan to help, 188; depression, 72, 119; living standard, 57

Vaccination: anaplasmosis, 216; brucellosis, 124–125, 216, 228–229; foot-and-mouth, 196, 216

Vertical integration: revival, 235–236

Vesicular stomatitis: discovered, described, 65, becomes serious, 198

Vetch: legume, 227

Veterinary medicine: advances, 164–165, 217; tick fever experiments, 39

Vitamins: antibiotics, 229; cattle feeding, 195, 235; silage, 212

Wages. *See* Labor

Wallace, Henry A.: set Forest fees, 138

Walsh, Thomas J.: Senator, grazing districts, 114

Warbles: efforts, eradicate, 197, 218, 230; grub infected cattle, 196–197

War Finance Corporation: ended, replaced, 90–91; lends to cattlemen, 61, 75; seeks repayment, 74–75

War Food Administration: conflict, OPA, 173; drouth, 180; rationing, 172; labor camps, 178; absorbs Food Production Administration, 177

War Food Board: activities, 171–172

War Production Board: rationing, 172

Washing machines: automatic, 221

Water: dams, rain water, 67, 180, 210, 227; facilities improved, 67, 98, 159, 180, 210, 227; sources dry up, 139

Weather: good, 20, 40, 44–45, 47, 61, 78, 87–88, 106–108, 124, 154, 180, 193; general, 61–63, 123–124, 153–154, 180, 208–209; drouth, 62, 153–154; hard winter, 45, 63; terrible, 123–124, 153–154

Webb, Walter P.: Plains described, 2

Weeds. *See* Herbicides

Weeks Law, 55

Welty, F. A.: quoted, pasture farmers, 96

West Coast. *See* Pacific Coast

Wheat: price entices growers, 51; production levels, 32–33, 65–66, 81, 148–149, 166, 184, 215; ranch farming, 183. *See also* Dry farming

Wilderness Bill, 236

Wilson, James: Secretary of Agriculture, interested, Brahmans, 24, 39

Wilson, Woodrow: reformer, 44, 48

Windbreaks. *See* Shelterbelts

Winter feeding. *See* Supplemental feeding

Wolves: nearly extinct, 110; predators, 181

Woodhead, P. V., 115

Works Progress Administration: efforts, Plains, 160

Worms: cattle, battle against, 165, 198, 217–218, 229–230

Wyoming: drouth, 45, 154; dry farming, 66; small farms, 192; prairie dog eradication, 79

X-disease: appears, 197–198; cure, 217

Young cattle: favored, 189–190, 204

Zebu, 99. *See also* Brahman; Africander; Santa Gertrudis